Mike Holt's

NEC Exam Practice Questions

Based on the 2005 *NEC*©

www.*NEC*code.com
1.888.NEC®code

Mike Holt Enterprises, Inc.
1.888.NEC.CODE • NECcode.com • Info@NECcode.com

NOTICE TO THE READER

Mike Holt's
NEC Exam Practice Questions
Cover Design: Tracy Jette
Layout Design and Typesetting: Cathleen Kwas

COPYRIGHT © 2005 Charles Michael Holt Sr.
ISBN: 1-932685-28-6

For more information, call 1-888-NEC CODE, or E-mail info@MikeHolt.com.

www.*NEC*code.com
1.888.NEC®code

This logo is a registered trademark of Mike Holt Enterprises, Inc.

To request examination copies of this or other Mike Holt Publications, call:
Phone: 1-888-NEC CODE • Fax: 1-954-720-7944
or E-mail: info@MikeHolt.com
or visit Mike Holt Online: www.NECcode.com

You can download a sample PDF of all our publications by visiting www.NECcode.com

I dedicate this book to the
Lord Jesus Christ,
my mentor and teacher.

ONE TEAM

To Our Instructors and Students:

We are committed to providing you the finest product with the fewest errors, but we are realistic and know that there will be errors found and reported after the printing of this book. The last thing we want is for you to have problems finding, communicating, or accessing this information. It is unacceptable to us for there to be even one error in our textbooks or answer keys. For this reason, we are asking you to work together with us as **One Team**.

Students: Please report any errors that you may find to your instructor.

Instructors: Please communicate these errors to us.

Our Commitment:

We will continue to list all of the corrections that come through for all of our textbooks and answer keys on our Website. We will always have the most up-to-date answer keys available to instructors to download from our instructor Website. The last thing that we want is for you to have problems finding this updated information, so we're outlining where to go for all of this below:

To view textbook and answer key corrections: Students and instructors go to our Website, www.MikeHolt.com, click on "Books" in the sidebar of links, and then click on "Corrections."

To download the most up-to-date answer keys: Instructors go to our Website, www.MikeHolt.com, click on "Instructors" in the sidebar of links and then click on "Answer Keys." On this page you will find instructions for how to access and download these answer keys.

If you are not registered as an instructor you will need to register. Your registration will be sent to our educational director who in turn reviews and approves your registration. In your approval E-mail will be the login and password so you can have access to all of the answer keys. If you have a situation that needs immediate attention, please contact the office directly at 1-888-NEC-CODE.

1.888.NEC.Code or visit us online at www.NECcode.com

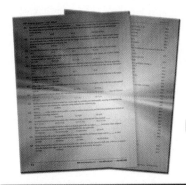

Table of Contents

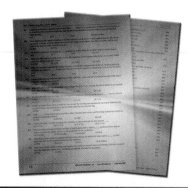

Introduction

The *NEC Exam Practice Questions* book contains 2,400 questions from the *National Electrical Code*. There are 12 review quizzes of 100 questions each that are in *Code* order and take you step by step through each of the nine chapters of the *National Electrical Code*.

The 12 practice quizzes of 50 questions each follow the *NEC* Review quizzes, but are presented in random order and contain questions different than those in the review quizzes.

In addition, this book contains 12 challenge quizzes of 50 questions each that cover all nine chapters of the *National Electrical Code*. The questions in the challenge quizzes do not follow the chapters of the *Code* book (as the other quizzes do); they are organized in a random manner, and you might find them harder to answer. Scores for the first few challenge quizzes might be somewhat lower than you would like to see. But, as you go through this book and take the review and practice quizzes, you'll learn a great deal and gain a better understanding of the material. This improved knowledge and understanding will help you improve on the challenge quizzes as you proceed.

This book is intended to be used with the *2005 National Electrical Code*.

Workbook Errors and Corrections

Humans develop the text and layout of this workbook, and since currently none of us is perfect, there may be a few errors. This could occur because the *NEC* is dramatically changed each *Code* cycle; new Articles are added, some deleted, some relocated, and many renumbered. In addition, this workbook must be written within a very narrow window of opportunity; after the *NEC* has been published (September), yet before it's enforceable (January).

You can be sure we work a tremendous number of hours and use all of our available resources to produce the finest product with the fewest errors. We take great care in researching the *Code* requirements to ensure this workbook is correct. If you feel there's an error of any type in this workbook (typo, grammar, or technical), no matter how insignificant, please let us know.

Any errors found after printing are listed on our Website, so if you find an error, first check to see if it has already been corrected. Go to www.MikeHolt.com, click on the "Books" link, and then the "Corrections" link (www.MikeHolt.com/book corrections.htm).

If you do not find the error listed on the Website, contact us by E-mailing corrections@MikeHolt.com, calling 1.888.NEC.CODE (1.888.632.2633), or faxing 954.720.7944. Be sure to include the book title, page number, and any other pertinent information.

Internet

Today as never before, you can get your technical questions answered by posting them to Mike Holt's Code Forum. Just visit www.MikeHolt.com and click on the "Code Forum" link.

Different Interpretations

Some electricians, contractors, instructors, inspectors, engineers, and others enjoy the challenge of discussing the *Code* requirements, hopefully in a positive and a productive manner. This action of challenging each other is important to the process of better understanding the *NEC*'s requirements and its intended application. However, if you're going to get into an *NEC* discussion, please do not spout out what you think without having the actual *Code* in your hand. The professional way of discussing an *NEC* requirement is by referring to a specific section, rather than by talking in vague generalities.

Passing the Exam

Passing an important electrical exam is the dream of all those who care about improving themselves and their families. Unfortunately, many don't pass the exam at all, and few pass it the first time. The primary reasons that people fail their exam is because they are not prepared on the technical material and/or they don't know how to take the exam.

This textbook was designed to help you prepare for your *National Electrical Code* exam.

Understanding the Emotional Aspects of Learning

To learn effectively, you must develop an attitude that learning is a process that will help you grow both personally and professionally. The learning process has an emotional as well as an intellectual component that we must recognize. To understand what affects our learning, consider the following:

Positive Image. Many feel disturbed by the expectations of being treated like children and we often feel threatened with the learning experience.

Uniqueness. Each of us will understand the subject matter from different perspectives and we all have some unique learning problems and needs.

Resistance to Change. People tend to resist change and resist information that appears to threaten their comfort level of knowledge. However, we often support new ideas that support our existing beliefs.

Dependence and Independence. The dependent person is afraid of disapproval and often will not participate in class discussion and will tend to wrestle alone. The independent person spends too much time asserting differences and too little time trying to understand others' views.

Fearful. Most of us feel insecure and afraid of learning, until we understand the process. We fear that our performance will not match the standard set by us or by others.

Egocentric. Our ego tendency is to prove someone is wrong, with a victorious surge of pride. Learning together without a win/lose attitude can be an exhilarating learning experience.

Emotional. It is difficult to discard our cherished ideas in the face of contrary facts when overpowered by the logic of others.

Getting the Best Grade

Studies have concluded that for students to get their best grades, they must learn to get the most from their natural abilities. It's not how long you study or how high your IQ is, it's what you do and how you study that counts the most. To get your best grade, you must make a decision to do your best and follow as many of the following techniques as possible.

Reality. These instructions are a basic guide to help you get the maximum grade. It is unreasonable to think that all of the instructions can be followed to the letter all of the time. Day-to-day events and unexpected situations must be taken into consideration.

Support. You need encouragement in your studies and you need support from your loved ones and employer. To properly prepare for your exam, you need to study 10 to 15 hours per week for about 3 to 6 months.

Communication with Your Family. Good communication with your family is very important because studying every night and on weekends can cause much tension and stress. Try to get their support, cooperation, and encouragement during this difficult time. Let them know the benefits to the family and what passing the exam means. Be sure to plan some special time with them during this preparation period; don't go overboard and leave them alone too long.

Stress. Stress can really take the wind out of you. It takes practice, but get into the habit of relaxing before you begin your studies. Stretch, do a few sit-ups and push-ups, take a 20-minute walk, or a few slow, deep

Mike Holt Enterprises, Inc. • www.NECcode.com • 1.888.NEC.Code

breaths. Close your eyes for a couple of minutes, and deliberately relax the muscle groups that are associated with tension, such as the shoulders, back, neck, and jaw.

Attitude. Maintaining a positive attitude is important. It helps keep you going and helps keep you from getting discouraged.

Training. Preparing for the exam is the same as training for any event. Get plenty of rest and avoid intoxicating drugs, including alcohol. Stretching or exercising each day for at least 10 minutes helps you get in a better mood. Eat light meals such as pasta, chicken, fish, vegetables, fruit, etc. Try to avoid red meat, butter, sugar, salt, and high-fat content foods. They slow you down and make you tired and sleepy.

Eye Care. It is very important to have your eyes checked! Human eyes were not designed to constantly focus on something less than arm's length away. Our eyes were designed for survival, spotting food and enemies at a distance. Your eyes will be under tremendous stress because of pro-longed, near-vision reading, which can result in headaches, fatigue, nausea, squinting, or eyes that burn, ache, water, or tire easily. Be sure to tell your eye doctor that you are  studying to pass an exam (bring this book and the *Code* book with you) and that you expect to do a tremendous amount of reading and writing. Reading glasses can reduce eye discomfort.

Reducing Eye Strain. Be sure to look up occasionally, away from near tasks to distant objects. Your work area should be three times brighter than the rest of the room. Don't read under a single lamp in a dark room. Try to eliminate glare. Mixing of fluorescent and incandescent lighting can be helpful.

Posture. Sit up straight, chest up, shoulders back, so both eyes are an equal distance from what you are viewing.

Getting Organized. Our lives are so busy that simply making time for homework and exam preparation is almost impossible. You can't waste time looking for a pencil or missing paper. Keep everything you need together. Maintain folders, one for notes, one for exams and answer keys, and one for miscellaneous items.

Study Location. It is very important that you have a private study area available at all times. Keep your materials there. The dining room table is not a good spot.

Time Management. Time management and planning are very important. There simply are not enough hours in the day to get everything done. Make a schedule that allows time for work, rest, study, meals, family, and recreation. Establish a schedule that is consistent from day-to-day. Have a calendar and immediately plan your exam preparation schedule. Try to follow the same routine

each week and try not to become overtired. Learn to pace yourself to accomplish as much as you can without the need for cramming.

Clean Up Your Act. Keep all of your papers neat, clean, and organized. Now is not the time to be sloppy. If you are not neat, now is an excellent time to begin.

Speak Up in Class. If you are in a class-room setting, the most important part of the learning process is class participation. If you don't understand the instructor's point, ask for clarification. Don't try to get attention by asking questions you already know the answer to.

Study With a Friend. Studying with a friend can make learning more enjoyable. You can push and encourage each other. You are more likely to study if someone else is depending on you. Students who study together perform above average because they try different approaches and explain their solutions to each other. Those who study alone spend most of their time reading and rereading the text and trying the same approach time after time even though it is unsuccessful.

Study Anywhere/Anytime. To make the most of your limited time, always keep a copy of the book(s) with you. Any time you get a minute free, study! Continue to study any chance you get. You can study at the supply house when waiting for your material; you can study during your coffee break, or even while you're at the doctor's office. Become creative!

You need to find your best study time. For some, it could be late at night when the house is quiet. For others, it's the first thing in the morning before things get going.

Set Priorities. Once you begin your study, stop all phone calls, TV shows, radio, snacks, and other interruptions. You can always take care of it later.

Preparing to Take the Exam

Have the Proper Supplies. First of all, make sure you have everything needed several days before the exam. The night before the exam is not the time to be out buying pencils, calculators, and batteries. The night before the exam, you should have a checklist (prepared in advance) of everything you could possibly need. The following is a sample checklist to get you started:

- Six sharpened #2H pencils or two mechanical pencils with extra #2H leads. The type with the larger lead is better for filling in the answer key.

- Two calculators. Most examining boards require quiet, paperless calculators. Solar calculators are great, but there may not be enough light to operate them.

- Spare batteries. Two sets of extra batteries should be taken. It's very unlikely you'll need them, but…

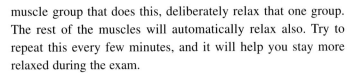

- Extra glasses if you use them.

- A wrist watch to ensure that you stay on track.

- All your reference materials, even the ones not on the list. Let the proctors tell you which ones are not permitted.

- Bring something to drink. Coffee is excellent.

- Some fruit, nuts, aspirin, etc.

- Know where the exam is going to take place and how long it takes to get there. Arrive at least 30 minutes early.

Meals. It is also a good idea to pack a lunch rather than going out. It can give you a little extra time to review the material for the afternoon portion of the exam, and it reduces the chance of coming back late.

Taking the Exam

Being prepared for an exam means more than just knowing electrical concepts, the *Code*, and the calculations. Have you felt prepared for an exam, then choked when actually taking it? Many good and knowledgeable people didn't pass their exam because they did not know "how to take an exam."

Taking exams is a learned process that takes practice and involves strategies. The following suggestions are designed to help you learn these methods:

Relax. This is easier said than done, but it is one of the most important factors in passing your exam. Stress and tension cause us to choke or forget. Everyone has had experiences where they became tense and couldn't think straight. The first step is becoming aware of the tension, and the second step is to make a deliberate effort to relax. Make sure you're comfortable; remove clothes if you are hot, or put on a jacket if you are cold.

There are many ways to relax and you have to find a method that works for you. Two of the easiest methods that work very well for many people follow:

Breathing Technique: Take a few slow deep breaths every few minutes. Do not confuse this with hyperventilation, which is abnormally fast breathing.

Single-Muscle Relaxation: When we are tense or stressful, many of us do things like clench our jaw, squint our eyes, or tense our shoulders without even being aware of it. If you find a

muscle group that does this, deliberately relax that one group. The rest of the muscles will automatically relax also. Try to repeat this every few minutes, and it will help you stay more relaxed during the exam.

Understand the Question. To answer a question correctly, you must first understand the question. One word in a question can totally change the meaning of it. Carefully read every word of every question. Underlining key words in the question will help you focus.

Skip the Difficult Questions. Contrary to popular belief, you do not have to answer one question before going on to the next one. The irony is that the question you get stuck on is one that you'll probably get wrong. This will result in not having enough time to answer the easy questions. You will get all stressed-out worrying that you will not complete the exam on time, and a chain reaction is started. More people fail their exams this way than for any other reason.

The following strategy should be used to avoid getting into this situation:

- **First Pass:** Answer the questions you know. Give yourself about 30 seconds for each question. If you can't find the answer in your reference book within the 30 seconds, go on to the next question. Chances are that you'll come across the answers while looking up another question. The total time for the first pass should be 25 percent of the exam time.

- **Second Pass:** This pass is done the same as the first pass except that you allow a little more time for each question, about 60 seconds. If you still can't find the answer, go on to the next one. Don't get stuck. Total time for the second pass should be about 30 percent of the exam time.

- **Third Pass:** See how much time is left and subtract 30 minutes. Spend the remaining time equally on each question. If you still haven't answered the question, it's time to make an educated guess. Never leave a question unanswered.

- **Fourth Pass:** Use the last 30 minutes of the exam to transfer your answers from the exam booklet to the answer key. Read each question and verify that you selected the correct answer on the test book. Transfer the answers carefully to the answer key. With the remaining time, see if you can find the answer to those questions you guessed at.

Guessing. When time is running out and you still have unanswered questions, GUESS! Never leave a question unanswered.

You can improve your chances of getting a question correct by the process of elimination. When one of the choices is "none of these," or "none of the above," it is usually not the correct answer. This improves your chances from one-out-of-four (25 percent), to one-out-of-three (33 percent). Guess "all of these" or "all of the above," and don't select the high or low number.

How do you pick one of the remaining answers? Some people toss a coin, others will count up how many of the answers were As, Bs, Cs, and Ds and use the one with the most as the basis for their guess.

 **Checking Your Work.** The first thing to check (and you should be watching out for this during the whole exam) is to make sure you mark the answer in the correct spot. People have failed the exam by one-half of a point. When they reviewed their exam, they found they correctly answered several questions on the test booklet, but marked the wrong spot on the exam answer sheet. They knew the answer was "(b) False" but marked in "(d)" in error. Another thing to be very careful of, is marking the answer for, let's say question 7, in the spot reserved for question 8.

Changing Answers. When re-reading the question and checking the answers during the fourth pass, resist the urge to change an answer. In most cases, your first choice is best and if you aren't sure, stick with the first choice. Only change answers if you are sure you made a mistake. Multiple choice exams are graded electronically so be sure to thoroughly erase any answer that you changed. Also erase any stray pencil marks from the answer sheet.

Rounding Off. You should always round your answers to the same number of places as the exam's answers.

Example: If an exam has multiple choice of:

(a) 2.2   (b) 2.1
(c) 2.3   (d) none of these

And your calculation comes out to 2.16, do not choose the answer (d) none of these. The correct answer is (a) 2.2, because the answers in this case are rounded off to the tenth.

Example: It could be rounded to tens, such as:

(a) 50   (b) 60
(c) 70   (d) none of these.

For this group, an answer such as 67 would be (c) 70, while an answer of 63 would be (b) 60. The general rule is to check the question's choice of answers then round off your answer to match it.

Things To Be Careful of Checklist

- Don't get stuck on any one question.

- Read each question carefully.

- Be sure you mark the answer in the correct spot on the answer sheet.

- Don't get flustered or extremely tense.

Summary Checklist

- Make sure everything is ready and packed the night before the exam.

- Don't try to cram the night before the exam—if you don't know it by then, it's too late!

- Have a good breakfast. Get the thermos and energy snacks ready.

- Take all your reference books. Let the proctors tell you what you can't use.

- Know where the exam is to be held and arrive early.

- Bring identification and your confirmation papers from the license board if this is required.

- Review your *NEC* while you wait for your exam to begin.

- Try to stay relaxed.

- Determine the time per question for each pass and don't forget to save 30 minutes for transferring your answers to the answer key.

- Remember—in the first pass answer only the easy questions. In the second pass, spend a little more time per question, but don't get stuck. In the third pass, use the remainder of the time minus 30 minutes. In the fourth pass, check your work and transfer the answers to the answer key.

The *National Electrical Code*

The *National Electrical Code (NEC)* is written for persons who understand electrical terms, theory, safety procedures, and electrical trade practices. These individuals include electricians, electrical contractors, electrical inspectors, electrical engineers, designers, and other qualified persons. The *Code* was not written to serve as an instructive or teaching manual for untrained individuals [90.1(C)].

Learning to use the *NEC* is somewhat like learning to play the game of chess; it's a great game if you enjoy mental warfare. You must first learn the names of the game pieces, how the pieces are placed on the board, and how each piece moves.

In the electrical world, this is equivalent to completing a comprehensive course on basic electrical theory, such as:

- What electricity is and how is it produced
- Dangers of electrical potential: fire, arc blast, arc fault, and electric shock
- Direct current
- Series and parallel circuits
- Electrical formulas
- Alternating current
- Induction, motors, generators, and transformers

Once you understand the fundamentals of the game of chess, you're ready to start playing the game. Unfortunately, at this point all you can do is make crude moves, because you really do not understand how all the information works together. To play chess well, you will need to learn how to use your knowledge by working on subtle strategies before you can work your way up to the more intriguing and complicated moves.

Again, back to the electrical world, this is equivalent to completing a course on the basics of electrical theory. You have the foundation upon which to build, but now you need to take it to the next level, which you can do by reading the Understanding the National Electrical Code, Volume 1 textbook, watching its companion video or DVD, and answering the *NEC* practice questions in this workbook.

Not a Game

Electrical work isn't a game, and it must be taken very seriously. Learning the basics of electricity, important terms and concepts, as well as the basic layout of the *NEC* gives you just enough knowledge to be dangerous. There are thousands of specific and unique applications of electrical installations, and the *Code* doesn't cover every one of them. To safely apply the *NEC*, you must understand the purpose of a rule and how it affects the safety aspects of the installation.

NEC Terms and Concepts

The *NEC* contains many technical terms, so it's crucial that *Code* users understand their meanings and their applications. If you do not understand a term used in a *Code* rule, it will be impossible to properly apply the *NEC* requirement. Be sure you understand that Article 100 defines the terms that apply to *two or more* Articles. For example, the term "Dwelling Unit" applies to many Articles. If you do not know what a Dwelling Unit is, how can you possibly apply the *Code* requirements for it?

In addition, many Articles have terms that are unique for that specific Article. This means that the definition of those terms is only applicable for that given Article. For example, Article 250 Grounding and Bonding has the definitions of a few terms that are only to be used within Article 250.

Small Words, Grammar, and Punctuation

It's not only the technical words that require close attention, because even the simplest of words can make a big difference to the intent of a rule. The word "or" can imply alternate choices for equipment wiring methods, while "and" can mean an additional requirement. Let's not forget about grammar and punctuation. The location of a comma "," can dramatically change the requirement of a rule.

Slang Terms or Technical Jargon

Electricians, engineers, and other trade-related professionals use slang terms or technical jargon that isn't shared by all. This

Mike Holt Enterprises, Inc. • www.NECcode.com • 1.888.NEC.Code

makes it very difficult to communicate because not everybody understands the intent or application of those slang terms. So where possible, be sure you use the proper word, and do not use a word if you do not understand its definition and application. For example, lots of electricians use the term "pigtail" when describing the short conductor for the connection of a receptacle, switch, luminaire, or equipment. Although they may understand it, not everyone does. **Figure 1**

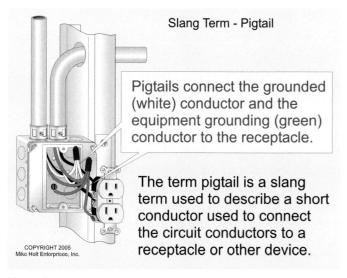

Figure 1

NEC Style and Layout

Before we get into the details of the *NEC*, we need to take a few moments to understand its style and layout. Understanding the structure and writing style of the *Code* is very important before it can be used effectively. If you think about it, how can you use something if you don't know how it works? Okay, let's get started. The *National Electrical Code* is organized into nine components.

- Table of Contents
- Chapters 1 through 9 (major categories)
- Articles 90 through 830 (individual subjects)
- Parts (divisions of an Article)
- Sections and Tables (*Code* requirements)
- Exceptions (*Code* permissions)
- Fine Print Notes (explanatory material)
- Index
- Annexes (information)

1. Table of Contents. The Table of Contents displays the layout of the Chapters, Articles, and Parts as well as the page numbers. It's an excellent resource and should be referred to periodically to observe the interrelationship of the various *NEC* components.

When attempting to locate the rules for a particular situation, knowledgeable *Code* users often go first to the Table of Contents to quickly find the specific *NEC* section that applies.

2. Chapters. There are nine Chapters, each of which is divided into Articles. The Articles fall into one of four groupings: General Requirements (Chapters 1 through 4), Specific Requirements (Chapters 5 through 7), Communications Systems (Chapter 8), and Tables (Chapter 9).

- Chapter 1 General
- Chapter 2 Wiring and Protection
- Chapter 3 Wiring Methods and Materials
- Chapter 4 Equipment for General Use
- Chapter 5 Special Occupancies
- Chapter 6 Special Equipment
- Chapter 7 Special Conditions
- Chapter 8 Communications Systems (Telephone, Data, Satellite, and Cable TV)
- Chapter 9 Tables—Conductor and Raceway Specifications

3. Articles. The *NEC* contains approximately 140 Articles, each of which covers a specific subject. For example:

- Article 110 General Requirements
- Article 250 Grounding and Bonding
- Article 300 Wiring Methods
- Article 430 Motors
- Article 500 Hazardous (Classified) Locations
- Article 680 Swimming Pools, Spas, Hot Tubs, and Fountains
- Article 725 Remote-Control, Signaling, and Power-Limited Circuits
- Article 800 Communications Systems

4. Parts. Larger Articles are subdivided into Parts. For example, Article 110 has been divided into multiple parts:

- Part I. General (Sections 110.1—110.23)
- Part II. 600 Volts, Nominal, or Less (110.26—110.27)
- Part III. Over 600 Volts, Nominal (110.30—110.59)

Note: Because the Parts of a *Code* Article aren't included in the Section numbers, we have a tendency to forget what "Part" the *NEC* rule is relating to. For example, Table 110.34(A) contains the working space clearances for electrical equipment. If we aren't careful, we might think this table applies to all electrical installations, but Table 110.34(A) is located in Part III, which contains the requirements for Over 600 Volts, Nominal installations. The rules for working clearances for electrical equipment for systems 600V or less are contained in Table 110.26(A)(1), which is located in Part II. 600 Volts, Nominal, or Less.

5. Sections and Tables.

Sections: Each *NEC* rule is called a *Code* Section. A *Code* Section may be broken down into subsections by letters in parentheses (A), (B), etc. Numbers in parentheses (1), (2), etc., may further break down a subsection, and lower-case letters (a), (b), etc., further break the rule down to the third level. For example, the rule requiring all receptacles in a dwelling unit bathroom to be GFCI protected is contained in Section 210.8(A)(1). Section 210.8(A)(1) is located in Chapter 2, Article 210, Section 8, sub-section (A), sub-subsection (1).

Many in the industry incorrectly use the term "Article" when referring to a *Code* Section. For example, they say "Article 210.8," when they should say "Section 210.8."

Tables: Many *Code* requirements are contained within Tables, which are lists of *NEC* requirements placed in a systematic arrangement. The titles of the Tables are extremely important; they must be carefully read in order to understand the contents, applications, limitations, etc., of each Table in the *Code*. Many times notes are provided in a table; be sure to read them as well, since they are also part of the requirement. For example, Note 1 for Table 300.5 explains how to measure the cover when burying cables and raceways, and Note 5 explains what to do if solid rock is encountered.

6. Exceptions.
Exceptions are *Code* requirements that provide an alternative method to a specific requirement. There are two types of exceptions—mandatory and permissive. When a rule has several exceptions, those exceptions with mandatory requirements are listed before the permissive exceptions.

Mandatory Exception: A mandatory exception uses the words "shall" or "shall not." The word "shall" in an exception means that if you're using the exception, you're required to do it in a particular way. The term "shall not" means it isn't permitted.

Permissive Exception: A permissive exception uses words such as "is permitted," which means that it's acceptable to do it in this way.

7. Fine Print Note (FPN).
A Fine Print Note contains explanatory material intended to clarify a rule or give assistance, but it isn't a *Code* requirement.

8. Index.
The Index contained in the *NEC* is excellent and is helpful in locating a specific rule.

9. Annexes.
Annexes aren't a part of the *NEC* requirements, and are included in the *Code* for informational purposes only.

- Annex A. Product Safety Standards
- Annex B. Application Information for Ampacity Calculation

- Annex C. Conduit and Tubing Fill Tables for Conductors and Fixture Wires of the Same Size
- Annex D. Examples
- Annex E. Types of Construction
- Annex F. Cross-Reference Tables (1999, 2002, and 2005 *NEC*)
- Annex G. Administration and Enforcement

Note: Changes to the *NEC* since the previous edition(s) are identified in the margins by a vertical line (|), but rules that have been relocated aren't identified as a change. In addition, the location from which the *Code* rule was removed has no identifier.

How to Locate a Specific Requirement

How to go about finding what you're looking for in the *Code* depends, to some degree, on your experience with the *NEC*. *Code* experts typically know the requirements so well that they just go to the *NEC* rule without any outside assistance. The Table of Contents might be the only thing very experienced *Code* users need to locate their requirement. On the other hand, average *Code* users should use all of the tools at their disposal, and that includes the Table of Contents and the Index.

Table of Contents: Let's work out a simple example: What *NEC* rule specifies the maximum number of disconnects permitted for a service? If you're an experienced *Code* user, you'll know that Article 230 applies to "Services," and because this Article is so large, it's divided up into multiple parts (actually 8 parts). With this knowledge, you can quickly go to the Table of Contents (page 70-2) and see that it lists the Service Equipment Disconnecting Means requirements in Part VI, starting at page 70-77.

Note: The number 70 precedes all page numbers because the *NEC* is standard number 70 within the collection of *NFPA* standards.

Index: If you used the Index, which lists subjects in alphabetical order, to look up the term "service disconnect," you would see that there's no listing. If you tried "disconnecting means," then "services," you would find the Index specifies that the rule is located at 230, Part VI. Because the *NEC* doesn't give a page number in the Index, you'll need to use the Table of Contents to get the page number, or flip through the *Code* to Article 230, then continue to flip until you find Part VI.

As you can see, although the index is very comprehensive, it's not that easy to use if you do not understand how the index works. But if you answer the over 1,200 *NEC* practice questions contained in this workbook, you'll become a master at finding things in the *Code* quickly.

Many people complain that the *NEC* only confuses them by taking them in circles. As you gain experience in using the *Code* and deepen your understanding of words, terms, principles, and practices, you will find the *NEC* much easier to understand and use than you originally thought.

Customizing Your *Code* Book

One way to increase your comfort level with the *Code* is to customize it to meet your needs. You can do this by highlighting and underlining important *NEC* requirements, and by attaching tabs to important pages.

Highlighting: As you answer the questions in this workbook, and read through the Understanding the National Electrical Code, Volume 1 textbook, be sure you highlight those requirements in the *Code* that are most important to you. Use yellow for general interest and orange for important requirements you want to find quickly. Be sure to highlight terms in the Index and Table of Contents as you use them.

Because of the size of the 2005 *NEC*, I recommend you highlight in green the Parts of Articles that are important for your applications, particularly:

    Article 230 Services
    Article 250 Grounding and Bonding
    Article 430 Motors, Motor Circuits, and Controllers

Underlining: Underline or circle key words and phrases in the *NEC* with a red pen (not a lead pencil) and use a 6 in. ruler to keep lines straight and neat. This is a very handy way to make important requirements stand out. A small 6 in. ruler also comes in handy for locating specific information in the many *Code* tables.

Tabbing the *NEC*: Placing tabs on important *Code* Articles, Sections, and Tables will make it very easy to access important *NEC* requirements. However, too many tabs will defeat the purpose. You can order a custom set of *Code* tabs, designed by Mike Holt, online at www.MikeHolt.com, or by calling us at 1.888.*NEC*.Code (1.888.632.2633).

About the Author

Mike Holt worked his way up through the electrical trade from an apprentice electrician to become one of the most recognized experts in the world as it relates to electrical power installation. He was a Journeyman Electrician, Master Electrician, and Electrical Contractor. Mike came from the real world, and he has a unique understanding of how the *NEC* relates to electrical installations from a practical standpoint. You will find his writing style to be simple, nontechnical, and practical.

Did you know that Mike didn't finish high school? So if you struggled in high school or if you didn't finish it at all, don't let this get you down, you're in good company. As a matter of fact, Mike Culbreath, Master Electrician, who produces the finest electrical graphics in the history of the electrical industry, didn't finish high school either! So two high school dropouts produce the text and graphics in Mike Holt's textbooks! However, realizing that success depends on one's continuing pursuit of education, Mike immediately attained his GED (as did Mike Culbreath) and ultimately attended the University of Miami's Graduate School for a Master's degree in Business Administration (MBA).

Mike Holt resides in Central Florida, is the father of seven children, and has many outside interests and activities. He is a former National Barefoot Waterskiing Champion (1988 and 1999), who set five barefoot water-ski records, and he continues to train year-round at a national competition level [www.barefootcentral.com].

Mike enjoys motocross racing, but at the age of 52 decided to retire from that activity (way too many broken bones, concussions, collapsed lung, etc., but what a rush). Mike also enjoys snow skiing and spending time with his family. What sets Mike apart from some is his commitment to living a balanced lifestyle; he places God first, then family, career, and self.

Unit 1
NEC Review Quiz
Articles 90 through 200

(• Indicates that 75% or fewer exam takers get the question correct)

Article 90 Introduction to the *National Electrical Code*

Article 90 opens by saying the *NEC* isn't intended as a design specification or instruction manual. The *National Electrical Code* has one purpose only. That is "the practical safeguarding of persons and property from hazards arising from the use of electricity."

Article 90 then describes the scope and arrangement of the *Code*.

1. The *NEC* is _____.

    (a) intended to be a design manual
    (b) meant to be used as an instruction guide for untrained persons
    (c) for the practical safeguarding of persons and property
    (d) published by the Bureau of Standards

    Answer: _____   Section: _____._____

2. •The *Code* contains provisions considered necessary for safety, which will not necessarily result in ___.

    (a) efficient use   (b) convenience
    (c) good service or future expansion of electrical use   (d) all of these

    Answer: _____   Section: _____._____

3. The following systems must be installed in accordance with the *NEC*:

    (a) signaling   (b) communications   (c) power and lighting   (d) all of these

    Answer: _____   Section: _____._____

4. The *Code* does not cover installations in ships, watercraft, railway rolling stock, aircraft, or automotive vehicles.

    (a) True   (b) False

    Answer: _____   Section: _____._____

5. Installations of communications equipment that are under the exclusive control of communications utilities, and located outdoors or in building spaces used exclusively for such installations _____ covered by the *Code*.

    (a) are   (b) are sometimes   (c) are not   (d) might be

    Answer: _____   Section: _____._____

6.   Service laterals installed by an electrical contractor must be installed in accordance with the *NEC*.

(a) True   (b) False

Answer: _____   Section: _____._____

7.   Utilities may be subject to compliance with codes and standards covering their regulated activities as adopted under governmental law or regulation.

(a) True   (b) False

Answer: _____   Section: _____._____

8.   Chapters 1 through 4 of the *NEC* apply _____.

(a) generally to all electrical installations   (b) to special occupancies and conditions
(c) to special equipment and material   (d) all of these

Answer: _____   Section: _____._____

9.   The requirements in "Annexes" must be complied with.

(a) True   (b) False

Answer: _____   Section: _____._____

10. The authority having jurisdiction is not required to enforce any requirements of Chapter 7 (Signaling Circuits) or Chapter 8 (Communications Circuits), because this is not within the scope of enforcement.

(a) True   (b) False

Answer: _____   Section: _____._____

11. A *Code* rule may be waived or alternative methods of installation approved that may be contrary to the *NEC*, if the authority having jurisdiction gives verbal or written consent.

(a) True   (b) False

Answer: _____   Section: _____._____

12. Explanatory material, such as references to other standards, references to related sections of the *NEC*, or information related to a *Code* rule, is included in the form of Fine Print Notes (FPNs).

(a) True   (b) False

Answer: _____   Section: _____._____

13. Compliance with either the metric or the inch-pound unit of measurement system is permitted.

(a) True   (b) False

Answer: _____   Section: _____._____

Chapter 1 General

Article 100 Definitions

Article 100—Definitions. Part I of Article 100 contains the definitions of terms used throughout the *Code* for systems that operate at 600V or less. The definitions of terms in Part II apply to systems that operate at over 600V.

14. Capable of being reached quickly for operation, renewal, or inspections without resorting to portable ladders and such is known as _____.

(a) accessible (equipment)   (b) accessible (wiring methods)
(c) accessible, readily   (d) all of these

Answer: _____   Section: _____._____

15. A junction box located above a suspended ceiling having removable panels is considered to be _____.

(a) concealed   (b) accessible   (c) readily accessible   (d) recessed

Answer: _____   Section: _____._____

16. •A generic term for a group of nonflammable synthetic chlorinated hydrocarbons used as electrical insulating media is _____.

(a) oil   (b) girasol   (c) askarel   (d) phenol

Answer: _____   Section: _____._____

17. Where no statutory requirement exists, the authority having jurisdiction could be a property owner or his/her agent, such as an architect or engineer.

(a) True   (b) False

Answer: _____   Section: _____._____

18. The connection between the grounded conductor and the equipment grounding conductor at the service is accomplished by installing a(n) _____ jumper.

(a) main bonding   (b) bonding   (c) equipment bonding   (d) circuit bonding

Answer: _____   Section: _____._____

19. The conductors between the final overcurrent protection device and the outlet(s) are known as the _____ conductors.

(a) feeder   (b) branch-circuit   (c) home run   (d) none of these

Answer: _____   Section: _____._____

20. A branch circuit that supplies only one utilization equipment is a(n) _____ branch circuit.

(a) individual   (b) general-purpose   (c) isolated   (d) special-purpose

Answer: _____   Section: _____._____

21. The *Code* defines a(n) _____ as a structure that stands alone or that is cut off from adjoining structures by firewalls, with all openings therein protected by approved fire doors.

(a) unit   (b) apartment   (c) building   (d) utility

Answer: _____   Section: _____._____

22. _____ is a qualifying term indicating that there is a purposely-introduced delay in the tripping action of the circuit breaker, which decreases as the magnitude of the current increases.

    (a) Adverse-time   (b) Inverse-time   (c) Time delay   (d) Timed unit

    Answer: _____   Section: _____._____

23. NM cable is considered _____ if rendered inaccessible by the structure or finish of the building.

    (a) inaccessible   (b) concealed   (c) hidden   (d) enclosed

    Answer: _____   Section: _____._____

24. A separate portion of a conduit or tubing system that provides access through a removable cover(s) to the interior of the system at a junction of two or more sections of the system, or at a terminal point of the system, is defined as a(n) _____.

    (a) junction box   (b) accessible raceway   (c) conduit body   (d) pressure connector

    Answer: _____   Section: _____._____

25. A load is considered to be continuous if the maximum current is expected to continue for _____ or more.

    (a) 1/2 hour   (b) 1 hour   (c) 2 hours   (d) 3 hours

    Answer: _____   Section: _____._____

26. •The _____ of any system is the ratio of the maximum demand of a system, or part of a system, to the total connected load of a system under consideration.

    (a) load   (b) demand factor   (c) minimum load   (d) computed factor

    Answer: _____   Section: _____._____

27. Which of the following does the *Code* recognize as a device?

    (a) Switch   (b) Light bulb   (c) Transformer   (d) Motor

    Answer: _____   Section: _____._____

28. Constructed so that dust will not enter the enclosing case under specified test conditions is known as _____.

    (a) dusttight   (b) dustproof   (c) dust rated   (d) all of these

    Answer: _____   Section: _____._____

29. Varying duty is defined as _____.

    (a) intermittent operation in which the load conditions are regularly recurrent
    (b) operation at a substantially constant load for an indefinite length of time
    (c) operation for alternate intervals of load and rest, or load, no load, and rest
    (d) operation at loads and for intervals of time, both of which may be subject to wide variations

    Answer: _____   Section: _____._____

30. Surrounded by a case, housing, fence, or wall(s) that prevents persons from accidentally contacting energized parts is called _____.

    (a) guarded   (b) covered   (c) protection   (d) enclosed

    Answer: _____   Section: _____._____

31. When the term exposed, as it relates to live parts, is used by the *Code*, it refers to _____.

    (a) capable of being inadvertently touched or approached nearer than a safe distance by a person
    (b) parts that are not suitably guarded, isolated, or insulated
    (c) wiring on, or attached to, the surface or behind panels designed to allow access
    (d) a and b

    Answer: _____   Section: _____._____

32. The *Code* defines a _____ as: "all circuit conductors between the service equipment, the source of a separately derived system, or other power supply source and the final branch-circuit overcurrent device."

    (a) feeder   (b) branch circuit   (c) service   (d) all of these

    Answer: _____   Section: _____._____

33. Connected to earth or to some conducting body that serves in place of the earth is called _____.

    (a) grounding   (b) bonded   (c) grounded   (d) all of these

    Answer: _____   Section: _____._____

34. _____ is defined as intentionally connected to earth through a ground connection or connections of sufficiently low impedance and having sufficient current-carrying capacity to prevent the buildup of voltages that may result in undue hazards to connected equipment or to persons.

    (a) Effectively grounded   (b) A proper wiring system   (c) A lighting rod   (d) A grounded conductor

    Answer: _____   Section: _____._____

35. A "Class A" GFCI protection device is designed to de-energize the circuit when the ground-fault current is approximately _____.

    (a) 4 mA   (b) 5 mA   (c) 6 mA   (d) any of these

    Answer: _____   Section: _____._____

36. A system intended to provide protection of equipment from damaging line-to-ground fault currents by operating to cause a disconnecting means to open all ungrounded conductors of the faulted circuit at levels less than the supply circuit overcurrent device is defined as _____.

    (a) ground-fault protection of equipment   (b) guarded
    (c) personal protection   (d) automatic protection

    Answer: _____   Section: _____._____

37. The grounding electrode conductor is the conductor used to connect the grounding electrode to the equipment grounding conductor and the grounded conductor at _____.

    (a) the service   (b) each building or structure supplied by feeder(s)
    (c) the source of a separately derived system   (d) all of these

    Answer: _____   Section: _____._____

38. A _____ is an accommodation that combines living, sleeping, sanitary, and storage facilities.

    (a) guest room   (b) guest suite   (c) dwelling unit   (d) single family dwelling

    Answer: _____   Section: _____._____

39. A handhole enclosure is an enclosure identified for use in underground systems, provided with an open or closed bottom, and sized to allow personnel to _____, for the purpose of installing, operating, or maintaining equipment or wiring or both.

    (a) enter and exit freely   (b) reach into but not enter   (c) have full working space   (d) examine visually

    Answer: _____   Section: _____._____

40. Recognized as suitable for the specific purpose, function, use, environment, and application is the definition of _____.

    (a) labeled   (b) identified (as applied to equipment)
    (c) listed   (d) approved

    Answer: _____   Section: _____._____

41. _____ means that an object is not readily accessible to persons unless special means for access are used.

    (a) Isolated   (b) Secluded   (c) Protected   (d) Locked

    Answer: _____   Section: _____._____

42. An outlet intended for the direct connection of a lampholder, a luminaire, or a pendant cord terminating in a lampholder is a(n) _____.

    (a) outlet   (b) receptacle outlet   (c) lighting outlet   (d) general-purpose outlet

    Answer: _____   Section: _____._____

43. A _____ location may be temporarily subject to dampness and wetness.

    (a) dry   (b) damp   (c) moist   (d) wet

    Answer: _____   Section: _____._____

44. The term "luminaire" includes "fixture(s)" and "lighting fixture(s)."

    (a) True   (b) False

    Answer: _____   Section: _____._____

45. A(n) _____ is a point on the wiring system at which current is taken to supply utilization equipment.

    (a) box   (b) receptacle   (c) outlet   (d) device

    Answer: _____   Section: _____._____

46. Outline lighting may not include light sources such as light emitting diodes (LEDs).

    (a) True   (b) False

    Answer: _____   Section: _____._____

47. An overload is the same thing as a short circuit or ground fault.

    (a) True   (b) False

    Answer: _____   Section: _____._____

48. The *Code* defines a(n) _____ as one familiar with the construction and operation of the electrical equipment and installations, and who has received safety training on the hazards involved.

(a) inspector   (b) master electrician   (c) journeyman electrician   (d) qualified person

Answer: _____   Section: _____._____

49. Something constructed, protected, or treated so as to prevent rain from interfering with the successful operation of the apparatus under specified test conditions is defined as _____.

(a) raintight   (b) waterproof   (c) weathertight   (d) rainproof

Answer: _____   Section: _____._____

50. A contact device installed at an outlet for the connection of an attachment plug is known as a(n) _____.

(a) attachment point   (b) tap   (c) receptacle   (d) wall plug

Answer: _____   Section: _____._____

51. When one electrical circuit controls another circuit through a relay, the first circuit is called a _____.

(a) control circuit   (b) remote-control circuit   (c) signal circuit   (d) controller

Answer: _____   Section: _____._____

52. A(n) _____ system is a premises wiring system whose power is derived from a source of electric energy or equipment other than a service, and that has no direct electrical connection, including a solidly connected grounded circuit conductor, to supply conductors originating in another system.

(a) separately derived   (b) classified   (c) direct   (d) emergency

Answer: _____   Section: _____._____

53. Overhead-service conductors from the last pole or other aerial support to and including the splices, if any, are called _____ conductors.

(a) service-entrance   (b) service-drop   (c) service   (d) overhead service

Answer: _____   Section: _____._____

54. The _____ is the necessary equipment, usually consisting of a circuit breaker(s) or switch(es) and fuse(s) and their accessories, connected to the load end of service conductors to a building or other structure, or an otherwise designated area, and intended to constitute the main control and cutoff of the supply.

(a) service equipment   (b) service
(c) service disconnect   (d) service overcurrent protection device

Answer: _____   Section: _____._____

55. The _____ is the point of connection between the facilities of the serving utility and the premises wiring.

(a) service entrance   (b) service point
(c) overcurrent protection (d) beginning of the wiring system

Answer: _____   Section: _____._____

56. The combination of all components and subsystems that convert solar energy into electrical energy is called a _____ system.

    (a) solar   (b) solar voltaic   (c) separately derived source   (d) solar photovoltaic

    Answer: _____   Section: _____._____

57. A _____ switch is a manually operated device used in conjunction with a transfer switch to provide a means of directly connecting load conductors to a power source, and of disconnecting the transfer switch.

    (a) transfer   (b) motor-circuit   (c) general-use snap   (d) bypass isolation

    Answer: _____   Section: _____._____

58. An isolating switch is one that is _____.

    (a) not readily accessible to persons unless special means for access is used
    (b) capable of interrupting the maximum operating overload current of a motor
    (c) intended for use in general distribution and branch circuits
    (d) intended for isolating an electrical circuit from the source of power

    Answer: _____   Section: _____._____

59. A thermal protector may consist of one or more heat-sensing elements integral with the motor or motor-compressor and an external control device.

    (a) True   (b) False

    Answer: _____   Section: _____._____

60. The voltage of a circuit is defined by the *Code* as the _____ root-mean-square (effective) difference of potential between any two conductors of the circuit.

    (a) lowest   (b) greatest   (c) average   (d) nominal

    Answer: _____   Section: _____._____

61. An enclosure or device constructed so that moisture will not enter the enclosure or device under specific test conditions is called _____.

    (a) watertight   (b) moistureproof   (c) waterproof   (d) rainproof

    Answer: _____   Section: _____._____

Article 110 Requirements for Electrical Installations

This article contains the general requirements for electrical installations.

62. In determining equipment to be installed, considerations such as the following should be evaluated:

    (a) Mechanical strength   (b) Cost   (c) Arcing effects   (d) a and c

    Answer: _____   Section: _____._____

63. To be *Code*-compliant, listed or labeled equipment must be installed and used in accordance with any instructions included in the _____.

    (a) catalog   (b) product   (c) listing or labeling   (d) all of these

    Answer: _____   Section: _____._____

64. Conductor sizes are expressed in American Wire Gage (AWG) or in _____.

    (a) in.   (b) circular mils   (c) sq in.   (d) AWG

    Answer: _____   Section: _____._____

65. A wiring method included in the *Code* is recognized as being a(n) _____ wiring method.

    (a) expensive   (b) efficient   (c) suitable   (d) cost-effective

    Answer: _____   Section: _____._____

66. Circuit-protective devices are used to clear a fault without the occurrence of extensive damage to the electrical components of the circuit. Faults can occur between two or more of the _____ or between any circuit conductor and the grounding conductor or enclosing metal raceway.

    (a) bonding jumpers   (b) grounding jumpers   (c) wiring harnesses   (d) circuit conductors

    Answer: _____   Section: _____._____

67. Unless identified for use in the operating environment, no conductors or equipment can be _____ having a deteriorating effect on the conductors or equipment.

    (a) located in damp or wet locations   (b) exposed to fumes, vapors, or gases
    (c) exposed to liquids or excessive temperatures   (d) all of these

    Answer: _____   Section: _____._____

68. Some cleaning and lubricating compounds contain chemicals that cause severe deteriorating reactions with plastics.

    (a) True   (b) False

    Answer: _____   Section: _____._____

69. Accepted industry workmanship practices are described in ANSI/NECA 1-2000, Standard Practices for Good Workmanship in Electrical Contracting, and other ANSI approved installation standards.

    (a) True   (b) False

    Answer: _____   Section: _____._____

70. Conductors must be _____ to provide ready and safe access in underground and subsurface enclosures into which persons enter for installation and maintenance.

    (a) bundled   (b) tied together   (c) color-coded   (d) racked

    Answer: _____   Section: _____._____

71. For mounting electrical equipment on a masonry wall, it is acceptable to drill a hole in the masonry and drive a wooden plug into the hole, then use sheet rock screws drilled into the wooden plug

    (a) True   (b) False

    Answer: _____   Section: _____._____

72. Many terminations and equipment are marked with _____.

    (a) an etching tool   (b) a removable label   (c) a tightening torque   (d) the manufacturer's initials

    Answer: _____   Section: _____._____

73. Connection by means of wire-binding screws, studs, or nuts having upturned lugs or the equivalent are permitted for _____ or smaller conductors.

(a) 10 AWG   (b) 8 AWG   (c) 6 AWG   (d) none of these

Answer: _____   Section: _____._____

74. The temperature rating associated with the ampacity of a _____ must be so selected and coordinated so as not to exceed the lowest temperature rating of any connected termination, conductor, or device.

(a) terminal   (b) conductor   (c) device   (d) all of these

Answer: _____   Section: _____._____

75. For circuits rated 100A or less, when the equipment terminals are listed for use with 75°C conductors, the _____ column of Table 310.16 must be used to determine the ampacity of THHN conductors installed.

(a) 60°C   (b) 75°C   (c) 30°C   (d) 90°C

Answer: _____   Section: _____._____

76. Conductors must have their ampacity determined using the _____ column of Table 310.16 for circuits rated over 100A, or marked for conductors larger than 1 AWG, unless the equipment terminals are listed for use with higher temperature rated conductors.

(a) 60°C   (b) 75°C   (c) 30°C   (d) 90°C

Answer: _____   Section: _____._____

77. On a _____ secondary where the midpoint of one phase winding is grounded, the phase conductor having the higher voltage-to-ground must be identified by an outer finish that is orange in color, or by tagging or other effective means. Such identification must be placed at each point where a connection is made if the grounded conductor is also present.

(a) 1-phase, 3-wire   (b) 3-phase, 4-wire delta-connected
(c) 3-phase, 4-wire wye-connected   (d) 3-phase, 3-wire delta-connected

Answer: _____   Section: _____._____

78. Identification of the high leg of a 3-phase, 4-wire delta connected system is required _____.

(a) at the service disconnect only
(b) at each point on the system where a connection is made if the equipment grounding conductor is also present
(c) at each point on the system where a connection is made if the grounding electrode conductor is also present
(d) at each point on the system where a connection is made if the grounded conductor is also present

Answer: _____   Section: _____._____

79. Switchboards, panelboards, industrial control panels, meter socket enclosures, and motor control centers in commercial and industrial occupancies that are likely to require _____ while energized must be field marked to warn qualified persons of the danger associated with an arc flash from line-to-line or ground faults.

(a) examination   (b) adjustment   (c) servicing or maintenance   (d) a, b, or c

Answer: _____   Section: _____._____

80. Each disconnecting means must be legibly marked to indicate its purpose unless located and arranged so _____.

     (a) that they can be locked out and tagged   (b) they are not readily accessible
     (c) the purpose is evident   (d) that they operate at less than 300 volts-to-ground

     Answer: _____   Section: _____._____

81. Sufficient access and _____ must be provided and maintained about all electrical equipment to permit ready and safe operation and maintenance of such equipment.

     (a) ventilation   (b) cleanliness   (c) circulation   (d) working space

     Answer: _____   Section: _____._____

82. Working-space distances for enclosed live parts must be measured from the _____ of equipment or apparatus, if such are enclosed.

     (a) enclosure   (b) opening   (c) a or b   (d) none of these

     Answer: _____   Section: _____._____

83. The minimum working clearance on a circuit that is 120V to ground, with exposed live parts on one side and no live or grounded parts on the other side of the working space, is _____.

     (a) 1 ft   (b) 3 ft   (c) 4 ft   (d) 6 ft

     Answer: _____   Section: _____._____

84. Concrete, brick, or tile walls are considered as _____, as it applies to working-space requirements.

     (a) inconsequential   (b) in the way   (c) grounded   (d) none of these

     Answer: _____   Section: _____._____

85. The working space in front of the electric equipment must not be less than _____ wide, or the width of the equipment, whichever is greater.

     (a) 15 in.   (b) 30 in.   (c) 40 in.   (d) 60 in.

     Answer: _____   Section: _____._____

86. When normally-enclosed live parts are exposed for inspection or servicing, the working space, if in a passageway or general open space, must be suitably _____.

     (a) accessible   (b) guarded   (c) open   (d) enclosed

     Answer: _____   Section: _____._____

87. For equipment rated 1,200A or more that contains overcurrent devices, switching devices, or control devices, at least one entrance, measuring not less than 24 in. wide and 6 1/2 ft high, must be provided at each end of the working space. Where the entrance to the working space has a personnel door, the door _____.

     (a) must open either in or out with simple pressure and must not have any lock
     (b) must open in the direction of egress and be equipped with panic hardware or other devices so the door can open under
         simple pressure
     (c) must be removed
     (d) must be equipped with an electronic opener

     Answer: _____   Section: _____._____

88. Illumination must be provided for all working spaces about service equipment, switchboards, panelboards, and motor control centers _____.

    (a) over 600V   (b) located indoors
    (c) Rated 1,200 amperes or more   (d) Using automatic means of control

    Answer: _____   Section: _____._____

89. The minimum headroom for working spaces about service equipment, switchboards, panelboards, or motor control centers must be 6 1/2 ft, except for service equipment or panelboards in existing dwelling units that do not exceed 200A.

    (a) True   (b) False

    Answer: _____   Section: _____._____

90. •Heating, cooling, or ventilating equipment (including ducts) that service the electrical room or space cannot be installed in the dedicated space above a panelboard or switchboard.

    (a) True   (b) False

    Answer: _____   Section: _____._____

91. Unless specified otherwise, live parts of electrical equipment operating at _____ or more must be guarded.

    (a) 12V   (b) 15V   (c) 50V   (d) 24V

    Answer: _____   Section: _____._____

92. Live parts of electrical equipment operating at _____ or more must be guarded against accidental contact by approved enclosures or by suitable permanent, substantial partitions, or screens arranged so that only qualified persons have access to the space within reach of the live parts.

    (a) 20V   (b) 30V   (c) 50V   (d) 100V

    Answer: _____   Section: _____._____

93. Entrances to rooms and other guarded locations containing exposed live parts must be marked with conspicuous _____ forbidding unqualified persons to enter.

    (a) warning signs   (b) alarms   (c) a and b   (d) neither a nor b

    Answer: _____   Section: _____._____

94. Openings in ventilated dry-type _____, or similar openings in other equipment over 600V, must be designed so that foreign objects inserted through these openings will be deflected from energized parts.

    (a) lampholders   (b) motors   (c) fuseholders   (d) transformers

    Answer: _____   Section: _____._____

95. •For switchboards and control panels, operating at over 600V, nominal, and exceeding 6 ft in width, there must be one entrance at each end of the equipment. _____ entrance(s) is (are) required for the working space if the depth of the working space is twice that required by 110.34(A).

    (a) One   (b) Two   (c) Three   (d) Four

    Answer: _____   Section: _____._____

96. _____ must be provided to give safe access to the working space around equipment over 600V installed on platforms, balconies, mezzanine floors, or in attic or roof rooms or spaces.

(a) Ladders   (b) Platforms or ladders
(c) Permanent ladders or stairways   (d) Openings

Answer: _____   Section: _____._____

97. When switches cutouts, or other equipment operating at 600V, nominal, or less are installed in a vault, room, or enclosure where there are exposed live parts or exposed wiring operating at over 600V, nominal, the high-voltage equipment must be effectively separated from the space occupied by _____ by a suitable partition, fence, or screen.

(a) the access area   (b) the low-voltage equipment
(c) unauthorized persons   (d) motor-control equipment

Answer: _____   Section: _____._____

98. Switches or other equipment operating at 600V, nominal, or less and serving only equipment within a high-voltage vault, room, or enclosure is permitted to be installed in the _____ enclosure, room, or vault without a partition, fence, or screen if accessible to qualified persons only.

(a) restricted   (b) medium-voltage   (c) sealed   (d) high-voltage

Answer: _____   Section: _____._____

99. Illumination must be provided for all working spaces about electrical equipment operating at over 600V. The lighting outlets must be arranged so that persons changing lamps or making repairs on the lighting system are not endangered by _____ or other equipment.

(a) live parts   (b) rotating parts   (c) bright lamps   (d) panelboards

Answer: _____   Section: _____._____

Chapter 2 Wiring and Protection

Article 200 Use and Identification of Grounded Conductors

This article contains the requirements for the use and identification of the grounded conductor and its terminals.

100. Article 200 contains the requirements for _____.

(a) identification of terminals   (b) grounded conductors in premises wiring systems
(c) identification of grounded conductors   (d) all of these

Answer: _____   Section: _____._____

Unit 1
NEC Practice Quiz
Articles 80 through 110

(• Indicates that 75% or fewer exam takers get the question correct)

1. Compliance with the provisions of the *Code* will result in _____.

    (a) good electrical service
    (b) an efficient electrical system
    (c) an electrical system essentially free from hazard
    (d) all of these

    Answer: _____   Section: _____._____

2. •A conductor encased within material of composition or thickness that is not recognized by this *Code* as electrical insulation is considered _____.

    (a) noninsulating   (b) bare   (c) covered   (d) protected

    Answer: _____   Section: _____._____

3. •Equipment approved for use in dry locations only must be protected against permanent damage from the weather during _____.

    (a) design   (b) building construction   (c) inspection   (d) none of these

    Answer: _____   Section: _____._____

4. •In a grounded system, the conductor that connects the grounded conductor of a service, a feeder supplying a separate building or structure, or the source of a separately derived system to the grounding electrode is called the _____ conductor.

    (a) main grounding   (b) common main   (c) equipment grounding   (d) grounding electrode

    Answer: _____   Section: _____._____

5. •The *Code* applies to the installation of _____.

    (a) electrical conductors and equipment within or on public and private buildings
    (b) outside conductors and equipment on the premises
    (c) optical fiber cable
    (d) all of these

    Answer: _____   Section: _____._____

6. •The required working clearance for access to live parts operating at 300V to ground, where there are exposed live parts on one side and grounded parts on the other side, is _____ according to Table 110.26(A).

    (a) 3 ft   (b) 3 1/2 ft   (c) 4 ft   (d) 4 1/2 ft

    Answer: _____   Section: _____._____

7.   •What size THHN conductor is required for a 50A circuit if the equipment is listed and identified for use with a 75°C conductor? Tip: Table 310.16 lists conductor ampacities.

(a) 10 AWG   (b) 8 AWG   (c) 6 AWG   (d) all of these

Answer: _____   Section: _____._____

8.   A _____ is a device or group of devices that serves to govern in some predetermined manner the electric power delivered to the apparatus to which it is connected.

(a) relay   (b) breaker   (c) transformer   (d) controller

Answer: _____   Section: _____._____

9.   A _____ is a single unit that provides independent living facilities for persons, including permanent provisions for living, sleeping, cooking, and sanitation.

(a) two-family dwelling   (b) one-family dwelling   (c) dwelling unit   (d) multifamily dwelling

Answer: _____   Section: _____._____

10. A circuit breaker is a device designed to _____ a circuit by nonautomatic means and to open the circuit automatically on a pre-determined overcurrent without damage to itself when properly applied within its rating.

(a) blow   (b) disconnect   (c) connect   (d) open and close

Answer: _____   Section: _____._____

11. A device intended for the protection of personnel, that functions to de-energize a circuit or portion thereof within an established period of time when a current-to-ground exceeds the values established for a "Class A Device," is a(n) _____.

(a) dual-element fuse   (b) inverse-time breaker
(c) ground-fault circuit interrupter   (d) safety switch

Answer: _____   Section: _____._____

12. A form of general-use switch constructed so that it can be installed in device boxes or on box covers, or otherwise used in conjunction with wiring systems recognized by the *Code* is called a _____ switch.

(a) transfer   (b) motor-circuit   (c) general-use snap   (d) bypass isolation

Answer: _____   Section: _____._____

13. A hoistway is any _____ in which an elevator or dumbwaiter is designed to operate.

(a) hatchway or well hole   (b) vertical opening or space   (c) shaftway   (d) all of these

Answer: _____   Section: _____._____

14. A raintight enclosure is constructed or protected so that exposure to a beating rain will not result in the entrance of water under specified test conditions.

(a) True   (b) False

Answer: _____   Section: _____._____

15. A signaling circuit is any electric circuit that energizes signaling equipment.

(a) True   (b) False

Answer: _____   Section: _____._____

16.   A single panel or group of panel units designed for assembly in the form of a single panel is called a _____.

      (a) switchboard   (b) disconnect   (c) panelboard   (d) switch

      Answer: _____   Section: _____._____

17.   A system or circuit conductor that is intentionally grounded is a(n) _____.

      (a) grounding conductor   (b) unidentified conductor   (c) grounded conductor   (d) none of these

      Answer: _____   Section: _____._____

18.   A(n) _____ branch circuit supplies energy to one or more outlets to which appliances are to be connected and has no permanently
      connected luminaires (lighting fixtures) that are not a part of an appliance.

      (a) general purpose   (b) multiwire   (c) individual   (d) appliance

      Answer: _____   Section: _____._____

19.   A(n) _____ enclosure is so constructed or protected that exposure to the weather will not interfere with successful operation.

      (a) weatherproof   (b) weathertight   (c) weather-resistant   (d) all weather

      Answer: _____   Section: _____._____

20.   A(n) _____ is a device, group of devices, or other means by which the conductors of a circuit can be disconnected from their
      source of supply.

      (a) feeder   (b) enclosure   (c) disconnecting means   (d) conductor interrupter

      Answer: _____   Section: _____._____

21.   Acceptable to the authority having jurisdiction means _____.

      (a) identified   (b) listed   (c) approved   (d) labeled

      Answer: _____   Section: _____._____

22.   According to the *Code*, automatic is self-acting, operating by its own mechanism when actuated by some impersonal influence,
      such as _____.

      (a) change in current strength   (b) temperature   (c) mechanical configuration   (d) all of these

      Answer: _____   Section: _____._____

23.   Admitting close approach, not guarded by locked doors, elevation, or other effective means, is commonly referred to as _____.

      (a) accessible (equipment)   (b) accessible (wiring methods)
      (c) accessible, readily   (d) all of these

      Answer: _____   Section: _____._____

24.   At least one entrance, not less than 24 in. wide and 6 ft 6 in. high, must be provided to give access to the working space about
      electrical equipment that operates at over 600V, nominal. For switchboards and control panels that exceed 6 ft in width, there
      must be one entrance at each end of such equipment, except where the working space is twice that required in 110.34(A).

      (a) True   (b) False

      Answer: _____   Section: _____._____

25. Conduit installed underground or encased in concrete slabs that are in direct contact with the earth is considered a _____ location.

(a) dry   (b) damp   (c) wet   (d) moist

Answer: _____   Section: _____._____

26. Electrical equipment that depends on _____ for cooling of exposed surfaces must be installed so that airflow over such surfaces is not prevented by walls or by adjacent installed equipment.

(a) outdoor air   (b) natural circulation of air and convection
(c) artificial cooling and circulation   (d) magnetic induction

Answer: _____   Section: _____._____

27. Electrical installations over 600V located in _____, where locks or other approved means control access, are considered to be accessible to qualified persons only.

(a) a room or closet   (b) a vault
(c) an area surrounded by a wall, screen, or fence   (d) any of these

Answer: _____   Section: _____._____

28. Enclosures housing electrical apparatus that are controlled by a lock are considered _____ to qualified persons.

(a) readily accessible   (b) accessible   (c) available   (d) none of these

Answer: _____   Section: _____._____

29. Equipment enclosed in a case or cabinet that is provided with a means of sealing or locking so that live parts cannot be made accessible without opening the enclosure is said to be _____.

(a) guarded   (b) protected   (c) sealable   (d) lockable

Answer: _____   Section: _____._____

30. Equipment intended to break current at other than fault levels must have an interrupting rating at nominal circuit voltage sufficient for the current that must be interrupted.

(a) True   (b) False

Answer: _____   Section: _____._____

31. Equipment or materials to which a symbol or other identifying mark of a product evaluation organization that is acceptable to the authority having jurisdiction has been attached is known as _____.

(a) listed   (b) labeled   (c) approved   (d) rated

Answer: _____   Section: _____._____

32. Equipment such as raceways, cables, wireways, cabinets, panels, etc. can be located above or below other electrical equipment when the associated equipment does not extend more than _____ from the front of the electrical equipment.

(a) 3 in.   (b) 6 in.   (c) 12 in.   (d) 30 in.

Answer: _____   Section: _____._____

33. For equipment rated 1,200A or more that contains overcurrent devices, switching devices, or control devices, there must be one entrance to the required working space not less than 24 in. wide and 6 ft 6 in. high at each end of the working space. Where the depth of the working space is twice that required by 110.26(A)(1), _____ entrance(s) are permitted.

    (a) one   (b) two   (c) three   (d) none of these

    Answer: _____   Section: _____._____

34. In the event the *Code* requires new products, constructions, or materials that are not yet available at the time a new edition is adopted, the _____ may permit the use of the products, constructions, or materials that comply with the most recent previous edition of this *Code* adopted by the jurisdiction.

    (a) architect   (b) master electrician
    (c) authority having jurisdiction   (d) supply house

    Answer: _____   Section: _____._____

35. In the *NEC*, conductors must be _____ unless otherwise provided.

    (a) bare   (b) stranded   (c) copper   (d) aluminum

    Answer: _____   Section: _____._____

36. Outline lighting may include an arrangement of _____ to outline or call attention to certain features such as the shape of a building or the decoration of a window.

    (a) incandescent lamps   (b) electric-discharge lighting
    (c) electrically powered light sources   (d) a, b, or c

    Answer: _____   Section: _____._____

37. Soldered splices must first be spliced or joined so as to be mechanically and electrically secure without solder and then be soldered.

    (a) True   (b) False

    Answer: _____   Section: _____._____

38. The authority having jurisdiction (AHJ) has the responsibility _____.

    (a) for making interpretations of the rules of the *Code*
    (b) for deciding upon the approval of equipment and materials
    (c) for waiving specific requirements in the *Code* and allowing alternate methods and material if safety is maintained
    (d) all of these

    Answer: _____   Section: _____._____

39. The *Code* covers all of the following electrical installations except _____.

    (a) floating buildings
    (b) in or on private and public buildings
    (c) industrial substations
    (d) electrical generation installations on property owned or leased by the electric utility company

    Answer: _____   Section: _____._____

40. The dedicated equipment space for electrical equipment that is required for panelboards is measured from the floor to a height of _____ above the equipment, or to the structural ceiling, whichever is lower.

(a) 3 ft   (b) 6 ft   (c) 12 ft   (d) 30 ft

Answer: _____   Section: _____._____

41. The high leg (wild leg) of a 3-phase, 4-wire delta-connected system must be identified by using _____.

(a) an outer finish that is red in color or by other effective means
(b) an outer finish that is orange in color or by other effective means
(c) permanent lettering on the conductor installed by the manufacturer of the wire
(d) this is no longer required

Answer: _____   Section: _____._____

42. The manufacturer's name, trademark, or other descriptive marking must be placed on all electric equipment. Where required by the *Code*, markings such as voltage, current, wattage, or other ratings must be provided with sufficient durability to withstand _____.

(a) the voltages encountered   (b) painting and other finishes applied
(c) the environment involved   (d) lack of planning by the installer

Answer: _____   Section: _____._____

43. The *NEC* term to define wiring methods that are not concealed is _____.

(a) open   (b) uncovered   (c) exposed   (d) bare

Answer: _____   Section: _____._____

44. The service conductors between the terminals of the service equipment and a point usually outside the building, clear of building walls, where they are joined by tap or splice to the service drop are called _____ service entrance conductors.

(a) underground   (b) complete   (c) overhead   (d) grounded

Answer: _____   Section: _____._____

45. To guard live parts over 50V but less than 600V, the equipment can be _____.

(a) located in a room accessible to qualified persons only   (b) located on a balcony
(c) elevated 8 ft or more above the floor   (d) any of these

Answer: _____   Section: _____._____

46. Unguarded live parts operating at 30,000V located above a working space must be elevated at least _____ above the working space.

(a) 24 ft   (b) 18 ft   (c) 12 ft   (d) 9 1/2 ft

Answer: _____   Section: _____._____

47. Unused cable or raceway openings in electrical equipment must be _____

(a) filled with cable clamps or connectors only
(b) taped over with electrical tape
(c) repaired only by welding or brazing in a metal slug
(d) effectively closed by fittings that provide protection substantially equivalent to the wall of the equipment

Answer: _____   Section: _____._____

48. Utilities include entities that are designated or recognized by governmental law or regulation by public service/utility commissions.

(a) True   (b) False

Answer: _____   Section: _____._____

49. Utilization equipment is equipment that utilizes electricity for _____ purposes.

(a) electromechanical   (b) heating   (c) lighting   (d) any of these

Answer: _____   Section: _____._____

50. Where switches, cutouts, or similar equipment operating at 600V, nominal, or less are installed in a vault, room, or enclosure where they are exposed to energized parts at over 600V, nominal, the high-voltage equipment must be effectively separated from the space occupied by the low-voltage equipment by a suitable _____.

(a) partition   (b) fence   (c) screen   (d) any of these

Answer: _____   Section: _____._____

Unit 1
NEC Challenge Quiz
Articles 90 through Annex C

(• Indicates that 75% or fewer exam takers get the question correct)

1. Branch-circuit conductors supplying a single continuous-duty motor must have an ampacity not less than _____ rating.

    (a) 125 percent of the motor's nameplate current rating
    (b) 125 percent of the motor's full-load current as determined by 430.6(A)(1)
    (c) 125 percent of the motor's full locked-rotor
    (d) 80 percent of the motor's full-load current

    Answer: _____   Section: _____._____

2. When HDPE enters a box, fitting, or other enclosure, a(n) _____ must be provided to protect the wire from abrasion where the box design does not provide such protection.

    (a) bushing   (b) adapter   (c) a or b   (d) reducing bushing

    Answer: _____   Section: _____._____

3. _____ conductor cables 4 AWG and larger marked for use in cable trays, or for CT use, are permitted within a raised floor of an information technology equipment room.

    (a) Green   (b) Insulated   (c) Single   (d) all of these

    Answer: _____   Section: _____._____

4. _____ connectors must not be used for concealed installations of liquidtight flexible metal conduit.

    (a) Straight   (b) Angle   (c) Grounding-type   (d) none of these

    Answer: _____   Section: _____._____

5. _____ must not be used for switching emergency lighting circuits.

    (a) Single-pole switches   (b) Switches connected in series
    (c) 3- and 4-way switches   (d) b and c

    Answer: _____   Section: _____._____

6. _____ protection for fixture wires must be as specified in 240.5.

    (a) Arc-fault   (b) Overcurrent   (c) Ground-fault   (d) Lightning

    Answer: _____   Section: _____._____

7.   _____ rated in amperes is permitted as a controller for all motors.

     (a) A branch-circuit inverse-time circuit breaker   (b) A molded-case switch
     (c) both a and b   (d) none of these

     Answer: _____   Section: _____._____

8.   •A _____ receptacle without GFCI protection can be located in a dwelling unit garage to supply one appliance, which is not easily moved, if the receptacle is located within the dedicated space for the appliance.

     (a) multioutlet   (b) duplex   (c) single   (d) none of these

     Answer: _____   Section: _____._____

9.   •A Class III, Division_____ location is where easily ignitible fibers or combustible flying material are stored or handled but not manufactured.

     (a) 1   (b) 2   (c) 3   (d) all of these

     Answer: _____   Section: _____._____

10.   •A device that, by insertion in a receptacle, establishes a connection between the conductors of the attached flexible cord and the conductors connected permanently to the receptacle is called a(n) _____.

     (a) attachment plug   (b) plug cap   (c) plug   (d) any of these

     Answer: _____   Section: _____._____

11.   •A single receptacle installed on an individual branch circuit must be rated at least _____ percent of the rating of the branch circuit.

     (a) 50   (b) 60   (c) 90   (d) 100

     Answer: _____   Section: _____._____

12.   •EMT must be supported within 3 ft of each coupling.

     (a) True   (b) False

     Answer: _____   Section: _____._____

13.   •For a circuit to be considered a multiwire branch circuit, it must have _____.

     (a) two or more ungrounded conductors with a voltage potential between them
     (b) a grounded conductor having equal voltage potential between it and each ungrounded conductor of the circuit
     (c) a grounded conductor connected to the grounded neutral terminal of the system
     (d) all of these

     Answer: _____   Section: _____._____

14.   •For box fill calculations, a reduction of _____ conductor(s) can be made for one hickey and two internal clamps.

     (a) 1   (b) 2   (c) 3   (d) zero

     Answer: _____   Section: _____._____

15.   •Metal enclosures for grounding electrode conductors must be electrically continuous, from the point of attachment to cabinets or equipment, to the grounding electrode.

     (a) True   (b) False

     Answer: _____   Section: _____._____

16. •Metal raceways, cable trays, cable armor, cable sheath, enclosures, frames, fittings, and other metal non-current-carrying parts that serve as the grounding conductor must be _____ where necessary to ensure electrical continuity and to have the capacity to conduct safely any fault current likely to be imposed.

(a) grounded   (b) effectively bonded   (c) soldered or welded   (d) any of these

Answer: _____   Section: _____._____

17. •Multiwire branch circuits must _____.

(a) supply only line-to-neutral loads
(b) not be allowed in dwelling units
(c) have their conductors originate from different panelboards
(d) none of these

Answer: _____   Section: _____._____

18. •Overhead service-drop conductors must have a horizontal clearance of _____ from a pool.

(a) 6 ft   (b) 10 ft   (c) 8 ft   (d) 4 ft

Answer: _____   Section: _____._____

19. •Service-entrance conductors must not be spliced or tapped.

(a) True   (b) False

Answer: _____   Section: _____._____

20. •The demand factors of Table 220.42 must apply to the computed load of feeders to areas in hospitals, hotels, and motels where the entire lighting is likely to be used at one time, as in operating rooms, ballrooms, or dining rooms.

(a) True   (b) False

Answer: _____   Section: _____._____

21. •The maximum unbalanced feeder load for household electric ranges, wall-mounted ovens, counter-mounted cooking units, and electric dryers must be considered as _____ percent of the load on the ungrounded conductors as determined in accordance with Table 220.55 for ranges and Table 220.54 for dryers.

(a) 50   (b) 70   (c) 85   (d) 115

Answer: _____   Section: _____._____

22. •Underground service conductors between the street main and the first point of connection to the service entrance are known as the _____.

(a) utility service   (b) service lateral   (c) service drop   (d) main service conductors

Answer: _____   Section: _____._____

23. •What size copper grounding electrode conductor is required for a service that has three sets of 500 kcmil copper conductors per phase?

(a) 1 AWG   (b) 1/0 AWG   (c) 2/0 AWG   (d) 3/0 AWG

Answer: _____   Section: _____._____

24.   •When installing direct-buried cables, a _____ must be used at the end of a conduit that terminates underground.

(a) splice kit   (b) terminal fitting   (c) bushing   (d) b or c

Answer: _____   Section: _____._____

25.   •When the service contains two to six service disconnecting means, they must be _____.

(a) the same size   (b) grouped at one location   (c) in the same enclosure   (d) none of these

Answer: _____   Section: _____._____

26.   15 and 20A, single-phase, 125V receptacles located within _____ of the inside walls of a pool or fountain must be protected by a ground-fault circuit interrupter.

(a) 8 ft   (b) 10 ft   (c) 15 ft   (d) 20 ft

Answer: _____   Section: _____._____

27.   A _____ is a building or portion of a building in which one or more self-propelled vehicles can be kept for use, sale, storage, rental, repair, exhibition, or demonstration purposes.

(a) garage   (b) residential garage   (c) service garage   (d) commercial garage

Answer: _____   Section: _____._____

28.   A _____ is a structure transportable in one or more sections that is built on a chassis and designed to be used as a dwelling, with or without a permanent foundation.

(a) manufactured home   (b) mobile home   (c) dwelling unit   (d) all of these

Answer: _____   Section: _____._____

29.   A _____ is an accommodation with two or more contiguous rooms comprising a compartment, with or without doors between such rooms, that provides living, sleeping, sanitary, and storage facilities.

(a) guest room   (b) guest suite   (c) dwelling unit   (d) single family dwelling

Answer: _____   Section: _____._____

30.   A _____ is permitted in lieu of a box or terminal fitting at the end of a conduit where the raceway terminates behind an unenclosed switchboard or similar equipment.

(a) bushing   (b) bonding bushing   (c) coupling   (d) connector

Answer: _____   Section: _____._____

31.   A 15 or 20A, 125V, single-phase receptacle outlet must be located within 25 ft of heating, air-conditioning, and refrigeration equipment for _____ occupancies.

(a) dwelling   (b) commercial   (c) industrial   (d) all of these

Answer: _____   Section: _____._____

32.   A box or conduit body is not required for splices and taps in direct-buried conductors and cables as long as the splice is made with a splicing device that is identified for the purpose.

(a) True   (b) False

Answer: _____   Section: _____._____

33. A cable tray is a unit or assembly of units or sections and associated fittings forming a _____ system used to securely fasten or support cables and raceways.

    (a) structural   (b) flexible   (c) movable   (d) secure

    Answer: _____   Section: _____._____

34. A Class I, Division 1 location is one in which _____.

    (a) ignitible concentrations of flammable gases or vapors can exist under normal operating conditions
    (b) ignitible concentrations of such gases or vapors may exist frequently because of repair or maintenance operations or because of leakage
    (c) breakdown or faulty operation of equipment or processes might release ignitible concentrations of flammable gases or vapors, and might also cause simultaneous failure of electrical equipment
    (d) all of these

    Answer: _____   Section: _____._____

35. A component of an electrical system that is intended to carry or control but not utilize electric energy is a(n) _____.

    (a) raceway   (b) fitting   (c) device   (d) enclosure

    Answer: _____   Section: _____._____

36. A conduit seal fitting must be installed in each conduit that passes from a Class I, Division 2 location into an unclassified location. Conduit boundary seals are not required to be _____, but must be identified for the purpose of minimizing the passage of gases under normal operating conditions.

    (a) listed   (b) installed   (c) explosionproof   (d) accessible

    Answer: _____   Section: _____._____

37. A cord connector on a permanently installed cord pendant is considered a receptacle outlet.

    (a) True   (b) False

    Answer: _____   Section: _____._____

38. A device that establishes an electrical connection to the earth is the _____.

    (a) grounding electrode conductor   (b) grounding conductor
    (c) grounding electrode   (d) grounded conductor

    Answer: _____   Section: _____._____

39. A disconnect must be provided in each ungrounded conductor for each capacitor bank, and must _____.

    (a) open all ungrounded conductors simultaneously
    (b) be permitted to disconnect the capacitor from the line as a regular operating procedure
    (c) be rated no less than 135 percent of the rated current of the capacitor
    (d) all of these

    Answer: _____   Section: _____._____

40. A fuel cell system typically consists of a reformer, stack, power inverter, and auxiliary equipment.

    (a) True   (b) False

    Answer: _____   Section: _____._____

41. A grounding electrode is required if a building or structure is supplied by a feeder or by more than one branch circuit.

(a) True   (b) False

Answer: _____   Section: _____._____

42. A horsepower-rated inverse-time circuit breaker can serve as both a motor controller and disconnecting means if _____.

(a) it opens all ungrounded conductors
(b) it is protected by an overcurrent device in each ungrounded conductor
(c) it is manually operable, or both power and manually operable
(d) all of these

Answer: _____   Section: _____._____

43. A lighting and appliance branch-circuit panelboard contains six 3-pole breakers and eight 2-pole breakers. The maximum allowable number of single-pole breakers that can be added to this panelboard is _____.

(a) 8   (b) 16   (c) 28   (d) 42

Answer: _____   Section: _____._____

44. A limited care facility is an area used on a(n) _____ basis for the housing of four or more persons who are incapable of self-preservation because of age, physical limitation due to accident or illness, or mental limitations, mental illness, or chemical dependency.

(a) occasional   (b) 10 hour or less per day   (c) 24 hour   (d) temporary

Answer: _____   Section: _____._____

45. A listed luminaire or a listed assembly is permitted to be cord-connected if located _____ the outlet box, the cord is continuously visible for its entire length outside the luminaire, and the cord is not subject to strain or physical damage.

(a) within   (b) directly below   (c) directly above   (d) adjacent to

Answer: _____   Section: _____._____

46. A minimum of _____ of working clearance is required to live parts operating at 300 volts-to-ground, where there are exposed live parts on one side and no live or grounded parts on the other side.

(a) 2 ft   (b) 3 ft   (c) 4 ft   (d) 6 ft

Answer: _____   Section: _____._____

47. A minimum of 70 percent of all recreational vehicle sites with electrical supply must each be equipped with a _____,125V receptacle.

(a) 15A   (b) 20A   (c) 30A   (d) 50A

Answer: _____   Section: _____._____

48. A motor control conductor that is tapped from the load side of a motor branch-circuit short-circuit and ground-fault protective device is not considered to be a branch-circuit conductor, and must be protected in accordance with 430.72.

(a) True   (b) False

Answer: _____   Section: _____._____

49.	A multiwire branch circuit is not permitted in a Class I, Zone 1, location unless all conductors of the circuit can be opened simultaneously.

	(a) True					(b) False

	Answer: _____	Section: _____._____

50.	A one-family or two-family dwelling unit requires a minimum of _____ GFCI receptacle(s) to be installed outdoors.

	(a) zero					(b) one					(c) two					(d) three

	Answer: _____	Section: _____._____

Unit 2
NEC Review Quiz
Articles 200 through 230

(• Indicates that 75% or fewer exam takers get the question correct)

Article 200 Use and Identification of Grounded conductors

1. Premises wiring must not be electrically connected to a supply system unless the supply system contains, for any grounded conductor of the interior system, a corresponding conductor that is ungrounded.

   (a) True   (b) False

   Answer: _____   Section: _____._____

2. The application of distinctive marking at the terminals during the process of installation must identify the grounded conductor of _____ metal-sheathed cable.

   (a) armored   (b) mineral-insulated   (c) copper   (d) aluminum

   Answer: _____   Section: _____._____

3. Grounded conductors larger than 6 AWG must be identified by _____.

   (a) a continuous white or gray outer finish along their entire length
   (b) three continuous white stripes along their entire length
   (c) distinctive white or gray tape or paint at terminations
   (d) a, b, or c

   Answer: _____   Section: _____._____

4. Where grounded conductors of different wiring systems are installed in the same raceway, cable, or enclosure, each grounded conductor must be identified in a manner that makes it possible to distinguish the grounded conductors for each system. This means of identification must be_____.

   (a) permanently posted at each branch-circuit panelboard
   (b) posted inside each junction box where both system neutrals are present
   (c) done using a listed labeling technique
   (d) all of these

   Answer: _____   Section: _____._____

5. A cable containing an insulated conductor with a white outer finish can be used for single pole, 3-way or 4-way switch loops, if it is permanently reidentified by painting or other effective means at its termination, and at each location where the conductor is visible and accessible.

   (a) True   (b) False

   Answer: _____   Section: _____._____

Mike Holt Enterprises, Inc. • www.NECcode.com • 1.888.NEC.Code

6. Receptacles, polarized attachment plugs, and cord connectors for plugs and polarized plugs must have the terminal intended for connection to the grounded conductor identified. Identification must be by a metal or metal coating that is substantially _____ in color, or by the word white or the letter W located adjacent to the identified terminal.

(a) green   (b) white   (c) gray   (d) b or c

Answer: _____ Section: _____._____

7. No _____ can be attached to any terminal or lead so as to reverse designated polarity.

(a) grounded conductor   (b) grounding conductor   (c) ungrounded conductor   (d) grounding connector

Answer: _____ Section: _____._____

Article 210 Branch Circuits

This article contains the requirements for branch circuits, such as conductor sizing, identification, GFCI protection of receptacles, and receptacle and lighting outlet requirements.

8. 120/208V or 480Y/227V, 3-phase, 4-wire, wye systems used to supply nonlinear loads such as personal computers, energy-efficient electronic ballasts, electronic dimming, etc., cause distortion of the phase and neutral currents producing high, unwanted, and potentially hazardous harmonic neutral currents. The *Code* cautions us that the system design for multiwire branch circuits should allow for the possibility of high harmonic neutral currents.

(a) True   (b) False

Answer: _____ Section: _____._____

9. When more than one nominal voltage system exists in a building, each ungrounded system conductor must be identified by system. The means of identification must be permanently posted at each branch-circuit panelboard.

(a) True   (b) False

Answer: _____ Section: _____._____

10. Where more than one nominal voltage system exists in a building, each _____ conductor of a branch circuit, where accessible, must be identified by system.

(a) grounded   (b) ungrounded   (c) grounding   (d) all of these

Answer: _____ Section: _____._____

11. A branch-circuit voltage that exceeds 277 volts-to-ground and does not exceed 600V between conductors is used to wire the auxiliary equipment of electrical discharge lamps mounted on poles. The minimum height of these luminaires must not be less than _____.

(a) 31 ft   (b) 15 ft   (c) 18 ft   (d) 22 ft

Answer: _____ Section: _____._____

12. Where two or more branch circuits supply devices or equipment on the same yoke, a means to disconnect simultaneously all ungrounded (hot) conductors that supply those devices or equipment must be provided _____.

(a) at the point where the branch circuit originates   (b) at the location of the device or equipment
(c) at the point where the feeder originates   (d) none of these

Answer: _____ Section: _____._____

13. All 15 and 20A, 125V single-phase receptacles installed in bathrooms of _____ must have ground-fault circuit-interrupter (GFCI) protection for personnel.

(a) guest rooms in hotels/motels   (b) dwelling units
(c) office buildings   (d) all of these

Answer: _____   Section: _____._____

14. GFCI protection is required for all 15 and 20A, 125V single-phase receptacles in accessory buildings that have a floor located at or below grade level not intended as _____ and limited to storage areas, work areas, or similar use.

(a) habitable   (b) finished   (c) a or b   (d) none of these

Answer: _____   Section: _____._____

15. GFCI protection for personnel is required for fixed electric snow melting or deicing equipment receptacles that are not readily accessible and are supplied by a dedicated branch circuit.

(a) True   (b) False

Answer: _____   Section: _____._____

16. GFCI protection for personnel is required for all 15 and 20A, 125V single-phase receptacles installed to serve the countertop surfaces in dwelling unit kitchens.

(a) True   (b) False

Answer: _____   Section: _____._____

17. All 15 and 20A, 125V single-phase receptacles installed in dwelling unit boathouses must have GFCI protection for personnel.

(a) True   (b) False

Answer: _____   Section: _____._____

18. GFCI protection for personnel is required for all 15 and 20A, 125V single-phase receptacles installed on rooftops in other than dwelling units, including those for fixed electric snow melting or deicing equipment.

(a) True   (b) False

Answer: _____   Section: _____._____

19. In locations other than dwelling units, a kitchen _____.

(a) is required to have GFCI protection on all 15 and 20A, 125V single-phase receptacles
(b) includes a sink
(c) includes permanent facilities for food preparation and cooking
(d) all of these

Answer: _____   Section: _____._____

20. Ground-fault circuit-interrupter protection for personnel must be provided for outlets that supply boat hoists installed in dwelling unit locations and supplied by a 15 or 20A, 120V branch circuit.

(a) True   (b) False

Answer: _____   Section: _____._____

21. Two or more _____, 120V small-appliance branch circuits must be provided to supply power for the receptacle outlets in the dwelling unit kitchen, dining room, breakfast room, pantry, or similar dining areas.

    (a) 15A   (b) 20A   (c) 30A   (d) either 20A or 30A

    Answer: _____   Section: _____._____

22. An individual 20A circuit is permitted to supply power to a single dwelling unit bathroom for receptacle outlet(s) and other equipment within the same bathroom.

    (a) True   (b) False

    Answer: _____   Section: _____._____

23. All 15 or 20A, 120V branch circuits that supply outlets in dwelling unit bedrooms must be AFCI protected by a listed arc-fault circuit interrupter of the combination type after January 1, 2008.

    (a) True   (b) False

    Answer: _____   Section: _____._____

24. _____ provided with permanent provisions for cooking must have branch circuits and outlets installed to meet the rules for dwelling units.

    (a) Guest rooms   (b) Guest suites   (c) Commercial kitchens   (d) a and b

    Answer: _____   Section: _____._____

25. The recommended maximum total voltage drop on both the feeder and branch-circuit conductors combined is _____ percent.

    (a) 3   (b) 2   (c) 5   (d) 4.6

    Answer: _____   Section: _____._____

26. Where a branch circuit supplies continuous loads, or any combination of continuous and noncontinuous loads, the rating of the overcurrent device must not be less than the noncontinuous load plus 125 percent of the continuous load.

    (a) True   (b) False

    Answer: _____   Section: _____._____

27. When connected to a branch circuit supplying _____ or more receptacles or outlets, a receptacle must not supply a total cord-and-plug connected load in excess of the maximum specified in Table 210.21(B)(2).

    (a) two   (b) three   (c) four   (d) five

    Answer: _____   Section: _____._____

28. •If a 20A branch circuit supplies multiple 125V receptacles, the receptacles must have an ampere rating of no less than _____.

    (a) 10A   (b) 15A   (c) 20A   (d) 30A

    Answer: _____   Section: _____._____

29. The total rating of utilization equipment fastened in place, other than luminaires, must not exceed _____ percent of the branch-circuit ampere rating where the circuit also supplies receptacles for cord-and-plug connected equipment not fastened in place and/or lighting units.

    (a) 50   (b) 75   (c) 100   (d) 125

    Answer: _____   Section: _____._____

30. _____ in dwelling units must supply only loads within that dwelling unit or loads associated only with that dwelling unit.

   (a) Service-entrance conductors   (b) Ground-fault protection
   (c) Branch circuits   (d) none of these

   Answer: _____   Section: _____._____

31. Receptacle outlets installed for a specific appliance in a dwelling unit, such as a clothes washer, dryer, range, or refrigerator, must be within _____ of the intended location of the appliance.

   (a) sight   (b) 6 ft
   (c) 3 ft   (d) readily accessible, no maximum distance

   Answer: _____   Section: _____._____

32. When applying the general provisions for receptacle spacing to the rooms of a dwelling unit, which require receptacles in the wall space, no point along the floor line in any wall space of a dwelling unit may be more than _____ from an outlet.

   (a) 12 ft   (b) 10 ft   (c) 8 ft   (d) 6 ft

   Answer: _____   Section: _____._____

33. In a dwelling unit, each wall space of _____ or wider requires a receptacle.

   (a) 2 ft   (b) 3 ft   (c) 4 ft   (d) 5 ft

   Answer: _____   Section: _____._____

34. In dwelling units, outdoor receptacles can be connected to one of the 20A small-appliance branch circuits.

   (a) True   (b) False

   Answer: _____   Section: _____._____

35. A receptacle connected to one of the small-appliance branch circuits can be used to supply an electric clock.

   (a) True   (b) False

   Answer: _____   Section: _____._____

36. Receptacles installed in a kitchen to serve countertop surfaces must be supplied by not fewer than _____small-appliance branch circuits.

   (a) one   (b) two   (c) three   (d) no minimum

   Answer: _____   Section: _____._____

37. A receptacle outlet must be installed at each wall counter space that is 12 in. or wider so that no point along the wall line is more than _____, measured horizontally, from a receptacle outlet in that space.

   (a) 10 in.   (b) 12 in.   (c) 16 in.   (d) 24 in.

   Answer: _____   Section: _____._____

38. At least one receptacle outlet must be installed at each peninsular countertop or island not containing a sink or range top, having a long dimension of _____ in. or greater, and a short dimension of _____ in. or greater.

   (a) 12, 24   (b) 24, 12   (c) 24, 48   (d) 48, 24

   Answer: _____   Section: _____._____

39.   For the purpose of determining the placement of receptacles in a dwelling unit kitchen, a(n) _____ countertop is measured from the connecting edge.

       (a) island   (b) usable   (c) peninsular   (d) cooking

       Answer: _____   Section: _____._____

40.   Kitchen and dining room countertop receptacle outlets in dwelling units must be installed above the countertop surface, and not more than ___ above the countertop.

       (a) 12 in.   (b) 20 in.   (c) 24 in.   (d) none of these

       Answer: _____   Section: _____._____

41.   The required receptacle for a dwelling unit countertop surface can be mounted a maximum height of _____ above a dwelling unit kitchen counter surface.

       (a) 10 in.   (b) 12 in.   (c) 18 in.   (d) 20 in.

       Answer: _____   Section: _____._____

42.   In dwelling units, the required wall receptacle outlet is allowed to be installed on the side or front of the basin cabinet if no lower than _____ below the countertop.

       (a) 12 in.   (b) 18 in.   (c) 24 in.   (d) 36 in.

       Answer: _____   Section: _____._____

43.   At least one receptacle outlet accessible from grade level and not more than _____ above grade must be installed at each dwelling unit of a multifamily dwelling located at grade level and provided with individual exterior entrance/egress.

       (a) 3 ft   (b) 6 1/2 ft   (c) 8 ft   (d) 24 in.

       Answer: _____   Section: _____._____

44.   For a one-family dwelling, at least one receptacle outlet is required in each _____.

       (a) basement   (b) attached garage
       (c) detached garage with electric power   (d) all of these

       Answer: _____   Section: _____._____

45.   Hallways in dwelling units that are _____ long or longer require a receptacle outlet.

       (a) 12 ft   (b) 10 ft   (c) 8 ft   (d) 15 ft

       Answer: _____   Section: _____._____

46.   Guest rooms or guest suites provided with permanent provisions for _____ must have receptacle outlets installed in accordance with all of the applicable requirements for a dwelling unit in accordance with 210.52.

       (a) whirlpool tubs   (b) bathing   (c) cooking   (d) internet access

       Answer: _____   Section: _____._____

47. The number of receptacle outlets for guest rooms in hotels and motels must not be less than that required for a dwelling unit, in accordance with 210.52(A). These receptacles can be located to be convenient for permanent furniture layout, but lesson fewer than _____ receptacle outlets must be readily accessible

    (a) 4   (b) 2   (c) 6   (d) 1

    Answer: _____   Section: _____._____

48. A 15 or 20A, 125V, single-phase receptacle outlet must be installed at an accessible location for the servicing of heating, air-conditioning, and refrigeration equipment. The receptacle must be located on the same level and within _____ of the heating, air-conditioning, and refrigeration equipment.

    (a) 10 ft   (b) 15 ft   (c) 20 ft   (d) 25 ft

    Answer: _____   Section: _____._____

49. In a dwelling unit, at least _____ wall switch-controlled lighting outlet(s) must be installed in every dwelling unit habitable room and bathroom.

    (a) one   (b) three   (c) six   (d) none of these

    Answer: _____   Section: _____._____

50. In _____ rooms other than kitchens and bathrooms of dwelling units, one or more receptacles controlled by a wall switch are permitted in lieu of lighting outlets.

    (a) habitable   (b) finished   (c) all   (d) a and b

    Answer: _____   Section: _____._____

51. In a dwelling unit, illumination from a lighting outlet must be provided at the exterior side of each outdoor entrance or exit that has grade-level access.

    (a) True   (b) False

    Answer: _____   Section: _____._____

52. Where a lighting outlet(s) is installed for interior stairways, there must be a wall switch at each floor landing that includes an entryway where the stairway between floor levels has four risers or more.

    (a) True   (b) False

    Answer: _____   Section: _____._____

53. In a dwelling unit, at least one lighting outlet _____ located at the point of entry to the attic, underfloor space, utility room, and basement must be installed where these spaces are used for storage or contain equipment requiring servicing.

    (a) that is unswitched and   (b) containing a switch
    (c) controlled by a wall switch   (d) b or c

    Answer: _____   Section: _____._____

54. For other than dwelling units, a lighting outlet containing a switch or controlled by a wall switch is required near equipment requiring servicing in attics or underfloor spaces, and at least one point of control must be located at the point of entrance to the attic or underfloor space.

    (a) True   (b) False

    Answer: _____   Section: _____._____

Article 215 Feeders

This article covers the requirements for installation, minimum size, and ampacity of feeders.

55.   The feeder conductor ampacity must not be less than that of the service-entrance conductors where the feeder conductors carry the total load supplied by service-entrance conductors with an ampacity of _____ or less.

(a) 100A   (b) 60A   (c) 55A   (d) 30A

Answer: _____   Section: _____._____

56.   Where installed in a metal raceway, all feeder conductors using a common grounded conductor must be _____.

(a) insulated for 600V   (b) enclosed within the same raceway
(c) shielded   (d) none of these

Answer: _____   Section: _____._____

57.   When a feeder supplies _____ in which equipment grounding conductors are required, the feeder must include or provide a grounding means to which the equipment grounding conductors of the branch circuits must be connected.

(a) equipment disconnecting means   (b) electrical systems
(c) branch circuits   (d) electric-discharge lighting equipment

Answer: _____   Section: _____._____

58.   Ground-fault protection of equipment is not required at the feeder disconnect if ground-fault protection of equipment is provided on the _____ side of the feeder.

(a) load   (b) supply   (c) service   (d) none of these

Answer: _____   Section: _____._____

Article 220 Branch-Circuit, Feeder, and Service Calculations

This article provides the requirements for sizing branch circuits, feeders, and services, and for determining the number of receptacles on a circuit and the number of branch circuits required.

59.   When computations in Article 220 result in a fraction of an ampere that is less than _____, such fractions can be dropped.

(a) 0.49   (b) 0.50   (c) 0.51   (d) none of these

Answer: _____   Section: _____._____

60.   •When determining the load for luminaires for branch circuits, the load must be based on the _____.

(a) wattage rating of the luminaire socket   (b) maximum VA rating of the equipment and lamps
(c) wattage rating of the lamps   (d) none of these

Answer: _____   Section: _____._____

61.   For other than dwelling occupancies, banks, or office buildings, each receptacle outlet must be computed at not less than _____ VA for each single or each multiple receptacle on one yoke.

(a) 1,500   (b) 180   (c) 20   (d) 3

Answer: _____   Section: _____._____

62. The 3 VA per square foot general lighting load for dwelling units includes general use receptacles and lighting outlets and no additional load calculations are required for these.

    (a) True   (b) False

    Answer: _____   Section: _____._____

63. The minimum feeder load for show-window lighting is _____ per-linear-foot.

    (a) 400 VA   (b) 200 VA   (c) 300 VA   (d) 180 VA

    Answer: _____   Section: _____._____

64. •Receptacle loads for nondwelling units, computed in accordance with 220.14(H) and (I), are permitted to be _____.

    (a) added to the lighting loads and made subject to the demand factors of Table 220.42
    (b) made subject to the demand factors of Table 220.44
    (c) made subject to the lighting demand loads of Table 220.12
    (d) a or b

    Answer: _____   Section: _____._____

65. The feeder and service load for fixed electric space heating must be computed at _____ percent of the total connected load.

    (a) 125   (b) 100   (c) 80   (d) 200

    Answer: _____   Section: _____._____

66. When sizing a feeder for the fixed appliance loads in dwelling units, a demand factor of 75 percent of the total nameplate ratings can be applied if there are _____ or more appliances fastened in place on the same feeder (not including washer, dryer, heating, or air conditioning).

    (a) two   (b) three   (c) four   (d) five

    Answer: _____   Section: _____._____

67. The load for electric clothes dryers in a dwelling unit must be _____ watts or the nameplate rating, whichever is larger, per dryer.

    (a) 1,500   (b) 4,500   (c) 5,000   (d) 8,000

    Answer: _____   Section: _____._____

68. The feeder demand load for four 6 kW cooktops is _____ kW.

    (a) 17   (b) 4   (c) 12   (d) 24

    Answer: _____   Section: _____._____

69. For identically sized ranges rated more than 12 kW but not more than 27 kW, the maximum demand in column C must be increased by _____ percent of the column C value for each additional kilowatt of rating, or major fraction thereof, by which the rating of individual ranges exceeds 12 kW.

    (a) 125   (b) 10   (c) 5   (d) 80

    Answer: _____   Section: _____._____

70. The feeder demand load for ranges individually rated more than 8 3/4 kW and of different ratings, but none exceeding 27 kW, is calculated by adding all of the ranges together and dividing by the total number of ranges to find an average value. The column C value for the number of ranges is then increased by _____ percent for each kW or major fraction that the average value exceeds 12 kW.

(a) 125   (b) 10   (c) 5   (d) 80

Answer: _____   Section: _____._____

71. Table 220.56 may be applied to compute the load for thermostatically controlled or intermittently used _____ and other kitchen equipment in a commercial kitchen.

(a) commercial electric cooking equipment   (b) dishwasher booster heaters
(c) water heaters   (d) all of these

Answer: _____   Section: _____._____

72. Where it is unlikely that two or more noncoincident loads will be in use simultaneously, it is permissible to use only the _____ loads on at any given time in computing the total load to a feeder.

(a) smaller of the   (b) largest of the   (c) difference between the   (d) none of these

Answer: _____   Section: _____._____

73. There must be no reduction in the size of the grounded conductor on _____ type loads.

(a) dwelling unit   (b) hospital   (c) nonlinear   (d) motel

Answer: _____   Section: _____._____

74. Feeder and service-entrance conductors with demand loads determined by the use of 220.82 are permitted to have the _____ load determined by 220.61.

(a) feeder   (b) circuit   (c) neutral   (d) none of these

Answer: _____   Section: _____._____

75. A demand factor of _____ percent applies to a multifamily dwelling with ten units if the optional calculation method is used.

(a) 75   (b) 60   (c) 50   (d) 43

Answer: _____   Section: _____._____

76. The calculated load to which the demand factors of Table 220.84 apply must include the _____ rating of all appliances that are fastened in place, permanently connected, or located to be on a specific circuit. These include ranges, wall-mounted ovens, counter-mounted cooking units, clothes dryers, water heaters, and space heaters.

(a) calculated   (b) nameplate   (c) circuit   (d) overcurrent protection

Answer: _____   Section: _____._____

77. Feeder conductors for new restaurants are not required to be of _____ ampacity than the service-entrance conductors.

(a) greater   (b) lesser   (c) equal   (d) none of these

Answer: _____   Section: _____._____

78. When a farm dwelling has electric heat and the farm operation has electric grain-drying systems, Part _____ of Article 220 cannot be used to compute the dwelling load where the dwelling and farm load are supplied by a common service.

(a) I   (b) II   (c) III   (d) IV

Answer: _____   Section: _____._____

Article 225 Outside Wiring

This article covers installation requirements for equipment, including conductors located outside, on, or between buildings, poles, and other structures on the premises.

79. Open individual conductors must not be smaller than _____ AWG copper for spans up to 50 ft in length and _____ AWG copper for a longer span, unless supported by a messenger wire.

(a) 10, 8   (b) 6, 8   (c) 6, 6   (d) 8, 8

Answer: _____   Section: _____._____

80. Where a mast is used for overhead conductor support of outside branch circuits and feeders, it must have adequate mechanical strength, or braces or guy wires to support it, to withstand the strain caused by the conductors. Only _____ conductors can be attached to the mast.

(a) communications   (b) fiber optic   (c) feeder or branch circuit   (d) all of these

Answer: _____   Section: _____._____

81. The minimum clearance for overhead conductors not exceeding 600V that pass over commercial areas subject to truck traffic is _____.

(a) 10 ft   (b) 12 ft   (c) 15 ft   (d) 18 ft

Answer: _____   Section: _____._____

82. If a set of 120/240V overhead conductors terminates at a through-the-roof raceway or approved support, with less than 6 ft of these conductors passing over the roof overhang, the minimum clearance above the roof for these conductors is _____.

(a) 12 in.   (b) 18 in.   (c) 2 ft   (d) 5 ft

Answer: _____   Section: _____._____

83. Overhead conductors to a building must maintain a vertical clearance of final spans above, or within _____ measured horizontally from the platforms, projections, or surfaces from which they might be reached.

(a) 3 ft   (b) 6 ft   (c) 8 ft   (d) 10 ft

Answer: _____   Section: _____._____

84. Raceways on exterior surfaces of buildings or other structures must be arranged to drain, and in _____ locations must be raintight.

(a) damp   (b) wet   (c) dry   (d) all of these

Answer: _____   Section: _____._____

85. A building or structure must be supplied by a maximum of _____ feeder(s) or branch circuit(s).

(a) one   (b) two   (c) three   (d) as many as desired

Answer: _____   Section: _____._____

86.   The building disconnecting means must be installed at a(n) _____location.

   (a) accessible   (b) readily accessible   (c) outdoor   (d) indoor

   Answer: _____   Section: _____._____

87.   •There must be no more than _____ disconnects installed for each electric supply.

   (a) two   (b) four   (c) six   (d) none of these

   Answer: _____   Section: _____._____

88.   The one or more additional disconnecting means for fire pumps or for emergency, legally required standby or optional standby
      systems as permitted by 225.30, must be installed sufficiently remote from the one to six disconnecting means for normal supply
      to minimize the possibility of _____ interruption of supply.

   (a) accidental   (b) intermittent   (c) simultaneous   (d) prolonged

   Answer: _____   Section: _____._____

89.   In a multiple-occupancy building where electrical maintenance is provided by the building management under continuous
      building management supervision, the building disconnecting means supplying more than one occupancy can be accessible to
      authorized _____ only.

   (a) inspectors   (b) tenants   (c) management personnel   (d) none of these

   Answer: _____   Section: _____._____

90.   •The building or structure disconnecting means must plainly indicate whether it is in the _____ position.

   (a) open or closed   (b) correct   (c) up or down   (d) none of these

   Answer: _____   Section: _____._____

91.   For installations consisting of not more than two 2-wire branch circuits, the building disconnecting means must have a rating of
      not less than _____.

   (a) 15A   (b) 20A   (c) 25A   (d) 30A

   Answer: _____   Section: _____._____

Article 230 Services

This article covers the installation requirements for service conductors and equipment. It's very important to know where the service
begins and ends when applying Articles 230 and 250.

Conductors supplied from a battery, uninterruptible power supply, solar photovoltaic system, generator, or transformer are not considered service conductors; they are feeder conductors.

92.   Additional services must be permitted for a single building or other structure sufficiently large to make two or more services nec-
      essary if permitted by _____.

   (a) architects   (b) special permission   (c) written authorization (d) master electricians

   Answer: _____   Section: _____._____

93. Where a building or structure is supplied by more than one service, or a combination of branch circuits, feeders, and services, a permanent plaque or directory must be installed at each service disconnect location denoting all other _____ supplying that building or structure and the area served by each.

    (a) services   (b) feeders   (c) branch circuits   (d) all of these

    Answer: _____   Section: _____._____

94. •Conductors other than service conductors must not be installed in the same _____.

    (a) service raceway   (b) service cable   (c) enclosure   (d) a or b

    Answer: _____   Section: _____._____

95. Service conductors installed as unjacketed multiconductor cable must have a minimum clearance of _____ from windows that are designed to be opened, doors, porches, stairs, fire escapes, or similar locations.

    (a) 3 ft   (b) 4 ft   (c) 6 ft   (d) 10 ft

    Answer: _____   Section: _____._____

96. _____ must not be installed beneath openings through which materials may be moved, such as openings in farm and commercial buildings, and must not be installed where they will obstruct entrance to these building openings.

    (a) Overcurrent protection devices   (b) Overhead-service conductors
    (c) Grounding conductors   (d) Wiring systems

    Answer: _____   Section: _____._____

97. Service-drop conductors must have _____.

    (a) sufficient ampacity to carry the current for the load   (b) adequate mechanical strength
    (c) a or b   (d) a and b

    Answer: _____   Section: _____._____

98. Service drops installed over roofs must have a vertical clearance of _____ above the roof surface.

    (a) 8 ft   (b) 12 ft   (c) 15 ft   (d) 3 ft

    Answer: _____   Section: _____._____

99. The requirement for maintaining a 3 ft vertical clearance from the edge of the roof does not apply to the final conductor span where the service drop is attached to _____.

    (a) a service pole   (b) the side of a building   (c) an antenna   (d) the base of a building

    Answer: _____   Section: _____._____

100. The minimum clearance for service drops not exceeding 600V that pass over commercial areas subject to truck traffic is _____.

    (a) 10 ft   (b) 12 ft   (c) 15 ft   (d) 18 ft

    Answer: _____   Section: _____._____

Unit 2
NEC Practice Quiz
Articles 200 through 230

(• Indicates that 75% or fewer exam takers get the question correct)

1. An insulated grounded conductor of _____ or smaller must be identified by a continuous white or gray outer finish, or by three continuous white stripes on other than green insulation along its entire length.

   (a) 3 AWG   (b) 4 AWG   (c) 6 AWG   (d) 8 AWG

   Answer: _____   Section: _____._____

2. _____ must not be installed beneath openings through which materials may be moved, such as openings in farm and commercial buildings, and must not be installed where they will obstruct entrance to these building openings.

   (a) Overcurrent protection devices   (b) Overhead branch-circuit and feeder conductors
   (c) Grounding conductors   (d) Wiring systems

   Answer: _____   Section: _____._____

3. •Service-entrance or feeder conductors whose demand load is determined by the optional calculation, as permitted in 220.88, are not permitted to have the neutral load determined by 220.61.

   (a) True   (b) False

   Answer: _____   Section: _____._____

4. A building or structure must be supplied by a maximum of _____ service(s).

   (a) one   (b) two   (c) three   (d) as many as desired

   Answer: _____   Section: _____._____

5. A receptacle connected to a small-appliance circuit can supply gas-fired ranges, ovens, or counter-mounted cooking units.

   (a) True   (b) False

   Answer: _____   Section: _____._____

6. A receptacle outlet for the laundry is not required in a dwelling unit in a multifamily building when laundry facilities that are available to all building occupants are provided on the premises.

   (a) True   (b) False

   Answer: _____   Section: _____._____

7. A receptacle outlet must be installed in dwelling units for every kitchen and dining area countertop space _____, and no point along the wall line can be more than 2 ft, measured horizontally, from a receptacle outlet in that space.

   (a) wider than 10 in.   (b) wider than 3 ft   (c) 18 in. or wider   (d) 12 in. or wider

   Answer: _____   Section: _____._____

8.   A single piece of equipment consisting of a multiple receptacle comprised of _____ or more receptacles must be computed at not less than 90 VA per receptacle.

      (a) 1   (b) 2   (c) 3   (d) 4

      Answer: _____   Section: _____._____

9.   All 15 and 20A, 125V single-phase receptacles installed in crawl spaces at or below grade level and in _____ of dwelling units must have GFCI protection for personnel.

      (a) unfinished attics   (b) finished attics   (c) unfinished basements   (d) finished basements

      Answer: _____   Section: _____._____

10.   All ungrounded (hot) conductors from two or more branch circuits terminating on multiple devices or equipment on the same yoke must have a means to be disconnected simultaneously in _____ occupancies.

      (a) dwelling unit   (b) commercial   (c) industrial   (d) all of these

      Answer: _____   Section: _____._____

11.   At least one receptacle outlet must be installed directly above a show-window for each _____, or major fraction thereof, of show-window area measured horizontally at its maximum width.

      (a) 10 ft   (b) 12 ft   (c) 18 ft   (d) 24 ft

      Answer: _____   Section: _____._____

12.   At least one wall switch-controlled lighting outlet must be installed in every habitable room and bathroom of a guest room or guest suite of hotels, motels, and similar occupancies. A receptacle outlet controlled by a wall switch may be used to meet this requirement in other than _____.

      (a) bathrooms   (b) kitchens   (c) sleeping areas   (d) both a and b

      Answer: _____   Section: _____._____

13.   Dwelling unit or mobile home feeder conductors need not be larger than the service conductors and are permitted to be sized according to 310.15(B)(6).

      (a) True   (b) False

      Answer: _____   Section: _____._____

14.   For other than dwelling units or guest rooms of hotels or motels, the feeder and service load calculation for track lighting is to be determined at 150 VA for every _____ of track installed.

      (a) 4 ft   (b) 6 ft   (c) 2 ft   (d) none of these

      Answer: _____   Section: _____._____

15.   GFCI protection for personnel is required for all 15 and 20A, 125V single-phase receptacles installed _____ of commercial, industrial, and all other nondwelling occupancies.

      (a) in storage rooms   (b) in equipment rooms   (c) in warehouses   (d) in bathrooms

      Answer: _____   Section: _____._____

16. GFCI protection for personnel is required for all 15 and 20A, 125V single-phase receptacles installed in a dwelling unit _____.

(a) attic   (b) garage   (c) laundry   (d) all of these

Answer: _____   Section: _____._____

17. Ground-fault protection of equipment is required for the feeder disconnect if _____.

(a) the feeder is rated 1,000A or more
(b) it is a solidly-grounded wye system
(c) it is more than 150 volts-to-ground, but not exceeding 600V phase-to-phase
(d) all of these

Answer: _____   Section: _____._____

18. Guest rooms in hotels, motels, and similar occupancies without permanent provisions for cooking must have receptacle outlets installed in accordance with 210.52(A) and 210.52(D).

(a) True   (b) False

Answer: _____   Section: _____._____

19. If a dwelling unit is served by a single 1-phase, 3-wire, 120/240V or 120/208V set of service-entrance or feeder conductors with an ampacity of _____ or greater, it is permissible to compute the feeder and service loads in accordance with 220.82 instead of the method specified in Part III of Article 220.

(a) 100   (b) 125   (c) 150   (d) 175

Answer: _____   Section: _____._____

20. In a dwelling unit, the minimum required receptacle outlets must be in addition to receptacle outlets that are _____.

(a) part of a luminaire or appliance   (b) located within cabinets or cupboards
(c) located more than 5 1/2 ft above the floor   (d) all of these

Answer: _____   Section: _____._____

21. In dwelling units, at least one wall receptacle outlet must be installed in bathrooms within _____ of the outside edge of each basin. The receptacle outlet must be located on a wall or partition that is adjacent to the basin or basin countertop.

(a) 12 in.   (b) 18 in.   (c) 24 in.   (d) 36 in.

Answer: _____   Section: _____._____

22. In other than dwelling units, GFCI protection is required _____.

(a) for outdoor 15 and 20A, 125V single-phase receptacles accessible to the public
(b) at an accessible location for HVAC equipment
(c) both a and b
(d) neither a nor b

Answer: _____   Section: _____._____

23. Loads that are computed for dwelling unit small-appliance branch circuits can be included with the _____ load and subject to the demand factors permitted in Table 220.42 for the general lighting load.

(a) general lighting   (b) feeder   (c) appliance   (d) receptacle

Answer: _____   Section: _____._____

24. More than one feeder or branch circuit is permitted to supply a single building or other structure sufficiently large to require two or more supplies if permitted by _____.

    (a) architects   (b) special permission   (c) written authorization   (d) master electricians

    Answer: _____   Section: _____._____

25. Multioutlet circuits rated 15 or 20A can supply fixed appliances (utilization equipment fastened in place) as long as the fixed appliances do not exceed _____ percent of the circuit rating.

    (a) 125   (b) 100   (c) 75   (d) 50

    Answer: _____   Section: _____._____

26. Overhead conductors installed over roofs must have a vertical clearance of _____ above the roof surface.

    (a) 8 ft   (b) 12 ft   (c) 15 ft   (d) 3 ft

    Answer: _____   Section: _____._____

27. Overhead-service conductors to a building must maintain a vertical clearance of final spans above, or within, _____ measured horizontally from the platforms, projections, or surfaces from which they might be reached.

    (a) 3 ft   (b) 6 ft   (c) 8 ft   (d) 10 ft

    Answer: _____   Section: _____._____

28. Receptacle outlets in floors are not counted as part of the required number of receptacle outlets to service dwelling unit wall spaces unless they are located within _____ of the wall.

    (a) 6 in.   (b) 12 in.   (c) 18 in.   (d) close to the wall

    Answer: _____   Section: _____._____

29. Service conductors supplying a building or other structure must not _____ of another building or other structure.

    (a) be installed on the exterior walls   (b) pass through the interior
    (c) a and b   (d) none of these

    Answer: _____   Section: _____._____

30. Service-drop conductors must have a minimum of _____ vertical clearance from final grade over residential property and driveways, as well as those commercial areas not subject to truck traffic where the voltage is limited to 300 volts-to-ground.

    (a) 10 ft   (b) 12 ft   (c) 15 ft   (d) 18 ft

    Answer: _____   Section: _____._____

31. The 3 VA per-square-foot general lighting load for dwelling units does not include _____.

    (a) open porches   (b) garages
    (c) unused or unfinished spaces not adaptable for future use   (d) all of these

    Answer: _____   Section: _____._____

32. The calculated load to which the demand factors of Table 220.84 apply must include 3 VA per _____ for general lighting and general-use receptacles.

    (a) inch   (b) foot   (c) square inch   (d) square foot

    Answer: _____   Section: _____._____

33. The feeder demand load for nine 16 kW ranges is _____.

(a) 15,000W   (b) 28,800W   (c) 20,000W   (d) 26,000W

Answer: _____   Section: _____._____

34. The grounded conductor of a 3-wire branch circuit supplying a household electric range is permitted to be smaller than the ungrounded conductors when the maximum demand of a range of 8.75 kW or more rating has been computed according to Column C of Table 220.19. However, the ampacity of the grounded conductor must not be less than _____ percent of the branch-circuit rating and not be smaller than _____ AWG.

(a) 50, 6   (b) 70, 6   (c) 50, 10   (d) 70, 10

Answer: _____   Section: _____._____

35. The identification of _____ to which a grounded conductor is to be connected must be substantially white in color.

(a) wire connectors   (b) circuit breakers   (c) terminals   (d) ground rods

Answer: _____   Section: _____._____

36. The location of the arc-fault circuit interrupter can be at other than the origination of the branch circuit if _____.

(a) the arc-fault circuit interrupter is installed within 6 ft of the branch-circuit overcurrent device
(b) the circuit conductors up to the arc-fault circuit interrupter are in a metal raceway or a cable with a metallic sheath
(c) both a and b
(d) none of these

Answer: _____   Section: _____._____

37. The minimum point of attachment of overhead conductors to a building must in no case be less than _____ above finished grade.

(a) 8 ft   (b) 10 ft   (c) 12 ft   (d) 15 ft

Answer: _____   Section: _____._____

38. The minimum size service-drop conductor permitted by the *Code* is _____ AWG copper or _____ AWG aluminum or copper-clad aluminum.

(a) 8, 6   (b) 6, 8   (c) 6, 6   (d) 8, 8

Answer: _____   Section: _____._____

39. The rating of a branch circuit is determined by the rating of the _____.

(a) ampacity of the largest device connected to the circuit
(b) average of the ampacity of all devices
(c) branch-circuit overcurrent protection
(d) ampacity of the branch circuit conductors according to Table 310.16

Answer: _____   Section: _____._____

40. The two to six disconnects as permitted by 225.33 must be _____. Each disconnect must be marked to indicate the load served.

(a) the same size   (b) grouped   (c) in the same enclosure   (d) none of these

Answer: _____   Section: _____._____

41. There must be a minimum of one _____ branch circuit for the laundry outlet(s) in a dwelling unit.

(a) 15A   (b) 20A   (c) 30A   (d) b and c

Answer: _____   Section: _____._____

42. To determine the feeder demand load for ten 3 kW household cooking appliances, use _____ of Table 220.19.

(a) Column A   (b) Column B   (c) Column C   (d) none of these

Answer: _____   Section: _____._____

43. What is the maximum cord-and-plug connected load permitted on a 15A receptacle that is supplied by a 20A circuit supplying multiple outlets?

(a) 12A   (b) 16A   (c) 20A   (d) 24A

Answer: _____   Section: _____._____

44. When applying the demand factors of Table 220.56, in no case can the feeder or service demand load be less than the sum of _____.

(a) the total number of receptacles at 180 VA per receptacle outlet
(b) the VA rating of all of the small appliance circuits combined
(c) the largest two kitchen equipment loads
(d) the kitchen heating and air conditioning loads

Answer: _____   Section: _____._____

45. When breaks occur in dwelling unit kitchen countertop spaces for ranges, refrigerators, sinks, etc., each countertop surface is considered a separate counter space for determining receptacle placement.

(a) True   (b) False

Answer: _____   Section: _____._____

46. When considering lighting outlets in dwelling units, a vehicle door in a garage is considered an outdoor entrance.

(a) True   (b) False

Answer: _____   Section: _____._____

47. When the building disconnecting means is a power-operated switch or circuit breaker, it must be able to be opened by hand in the event of a _____.

(a) ground fault   (b) short circuit   (c) power surge   (d) power-supply failure

Answer: _____   Section: _____._____

48. Where grounded conductors of different wiring systems are installed in the same raceway, cable, or enclosure, each grounded conductor must be identified by a different one of the acceptable methods in order to distinguish the grounded conductors of each system from the other.

(a) True   (b) False

Answer: _____   Section: _____._____

49. Where more than one nominal voltage system exists in a building, each ungrounded conductor of a branch circuit, where accessible, must be identified by system. The identification can be _____ and must be permanently posted at each branch-circuit panelboard.

    (a) color-coding   (b) phase tape   (c) tagging   (d) any of these

    Answer: _____   Section: _____._____

50. Which rooms in a dwelling unit must have a switch-controlled lighting outlet?

    (a) Every habitable room   (b) Bathrooms   (c) Hallways and stairways   (d) all of these

    Answer: _____   Section: _____._____

1. A permanently-mounted luminaire (fixture) in a commercial garage and located over lanes on which vehicles are commonly driven must be located not less than _____ above floor level.

   (a) 10 ft   (b) 12 ft   (c) 14 ft   (d) none of these

   Answer: _____   Section: _____._____

2. A pool capable of holding water to a maximum depth of _____ is a storable pool.

   (a) 18 in.   (b) 36 in.   (c) 42 in.   (d) none of these

   Answer: _____   Section: _____._____

3. A pool light junction box that has a raceway that extends directly to underwater pool light forming shells must be located not less than _____ from the outdoor pool or spa.

   (a) 2 ft   (b) 3 ft   (c) 4 ft   (d) 6 ft

   Answer: _____   Section: _____._____

4. A sealing fitting must be installed within _____ of either side of the boundary where a conduit leaves a Class I, Division 1 location. The sealing fitting must be designed and installed so as to minimize the amount of gas or vapor within the Division 1 portion of the conduit being communicated beyond the seal.

   (a) 5 ft   (b) 6 ft   (c) 8 ft   (d) 10 ft

   Answer: _____   Section: _____._____

5. A single receptacle is a single contact device with no other contact device on the same _____.

   (a) circuit   (b) yoke   (c) run   (d) equipment

   Answer: _____   Section: _____._____

6. A solderless pressure connector is a device that _____ between two or more conductors or between one or more conductors and a terminal by means of mechanical pressure and without the use of solder.

   (a) provides access   (b) protects the wiring   (c) is never needed   (d) establishes a connection

   Answer: _____   Section: _____._____

7. A standard circuit breaker mounted in a Class I, Division 2 location with make-and-break contacts, and not hermetically sealed or oil-immersed, must be installed in a Class I, Division 1 rated enclosure.

   (a) True   (b) False

   Answer: _____   Section: _____._____

8.   A strut-type channel raceway is a metallic raceway intended to be mounted to the surface of, or suspended from, a structure with associated accessories for the installation of electrical conductors.

     (a) True   (b) False

     Answer: _____   Section: _____._____

9.   A surface mount strut-type channel raceway must be secured to the mounting surface with retention straps external to the channel at intervals not exceeding _____ and within 3 ft of each outlet box, cabinet, junction box, or other channel raceway termination.

     (a) 3 ft   (b) 5 ft   (c) 6 ft   (d) 10 ft

     Answer: _____   Section: _____._____

10. A surge arrester is a protective device for limiting surge voltages by _____ or bypassing surge current.

     (a) decreasing   (b) discharging   (c) limiting   (d) derating

     Answer: _____   Section: _____._____

11. A transfer switch is required for all fixed or portable optional standby power systems for buildings or structures for which an electric-utility supply is either the normal or standby source.

     (a) True   (b) False

     Answer: _____   Section: _____._____

12. A value assigned to a circuit or system for the purpose of conveniently designating its voltage class such as 120/240V is called _____ voltage.

     (a) root-mean-square (b) circuit   (c) nominal   (d) source

     Answer: _____   Section: _____._____

13. A wall-mounted luminaire weighing not more than _____ can be supported to a device box with no fewer than two No. 6 or larger screws.

     (a) 4 lbs   (b) 6 lbs   (c) 8 lbs   (d) 10 lbs

     Answer: _____   Section: _____._____

14. A(n) _____ is intended to provide limited overcurrent protection for specific applications and utilization equipment, such as luminaires and appliances. This limited protection is in addition to the protection provided by the required branch circuit overcurrent protective device.

     (a) supplementary overcurrent protective device   (b) transient voltage surge suppressor
     (c) arc-fault circuit interrupter   (d) Class A GFCI

     Answer: _____   Section: _____._____

15. AC circuits of less than 50V must be grounded if supplied by a transformer whose supply system exceeds 150 volts-to-ground.

     (a) True   (b) False

     Answer: _____   Section: _____._____

16. Additional services are permitted for different voltages, frequencies, or phases, or for different uses such as for _____.

    (a) gymnasiums
    (b) different rate schedules
    (c) flea markets
    (d) special entertainment events

    Answer: _____   Section: _____._____

17. Agricultural buildings where excessive dust and dust with water may accumulate, are defined as including all areas of _____ confinement systems, where litter dust or feed dust, including mineral feed particles may accumulate.

    (a) poultry
    (b) livestock
    (c) fish
    (d) all of these

    Answer: _____   Section: _____._____

18. All 125-volt, single-phase, 15 and 20 ampere receptacles installed in aircraft hangers in areas where _____ is (are) used must have ground fault circuit interrupter protection for personnel.

    (a) electrical diagnostic equipment
    (b) electrical hand tools
    (c) portable lighting equipment
    (d) any of these

    Answer: _____   Section: _____._____

19. All 15 and 20A, 125V single-phase receptacles _____ of commercial occupancies must have GFCI protection for personnel.

    (a) in bathrooms
    (b) on rooftops
    (c) in kitchens
    (d) all of these

    Answer: _____   Section: _____._____

20. All 15 and 20A, 125V single-phase receptacles installed in pits, in hoistways, on elevator car tops, and in escalator and moving walk wellways must be _____.

    (a) on a GFCI-protected circuit
    (b) of the GFCI type
    (c) a or b
    (d) none of these

    Answer: _____   Section: _____._____

21. All 15 and 20A, 125V, single-phase general-purpose receptacles installed _____ of agricultural buildings must have ground-fault circuit-interrupter protection for personnel.

    (a) in areas having an equipotential plane
    (b) outdoors
    (c) in dirt confinement areas for livestock
    (d) any of these

    Answer: _____   Section: _____._____

22. All 15, 20, and 30A, 125V, single-phase receptacle outlets used by personnel for temporary power must have ground-fault circuit-interrupter protection for personnel. GFCI protection can be incorporated into a _____ or other devices incorporating listed GFCI protection for personnel identified for portable use.

    (a) circuit breaker
    (b) receptacle
    (c) cord set
    (d) any of these

    Answer: _____   Section: _____._____

23. All accessible portions of abandoned CATV cable must be removed.

    (a) True
    (b) False

    Answer: _____   Section: _____._____

24.   All accessible portions of abandoned communications cable must be removed.

(a) True   (b) False

Answer: _____   Section: _____._____

25.   All accessible portions of abandoned fire alarm cable must be removed.

(a) True   (b) False

Answer: _____   Section: _____._____

26.   All applicable articles of the *Code* apply to intrinsically safe systems except where specifically modified by article 504.

(a) True   (b) False

Answer: _____   Section: _____._____

27.   All areas designated as hazardous (classified) must be properly _____ and the documentation must be available to those authorized to design, install, inspect, maintain, or operate electrical equipment at these locations.

(a) cleaned   (b) documented   (c) maintained   (d) all of these

Answer: _____   Section: _____._____

28.   All branch circuits that supply 15 and 20A, 125V single-phase outlets installed in dwelling unit bedrooms must be protected by
a(n) _____ listed to provide protection of the entire branch circuit.

(a) AFCI   (b) GFCI   (c) a and b   (d) none of these

Answer: _____   Section: _____._____

29.   All cut ends of rigid metal conduit must be _____or otherwise finished to remove rough edges.

(a) threaded   (b) reamed   (c) painted   (d) galvanized

Answer: _____   Section: _____._____

30.   All electric equipment, including power-supply cords, used with storable pools must be protected by _____.

(a) fuses   (b) circuit breakers   (c) double-insulation   (d) GFCIs

Answer: _____   Section: _____._____

31.   All electrical connections in marinas and boatyards must be located _____.

(a) at least 12 in. above the deck of a floating pier   (b) not less than 12 in. above the deck of a fixed pier
(c) not below the electrical datum plane   (d) all of these

Answer: _____   Section: _____._____

32.   All joints between lengths of rigid nonmetallic conduit, and between conduit and couplings, fittings, and boxes must be made by
_____.

(a) the authority having jurisdiction   (b) set screw fittings
(c) an approved method   (d) expansion fittings

Answer: _____   Section: _____._____

33. All receptacles for temporary branch circuits are required to be electrically connected to the _____ conductor.

    (a) grounded   (b) grounding   (c) equipment grounding   (d) grounding electrode

    Answer: _____   Section: _____._____

34. All threaded conduit or fittings referred to in hazardous (classified) locations must be made wrenchtight in order to _____.

    (a) prevent sparking when a fault current flows
    (b) ensure the explosionproof or flameproof integrity of the conduit system
    (c) a and b
    (d) none of these

    Answer: _____   Section: _____._____

35. All wiring for Class 1 circuits must be installed in accordance with Article 300 and the other appropriate articles in Chapter 4.

    (a) True   (b) False

    Answer: _____   Section: _____._____

36. All wiring must be installed so that the completed system will be free from _____, other than required or permitted in Article 250.

    (a) short circuits   (b) grounds   (c) a and b   (d) none of these

    Answer: _____   Section: _____._____

37. Aluminum cable trays must not be used as an equipment grounding conductor for circuits with ground-fault protection above _____.

    (a) 2,000A   (b) 300A   (c) 500A   (d) 1,200A

    Answer: _____   Section: _____._____

38. Aluminum conductors, and copper-clad aluminum conductors are permitted only for branch-circuit wiring in mobile homes.

    (a) True   (b) False

    Answer: _____   Section: _____._____

39. An 8 AWG or larger solid copper equipotential bonding conductor must be extended or attached to any remote panelboard or service equipment enclosure to eliminate voltage gradients in the pool area.

    (a) True   (b) False

    Answer: _____   Section: _____._____

40. An 8 x 8 x 4 in. deep junction/splice box requires 6 in. of free conductor, measured from the point in the box where the conductors enter the enclosure. The 3 in. of conductor outside-the-box rule _____.

    (a) does apply   (b) does not apply   (c) sometimes applies   (d) none of these

    Answer: _____   Section: _____._____

41. An alternate ac power source such as an onsite generator is not a separately derived system if the _____ is solidly interconnected to a service-supplied system neutral.

    (a) ignition system   (b) fuel cell   (c) neutral   (d) line conductor

    Answer: _____   Section: _____._____

42. An electric vehicle connector is a device that, by insertion into an electric vehicle inlet, establishes an electrical connection to the electric vehicle for the purpose of charging and information exchange.

    (a) True   (b) False

    Answer: _____   Section: _____._____

43. An equipment grounding conductor must be identified by _____.

    (a) a continuous outer finish that is green
    (b) being bare
    (c) a continuous outer finish that is green with one or more yellow stripes
    (d) any of these

    Answer: _____   Section: _____._____

44. An equipotential plane is an area where wire mesh or other conductive elements are embedded in or placed under concrete bonded to _____.

    (a) all metal structures   (b) fixed nonelectrical equipment that may become energized
    (c) the electrical grounding system   (d) all of these

    Answer: _____   Section: _____._____

45. An equipotential plane must be installed in all concrete floor confinement areas of livestock buildings and all outdoor confinement areas that contain metallic equipment that is accessible to animals and that may become energized.

    (a) True   (b) False

    Answer: _____   Section: _____._____

46. An exothermic or irreversible compression connection to fireproofed structural metal is required to be accessible.

    (a) True   (b) False

    Answer: _____   Section: _____._____

47. An exposed wiring system for indoor wet locations where walls are frequently washed must be mounted so that there is at least _____ between the mounting surface and the electrical equipment.

    (a) a 1/4 in. airspace   (b) separation by insulated bushings
    (c) separation by noncombustible tubing   (d) none of these

    Answer: _____   Section: _____._____

48. Any current in excess of the rated current of equipment, or the ampacity of a conductor, is called _____.

    (a) trip current   (b) faulted   (c) overcurrent   (d) shorted

    Answer: _____   Section: _____._____

49. Any pit or depression below a garage floor level of a lubrication or service room where Class I liquids are not transferred is considered to be a Class I, Division _____ location up to floor level and extending 18 in. above floor level and 3 ft horizontally.

    (a) 1   (b) 2   (c) 3   (d) not classified

    Answer: _____   Section: _____._____

50.   Any pit or depression below the level of the aircraft hangar floor is classified as a _____ location that extends up to said floor level.

(a) Class I, Division 1 or Zone 1   (b) Class I, Division 2
(c) Class II, Division 1   (d) Class III

Answer: _____   Section: _____._____

Unit 3
NEC Review Quiz
Articles 230 through 250

(• Indicates that 75% or fewer exam takers get the question correct)

Article 230 Services (continued)

1. The minimum point of attachment of the service-drop conductors to a building must in no case be less than _____ above finished grade.

    (a) 8 ft   (b) 10 ft   (c) 12 ft   (d) 15 ft

    Answer: _____   Section: _____._____

2. Service-lateral conductors are required to be insulated except for the grounded conductor when it is _____.

    (a) bare copper used in a raceway
    (b) bare copper and part of a cable assembly that is identified for underground use
    (c) copper-clad aluminum
    (d) a or b

    Answer: _____   Section: _____._____

3. Underground copper service conductors must not be smaller than _____ AWG copper.

    (a) 3   (b) 4   (c) 6   (d) 8

    Answer: _____   Section: _____._____

4. When two to six service disconnecting means in separate enclosures are grouped at one location and supply separate loads from one service drop or lateral, _____ set(s) of service-entrance conductors are permitted to supply each or several such service equipment enclosures.

    (a) one   (b) two   (c) three   (d) four

    Answer: _____   Section: _____._____

5. Service conductors must be sized no less than _____ percent of the continuous load, plus 100 percent of the noncontinuous load.

    (a) 100   (b) 115   (c) 125   (d) 150

    Answer: _____   Section: _____._____

6. Cable tray systems are permitted to support service-entrance conductors. Cable trays used to support service-entrance conductors can contain only service-entrance conductors _____.

    (a) unless a solid fixed barrier separates the service-entrance conductors
    (b) only for under 300V
    (c) only in industrial locations
    (d) only for over 600V

    Answer: _____   Section: _____._____

7. Service-entrance conductors can be spliced or tapped by clamped or bolted connections at any time as long as _____.

    (a) the free ends of conductors are covered with an insulation that is equivalent to that of the conductors or with an insulating device identified for the purpose
    (b) wire connectors or other splicing means installed on conductors that are buried in the earth are listed for direct burial
    (c) no splice is made in a raceway
    (d) all of these

    Answer: _____   Section: _____._____

8. Service cables that are subject to physical damage must be protected by _____.

    (a) rigid metal conduit   (b) intermediate metal conduit
    (c) schedule 80 rigid nonmetallic conduit   (d) any of these

    Answer: _____   Section: _____._____

9. Service cables mounted in contact with a building must be supported at intervals not exceeding _____.

    (a) 4 ft   (b) 3 ft   (c) 30 in.   (d) 24 in.

    Answer: _____   Section: _____._____

10. Where individual open conductors are not exposed to the weather, the conductors must be mounted on _____ knobs.

    (a) door   (b) insulated metal   (c) glass or porcelain   (d) none of these

    Answer: _____   Section: _____._____

11. When individual open conductors enter a building or other structure, they must enter through roof bushings or through the wall in an upward slant through individual, noncombustible, nonabsorbent insulating _____.

    (a) tubes   (b) raceways   (c) chases   (d) standoffs

    Answer: _____   Section: _____._____

12. Service cables must be equipped with a raintight _____.

    (a) raceway   (b) service head   (c) cover   (d) all of these

    Answer: _____   Section: _____._____

13. Service heads must be located _____.

    (a) above the point of attachment   (b) below the point of attachment
    (c) even with the point of attachment   (d) none of these

    Answer: _____   Section: _____._____

14. Service-drop conductors and service-entrance conductors must be arranged so that _____ will not enter the service raceway or equipment.

(a) dust   (b) vapor   (c) water   (d) none of these

Answer: _____   Section: _____._____

15. The service disconnecting means must be installed at a(n) _____location.

(a) dry   (b) readily accessible   (c) outdoor   (d) indoor

Answer: _____   Section: _____._____

16. Each service disconnecting means must be permanently marked to identify it as a service disconnecting means.

(a) True   (b) False

Answer: _____   Section: _____._____

17. Each service disconnecting means must be suitable for _____.

(a) hazardous locations   (b) wet locations   (c) dry locations   (d) the prevailing conditions

Answer: _____   Section: _____._____

18. Disconnecting means used solely for power monitoring equipment, transient voltage surge suppressors, or the control circuit of the ground-fault protection system or power-operable service disconnecting means, installed as part of the listed equipment, are not considered a service disconnecting means.

(a) True   (b) False

Answer: _____   Section: _____._____

19. The additional service disconnecting means for fire pumps or for emergency, legally required standby, or optional standby services permitted by 230.2, must be installed remote from the one to six service disconnecting means for normal service to minimize the possibility of _____ interruption of supply.

(a) accidental   (b) intermittent   (c) simultaneous   (d) prolonged

Answer: _____   Section: _____._____

20. In a multiple-occupancy building where electric service and electrical maintenance are provided by the building management under continuous building management supervision, the service disconnecting means supplying more than one occupancy can be accessible to authorized _____ only.

(a) inspectors   (b) tenants   (c) management personnel   (d) none of these

Answer: _____   Section: _____._____

21. •The service disconnecting means must plainly indicate whether it is in the _____ position.

(a) open or closed   (b) tripped   (c) up or down   (d) correct

Answer: _____   Section: _____._____

22. For installations consisting of not more than two 2-wire branch circuits, the service disconnecting means must have a rating of not less than _____.

(a) 15A   (b) 20A   (c) 25A   (d) 30A

Answer: _____   Section: _____._____

23. The service conductors must be connected to the service disconnecting means by _____ or other approved means.

    (a) pressure connectors   (b) clamps   (c) solder   (d) a or b

    Answer: _____   Section: _____._____

24. _____ for power-operable service disconnects can be connected on the supply side of the service disconnecting means, if suitable overcurrent protection and disconnecting means are provided.

    (a) Control circuits   (b) Distribution panels (c) Grounding conductors (d) none of these

    Answer: _____   Section: _____._____

25. In a service, overcurrent protection devices must never be placed in the grounded service conductor with the exception of a circuit breaker that simultaneously opens all conductors of the circuit.

    (a) True   (b) False

    Answer: _____   Section: _____._____

26. Where necessary to prevent tampering, an automatic overcurrent protection device that protects service conductors supplying only a specific load, such as a water heater, are permitted to be _____ where located so as to be accessible.

    (a) locked   (b) sealed   (c) a or b   (d) none of these

    Answer: _____   Section: _____._____

27. As defined by 230.95, the rating of the service disconnect is considered to be the rating of the largest _____ that can be installed or the highest continuous-current trip setting for which the actual overcurrent protection device installed in a circuit breaker is rated or can be adjusted.

    (a) fuse   (b) circuit   (c) wire   (d) all of these

    Answer: _____   Section: _____._____

28. The maximum setting of the ground-fault protection in a service disconnecting means must be _____.

    (a) 800A   (b) 1,000A   (c) 1,200A   (d) 2,000A

    Answer: _____   Section: _____._____

29. Ground-fault protection that functions to open the service disconnect _____ protect(s) service conductors or the service equipment on the line side.

    (a) will   (b) will not   (c) adequately   (d) totally

    Answer: _____   Section: _____._____

30. Where ground-fault protection is provided for the _____ disconnect and interconnection is made with another supply system by a transfer device, means or devices may be needed to ensure proper ground-fault sensing by the ground-fault protection equipment.

    (a) circuit   (b) service
    (c) switch and fuse combination   (d) b and c

    Answer: _____   Section: _____._____

Article 240 Overcurrent Protection

This article provides the general requirements for overcurrent protection and overcurrent protective devices. Overcurrent protection for conductors and equipment is provided to open the circuit if the current reaches a value that will cause an excessive or dangerous temperature on the conductors or conductor insulation.

31. Overcurrent protection for conductors and equipment is designed to _____ the circuit if the current reaches a value that will cause an excessive or dangerous temperature in conductors or conductor insulation.

    (a) open   (b) close   (c) monitor   (d) record

    Answer: _____   Section: _____._____

32. Conductor overload protection is not required where the interruption of the _____ would create a hazard, such as in a material-handling magnet circuit or fire-pump circuit. However, short-circuit protection is required.

    (a) circuit   (b) line   (c) phase   (d) system

    Answer: _____   Section: _____._____

33. 240.4(E) allows tap conductors to be protected against overcurrent in accordance with other *Code* sections that deal with the specific situation outside Article 240.

    (a) True   (b) False

    Answer: _____   Section: _____._____

34. Where flexible cord is used in listed extension cord sets, the conductors are considered protected against overcurrent when used within _____.

    (a) indoor installations   (b) non-hazardous locations
    (c) the extension cord's listing requirements   (d) 50 ft of the branch-circuit panelboard

    Answer: _____   Section: _____._____

35. The standard ampere ratings for fuses and inverse-time circuit breakers are listed in 240.6(a). Additional standard ratings for fuses include _____.

    (a) 1A   (b) 6A   (c) 601A   (d) all of these

    Answer: _____   Section: _____._____

36. Supplementary overcurrent protection _____.

    (a) must not be used in luminaires.
    (b) may be used as a substitute for a branch-circuit overcurrent protection device.
    (c) may be used to protect internal circuits of equipment.
    (d) must be readily accessible.

    Answer: _____   Section: _____._____

37. When an orderly shutdown is required to minimize hazard(s) to personnel and equipment, a system of coordination based on two conditions is permitted. Those two conditions are _____ short-circuit protection, and _____ indication based on monitoring systems or devices.

    (a) uncoordinated, overcurrent   (b) coordinated, overcurrent
    (c) coordinated, overload   (d) none of these

    Answer: _____   Section: _____._____

38. A(n) _____ is considered equivalent to an overcurrent trip unit.

    (a) current transformer　　(b) overcurrent relay　　(c) a and b　　(d) a or b

    Answer: _____　Section: _____._____

39. Circuit breakers must _____ all ungrounded conductors of the circuit.

    (a) open　　(b) close　　(c) isolate　　(d) inhibit

    Answer: _____　Section: _____._____

40. Single-pole breakers with identified handle ties can be used to protect each ungrounded conductor for line-to-line connected loads.

    (a) True　　(b) False

    Answer: _____　Section: _____._____

41. A feeder tap of 10 ft or less can be made without overcurrent protection at the tap when the rating of the overcurrent device on the line side of the tap conductors does not exceed _____ times the ampacity of the tap conductor.

    (a) 10　　(b) 5　　(c) 125　　(d) 25

    Answer: _____　Section: _____._____

42. One of the requirements that permit conductors supplying a transformer to be tapped, without overcurrent protection at the tap, is that the conductors supplied by the _____ of a transformer must have an ampacity, when multiplied by the ratio of the primary-to-secondary voltage, of at least one-third the rating of the overcurrent device protecting the feeder conductors.

    (a) primary　　(b) secondary　　(c) tertiary　　(d) none of these

    Answer: _____　Section: _____._____

43. The "next size up protection rule" of 240.4(B) is permitted for transformer secondary tap conductors.

    (a) True　　(b) False

    Answer: _____　Section: _____._____

44. No overcurrent protection device can be connected in series with any conductor that is intentionally grounded except where the overcurrent protection device opens all conductors of the circuit, including the _____ conductor, and is designed so that no pole can operate independently (except as allowed for motor overload protection in 430.36 or 430.37).

    (a) ungrounded　　(b) grounding　　(c) grounded　　(d) none of these

    Answer: _____　Section: _____._____

45. Overcurrent protection devices must be _____.

    (a) accessible (as applied to wiring methods)　　(b) accessible (as applied to equipment)
    (c) readily accessible　　(d) inaccessible to unauthorized personnel

    Answer: _____　Section: _____._____

46. Overcurrent protection devices are not permitted to be located _____.

    (a) where exposed to physical damage　　(b) near easily ignitable materials, such as in clothes closets
    (c) in bathrooms of dwelling units　　(d) all of these

    Answer: _____　Section: _____._____

47. Handles or levers of circuit breakers, and similar parts that may move suddenly in such a way that persons in the vicinity are likely to be injured by being struck by them, must be _____.

(a) guarded   (b) isolated   (c) a and b   (d) a or b

Answer: _____   Section: _____._____

48. Plug fuses of the Edison-base type have a maximum rating of _____.

(a) 20A   (b) 30A   (c) 40A   (d) 50A

Answer: _____   Section: _____._____

49. Fuseholders of the Edison-base type must be installed only where they are made to accept _____ fuses by the use of adapters.

(a) Edison-base   (b) medium-base   (c) heavy-duty base   (d) Type S

Answer: _____   Section: _____._____

50. Type _____ fuse adapters must be designed so that once inserted in a fuseholder they cannot be removed.

(a) A   (b) E   (c) S   (d) P

Answer: _____   Section: _____._____

51. Dimensions of Type S fuses, fuseholders, and adapters must be standardized to permit interchangeability regardless of the _____.

(a) model   (b) manufacturer   (c) amperage   (d) voltage

Answer: _____   Section: _____._____

52. Fuseholders for cartridge fuses must be so designed that it is difficult to put a fuse of any given class into a fuseholder that is designed for a _____ lower or a _____ higher than that of the class to which the fuse belongs.

(a) voltage, wattage   (b) wattage, voltage   (c) voltage, current   (d) current, voltage

Answer: _____   Section: _____._____

53. Cartridge fuses and fuseholders must be classified according to _____ ranges.

(a) voltage   (b) amperage   (c) voltage or amperage   (d) voltage and amperage

Answer: _____   Section: _____._____

54. Circuit breakers must be capable of being closed and opened by manual operation. Their normal method of operation by other means, such as electrical or pneumatic must be permitted if means for _____ operation are also provided.

(a) automated   (b) timed   (c) manual   (d) shunt trip

Answer: _____   Section: _____._____

55. A(n) _____ must be of such design that any alteration of its trip point (calibration) or the time required for its operation will require dismantling of the device or breaking of a seal for other than intended adjustments.

(a) Type S fuse   (b) Edison-base fuse   (c) circuit breaker   (d) fuseholder

Answer: _____   Section: _____._____

56. Circuit breakers must be marked with their ampere rating in a manner that will be durable and visible after installation. Such marking can be made visible by removal of a _____.

   (a) trim   (b) cover   (c) box   (d) a or b

   Answer: _____   Section: _____._____

57. Circuit breakers having an interrupting current rating of other than _____ must have their interrupting rating marked on the circuit breaker.

   (a) 50,000A   (b) 10,000A   (c) 15,000A   (d) 5,000A

   Answer: _____   Section: _____._____

58. Circuit breakers used to switch high-intensity discharge lighting circuits must be listed and marked as _____.

   (a) SWD   (b) HID   (c) a or b   (d) a and b

   Answer: _____   Section: _____._____

59. A circuit breaker with a straight voltage rating (240V or 480V) can be used on a circuit where the nominal voltage between any two conductors does not exceed the circuit breaker's voltage rating.

   (a) True   (b) False

   Answer: _____   Section: _____._____

Article 250 Grounding and Bonding

Article 250 covers the requirements for providing a low-impedance path to conduct undesired high voltage to the earth, and requirements for the low-impedance fault-current path necessary to facilitate the operation of overcurrent protection devices.

60. A ground-fault current path is an electrically conductive path from the point of a line-to-case fault extending to the _____.

   (a) ground   (b) earth   (c) electrical supply source   (d) none of these

   Answer: _____   Section: _____._____

61. An effective ground-fault current path is an intentionally constructed low-impedance path designed and intended to carry fault current from the point of a line-to-case fault on a wiring system to _____.

   (a) ground   (b) earth
   (c) the electrical supply source   (d) none of these

   Answer: _____   Section: _____._____

62. Electrical systems that are grounded must be connected to earth in a manner that will _____.

   (a) limit voltages due to lightning, line surges, or unintentional contact with higher voltage lines
   (b) stabilize the voltage-to-ground during normal operation
   (c) facilitate overcurrent protection device operation in case of ground faults
   (d) a and b

   Answer: _____   Section: _____._____

63.   Electrical systems are grounded to the _____ to stabilize the system voltage.

(a) ground   (b) earth   (c) electrical supply source   (d) none of these

Answer: _____   Section: _____ . _____

64.   For grounded systems, the metal parts of electrical equipment in a building or structure must be connected to the _____ for the purpose of limiting the voltage to ground on these materials.

(a) ground   (b) earth   (c) electrical supply source   (d) none of these

Answer: _____   Section: _____ . _____

65.   For grounded systems, the electrical equipment and wiring, and other electrically conductive material likely to become energized, are installed in a manner that creates a permanent, low-impedance circuit capable of safely carrying the maximum ground-fault current likely to be imposed on it from where a ground fault may occur to the _____ .

(a) ground   (b) earth   (c) electrical supply source   (d) none of these

Answer: _____   Section: _____ . _____

66.   For grounded systems, the earth can be considered as an effective ground-fault current path.

(a) True   (b) False

Answer: _____   Section: _____ . _____

67.   The grounding of electrical systems, circuit conductors, surge arresters, and conductive non-current-carrying materials and equipment must be installed and arranged in a manner that will prevent objectionable current over the grounding conductors or grounding paths.

(a) True   (b) False

Answer: _____   Section: _____ . _____

68.   •Currents that introduce noise or data errors in electronic equipment are considered objectionable currents.

(a) True   (b) False

Answer: _____   Section: _____ . _____

69.   Sheet-metal screws can be used to connect grounding (or bonding) conductors or connection devices to enclosures.

(a) True   (b) False

Answer: _____   Section: _____ . _____

70.   _____ on equipment to be grounded must be removed from contact surfaces to ensure good electrical continuity.

(a) Paint   (b) Lacquer   (c) Enamel   (d) any of these

Answer: _____   Section: _____ . _____

71.   AC systems of 50 to 1,000V that supply premises wiring systems must be grounded where the system can be grounded so that the maximum voltage-to-ground on the ungrounded conductors does not exceed _____ .

(a) 1,000V   (b) 300V   (c) 150V   (d) 50V

Answer: _____   Section: _____ . _____

72. AC systems of 50 to 1,000V that supply premises wiring systems must be grounded where supplied by a 3-phase, 4-wire, delta connected system.

    (a) True   (b) False

    Answer: _____   Section: _____._____

73. •When grounding service-supplied alternating-current systems, the grounding electrode conductor must be connected (bonded) to the grounded service conductor (neutral) at _____.

    (a) the load end of the service drop   (b) the meter equipment
    (c) the service disconnect   (d) any of these

    Answer: _____   Section: _____._____

74. A grounding connection must not be made to any grounded circuit conductor on the _____ side of the service disconnecting means except as permitted for separately derived systems or separate buildings.

    (a) supply   (b) power   (c) line   (d) load

    Answer: _____   Section: _____._____

75. The grounded conductor brought to service equipment must be routed with the phase conductors and must not be smaller than specified in Table _____ when the service-entrance conductors are not larger than 1,100 kcmil copper.

    (a) 250.66   (b) 250.122   (c) 310.16   (d) 430.52

    Answer: _____   Section: _____._____

76. Where the service-entrance phase conductors are installed in parallel, the size of the grounded conductor in each raceway must be based on the size of the ungrounded service-entrance conductor in the raceway, but not smaller than _____ AWG.

    (a) 6   (b) 1   (c) 1/0   (d) none of these

    Answer: _____   Section: _____._____

77. A main bonding jumper must be a _____ or similar conductor.

    (a) wire   (b) bus   (c) screw   (d) any of these

    Answer: _____   Section: _____._____

78. The grounding electrode conductor for a single separately derived system must connect the grounded conductor of the derived system to the grounding electrode.

    (a) True   (b) False

    Answer: _____   Section: _____._____

79. Grounding electrode taps from a separately derived system to a common grounding electrode conductor are permitted when a building or structure has multiple separately derived systems.

    (a) True   (b) False

    Answer: _____   Section: _____._____

80. Where a grounded conductor is installed and the neutral-to-case bond is not at the source of the separately derived system, the grounded conductor must be routed with the derived phase conductors and must not be smaller than the required grounding electrode conductor specified in Table 250.66, but must not be required to be larger than the largest ungrounded derived phase conductor.

    (a) True   (b) False

    Answer: _____   Section: _____._____

81. A grounding electrode at a separate building or structure is required where one multiwire branch circuit serves the building or structure.

    (a) True   (b) False

    Answer: _____   Section: _____._____

82. When supplying a grounded system at a separate building or structure, if the equipment grounding conductor is not run with the supply conductors and there are no continuous metallic paths bonded to the grounding system in both buildings involved, and ground fault protection of equipment has not been installed on the common ac service, then the grounded circuit conductor must be connected to the building disconnecting means and to the grounding electrode at the separate building.

    (a) True   (b) False

    Answer: _____   Section: _____._____

83. The frame of a portable generator is not required to be grounded and is not to be connected to a(n) _____ for a system supplied by cord and plug using receptacles mounted on the generator with the grounding terminals of the receptacles bonded to the generator frame.

    (a) grounding electrode   (b) grounded conductor
    (c) ungrounded conductor   (d) equipment grounding conductor

    Answer: _____   Section: _____._____

84. Where none of the items in 250.52(A)(1) through (A)(6) are present for use as a grounding electrode, one or more of the following must be installed and used as the grounding electrode: _____.

    (a) a ground ring   (b) rod and pipe electrodes or plate electrodes
    (c) local metal underground systems or structures   (d) any of these

    Answer: _____   Section: _____._____

85. Interior metal water piping located more than _____ from the point of entrance to the building cannot be used as a part of the grounding electrode system, or as a conductor to interconnect electrodes that are part of the grounding electrode system.

    (a) 2 ft   (b) 4 ft   (c) 5 ft   (d) 6 ft

    Answer: _____   Section: _____._____

86. A bare 4 AWG copper conductor installed near the bottom of a concrete foundation or footing that is in direct contact with the earth may be used as a grounding electrode when the conductor is at least _____ in length.

    (a) 25 ft   (b) 15 ft   (c) 10 ft   (d) 20 ft

    Answer: _____   Section: _____._____

87. Electrodes of pipe or conduit must not be smaller than _____ and, where of iron or steel, must have the outer surface galvanized or otherwise metal-coated for corrosion protection.

    (a) 1/2 in.   (b) 3/4 in.   (c) 1 in.   (d) none of these

    Answer: _____   Section: _____._____

88. A metal underground water pipe must be supplemented by an additional electrode of a type specified in 250.52(A)(2) through (A)(7). Where the supplemental electrode is a rod, pipe, or plate electrode, that portion of the bonding jumper that is the sole connection to the supplemental grounding electrode is not required to be larger than _____ AWG copper wire.

    (a) 8   (b) 6   (c) 4   (d) 1

    Answer: _____   Section: _____._____

89. Ground rod electrodes must be installed so that at least _____ of the length is in contact with the soil. Where rock bottom is encountered, the rod must be driven at an angle not to exceed 45 degrees.

    (a) 8 ft   (b) 5 ft   (c) 1/2   (d) 80 percent

    Answer: _____   Section: _____._____

90. When driving a ground rod electrode, if rock bottom is encountered, the rod is allowed to be bent over in a trench and buried or shortened with a hack saw.

    (a) True   (b) False

    Answer: _____   Section: _____._____

91. The supplementary electrode allowed by the *Code* is different from a supplemental electrode, and is allowed to be connected to the equipment grounding conductors but cannot be used in place of an effective ground-fault current path for electrical equipment.

    (a) True   (b) False

    Answer: _____   Section: _____._____

92. When multiple ground rods are used for a grounding electrode, they must be separated not less than _____ apart.

    (a) 6 ft   (b) 8 ft   (c) 20 ft   (d) 12 ft

    Answer: _____   Section: _____._____

93. Where separate services supply a building and are required to be connected to a grounding electrode, the same grounding electrode must be used. Two or more grounding electrodes that are _____ are considered as a single grounding electrode system in this sense.

    (a) effectively bonded together   (b) spaced no more than 6 ft apart
    (c) a and b   (d) none of these

    Answer: _____   Section: _____._____

94. The grounding electrode conductor must be made of which of the following materials?

    (a) Copper   (b) Aluminum   (c) Copper-clad aluminum   (d) any of these

    Answer: _____   Section: _____._____

95. Grounding electrode conductors smaller than _____ must be in rigid metal conduit, intermediate metal conduit, rigid nonmetallic conduit, electrical metallic tubing, or cable armor.

(a) 6 AWG   (b) 8 AWG   (c) 10 AWG   (d) 4 AWG

Answer: _____   Section: _____._____

96. The grounding electrode conductor must be installed in one continuous length without a splice or joint, unless spliced _____.

(a) by connecting to a busbar
(b) by irreversible compression-type connectors listed as grounding and bonding
(c) by the exothermic welding process.
(d) any of these

Answer: _____   Section: _____._____

97. The grounding electrode conductor can be run to any convenient grounding electrode available in the grounding electrode system or to one or more grounding electrodes individually.

(a) True   (b) False

Answer: _____   Section: _____._____

98. •The largest size grounding electrode conductor required for any service is a _____ copper.

(a) 6 AWG   (b) 1/0 AWG   (c) 3/0 AWG   (d) 250 kcmil

Answer: _____   Section: _____._____

99. In an ac system, the size of the grounding electrode conductor to a concrete-encased electrode is not required to be larger than _____ copper wire.

(a) 4 AWG   (b) 6 AWG   (c) 8 AWG   (d) 10 AWG

Answer: _____   Section: _____._____

100. Grounding electrode conductor connections to a concrete-encased or buried grounding electrode are required to be readily accessible.

(a) True   (b) False

Answer: _____   Section: _____._____

Unit 3
NEC Practice Quiz
Articles 230 through 250

(• Indicates that 75% or fewer exam takers get the question correct)

1. Where raceway-type service masts are used, all raceway fittings must be _____ for use with service masts.

   (a) identified   (b) approved   (c) heavy-duty   (d) listed

   Answer: _____   Section: _____._____

2. •A service that contains 12 AWG service-entrance conductors, as permitted by 230.23(B) Ex., requires a grounding electrode conductor sized no less than _____.

   (a) 6 AWG   (b) 4 AWG   (c) 8 AWG   (d) 10 AWG

   Answer: _____   Section: _____._____

3. •Where the resistance-to-ground of a single rod electrode exceeds 25 ohms, _____.

   (a) other means besides made electrodes must be used in order to provide grounding
   (b) at least one additional electrode must be added
   (c) no additional electrodes are required
   (d) the electrode can be omitted

   Answer: _____   Section: _____._____

4. •Which of the following statements about Type S fuses is (are) true?

   (a) Adapters must fit Edison-base fuseholders.   (b) Adapters are designed to be easily removed.
   (c) Type S fuses must be classified as not over 125V and 30A.   (d) a and c

   Answer: _____   Section: _____._____

5. A circuit breaker with a slash rating (120/240V or 277/480V) can be used on a solidly-grounded circuit where the nominal voltage of any conductor to _____ does not exceed the lower of the two values, and the nominal voltage between any two conductors does not exceed the higher value.

   (a) another conductor   (b) an enclosure   (c) earth   (d) ground

   Answer: _____   Section: _____._____

6. A device that, when interrupting currents in its current-limiting range, will reduce the current flowing in the faulted circuit to a magnitude substantially less than that obtainable in the same circuit if the device were replaced with a solid conductor having comparable impedance, is defined as a(n) _____ protective device.

   (a) short-circuit   (b) overload   (c) ground-fault   (d) current-limiting

   Answer: _____   Section: _____._____

7.   AC systems of 50 to 1,000V that supply premises wiring systems must be grounded where supplied by a 3-phase, 4-wire, wye connected system.

      (a) True   (b) False

      Answer: _____   Section: _____._____

8.   Air terminal conductors or electrodes used for grounding air terminals _____ be used as the grounding electrodes required by 250.50 for grounding wiring systems and equipment.

      (a) must   (b) must not   (c) can   (d) any of these

      Answer: _____   Section: _____._____

9.   An 800A fuse rated at 600V _____ on a 250V system.

      (a) must not be used   (b) must be used   (c) can be installed   (d) none of these

      Answer: _____   Section: _____._____

10.   An effective ground-fault current path is created when all electrically conductive materials that are likely to be energized are bonded together and to the _____.

      (a) ground   (b) earth   (c) electrical supply source   (d) none of these

      Answer: _____   Section: _____._____

11.   Branch-circuit overcurrent protection devices are not required to be accessible to occupants of guest rooms of hotels and motels if maintenance is provided in a facility that is under continuous building management.

      (a) True   (b) False

      Answer: _____   Section: _____._____

12.   Breakers or fuses can be used in parallel when _____.

      (a) they are factory assembled in parallel   (b) they are listed as a unit
      (c) a and b   (d) a or b

      Answer: _____   Section: _____._____

13.   Cartridge fuses and fuseholders of the 300V type are not permitted on circuits exceeding 300V _____.

      (a) between conductors   (b) to ground   (c) or less   (d) a or c

      Answer: _____   Section: _____._____

14.   Circuit breakers must be marked with their _____ rating in a manner that will be durable and visible after installation.

      (a) voltage   (b) ampere   (c) type   (d) all of these

      Answer: _____   Section: _____._____

15.   Circuit breakers used as switches in 120V or 277V fluorescent-lighting circuits must be listed and marked _____.

      (a) UL   (b) SWD or HID   (c) Amps   (d) VA

      Answer: _____   Section: _____._____

16. Except where limited by 210.4(B), individual single-pole circuit breakers, with or without approved handle ties, are permitted as the protection for each ungrounded conductor of multiwire branch circuits that serve only 1-phase line-to-neutral loads.

    (a) True   (b) False

    Answer: _____   Section: _____._____

17. Flexible cords approved for and used with a specific listed appliance or portable lamp are considered to be protected when _____.

    (a) not more than 6 ft in length   (b) 20 AWG and larger
    (c) applied within the listing requirements   (d) 16 AWG and larger

    Answer: _____   Section: _____._____

18. For grounded systems, electrical equipment and wiring, and other electrically conductive material likely to become energized, must be installed in a manner that creates a _____ from any point on the wiring system where a ground fault may occur to the electrical supply source.

    (a) permanent path
    (b) low-impedance path
    (c) path capable of safely carrying the ground-fault current likely to be imposed on it
    (d) all of these

    Answer: _____   Section: _____._____

19. For grounded systems, non-current-carrying conductive materials enclosing electrical conductors or equipment, or forming part of such equipment, must be connected to earth so as to limit the voltage-to-ground on these materials.

    (a) True   (b) False

    Answer: _____   Section: _____._____

20. For industrial installations only, a tap can be made without overcurrent protection when the transformer secondary conductors have a total length of not more than _____ . The tap conductors must have an ampacity not less than the secondary current rating of the transformer and the sum of the ratings of the overcurrent devices.

    (a) 8 ft   (b) 25 ft   (c) 35 ft   (d) 75 ft

    Answer: _____   Section: _____._____

21. For installations that supply only limited loads of a single branch circuit, the service disconnecting means must have a rating of not less than _____.

    (a) 15A   (b) 20A   (c) 25A   (d) 30A

    Answer: _____   Section: _____._____

22. Ground-fault protection at service equipment may make it necessary to review the overall wiring system for proper selective overcurrent protection _____.

    (a) rating   (b) coordination   (c) devices   (d) none of these

    Answer: _____   Section: _____._____

23. Ground-fault protection of equipment must be provided for solidly-grounded wye electrical services of more than 150 volts-to-ground, but not exceeding 600V phase-to-phase for each service disconnecting means rated _____ or more.

    (a) 1,000A   (b) 1,500A   (c) 2,000A   (d) 2,500A

    Answer: _____   Section: _____._____

24. Ground-fault protection of equipment must be provided in accordance with the provisions of 230.95 for solidly grounded wye electrical systems of more than 150 volts-to-ground, but not exceeding 600V phase-to-phase for each individual device used as a building or structure main disconnecting means rated _____, or more.

    (a) 1,000A   (b) 1,500A   (c) 2,000A   (d) 2,500A

    Answer: _____   Section: _____._____

25. Grounding electrode conductor fittings must be protected from physical damage by being enclosed in _____ where there may be a possibility of physical damage.

    (a) metal   (b) wood   (c) the equivalent of a or b   (d) none of these

    Answer: _____   Section: _____._____

26. Grounding electrode conductors _____ and larger that are not subject to physical damage can be run exposed along the surface, if securely fastened to the construction.

    (a) 6 AWG   (b) 8 AWG   (c) 10 AWG   (d) 4 AWG

    Answer: _____   Section: _____._____

27. Grounding electrodes consisting of stainless-steel rods or nonferrous rods that are less than 5/8 in. in diameter must be listed and cannot be less than _____ in diameter.

    (a) 1/2 in.   (b) 3/4 in.   (c) 1 in.   (d) 1 1/4 in.

    Answer: _____   Section: _____._____

28. In a multiple-occupancy building, each occupant must have access to the occupant's _____.

    (a) service disconnecting means (b) service drops   (c) distribution transformer   (d) lateral conductors

    Answer: _____   Section: _____._____

29. Meter disconnect switches that have a short-circuit current rating equal to or greater than the available short-circuit current are permitted ahead of the service-disconnecting means.

    (a) True   (b) False

    Answer: _____   Section: _____._____

30. Overcurrent protection for tap conductors not over 25 ft is not required at the point where the conductors receive their supply providing the _____.

    (a) ampacity of the tap conductors is not less than one-third the rating of the overcurrent device protecting the feeder conductors being tapped
    (b) tap conductors terminate in a single circuit breaker or set of fuses that limit the load to the ampacity of the tap conductors
    (c) tap conductors are suitably protected from physical damage
    (d) all of these

    Answer: _____   Section: _____._____

31. Plug fuses of 15A or less must be identified by a(n) _____ configuration of the window, cap, or other prominent part to distinguish them from fuses of higher ampere ratings.

    (a) octagonal   (b) rectangular   (c) hexagonal   (d) triangular

    Answer: _____   Section: _____._____

32. Service cables, where subject to physical damage, must be protected.

    (a) True   (b) False

    Answer: _____   Section: _____._____

33. Service disconnecting means must not be installed in bathrooms.

    (a) True   (b) False

    Answer: _____   Section: _____._____

34. Service heads for service raceways must be _____.

    (a) raintight   (b) weatherproof   (c) rainproof   (d) watertight

    Answer: _____   Section: _____._____

35. Service lateral conductors that supply power to limited loads of a single branch circuit must not be smaller than _____.

    (a) 4 AWG copper   (b) 8 AWG aluminum   (c) 12 AWG copper   (d) none of these

    Answer: _____   Section: _____._____

36. Temporary current flowing on the effective ground-fault current path during a ground fault condition is considered by the *Code* to be objectionable current.

    (a) True   (b) False

    Answer: _____   Section: _____._____

37. The connection of the grounding electrode conductor to a buried grounding electrode (driven ground rod) must be made with a listed terminal device that is accessible.

    (a) True   (b) False

    Answer: _____   Section: _____._____

38. The frame of a vehicle-mounted generator is not required to be connected to a(n) _____ for a system supplied by cord and plug using receptacles mounted on the vehicle or the generator when the grounding terminals of the receptacles are bonded to the generator frame and the generator frame is bonded to the vehicle frame.

    (a) grounding electrode   (b) grounded conductor   (c) ungrounded conductor   (d) equipment grounding
        conductor

    Answer: _____   Section: _____._____

39. The grounding electrode conductor at the service is permitted to terminate on an equipment grounding terminal bar if a (main) bonding jumper is installed between the grounded conductor bus and the equipment grounding terminal.

    (a) True   (b) False

    Answer: _____   Section: _____._____

40.   The grounding electrode for a separately derived system must be as near as practicable to, and preferably in the same area as, the grounding electrode conductor connection to the system. The grounding electrode must be the nearest one of the following:

(a) An effectively grounded metal member of the building structure.
(b) An effectively grounded metal water pipe, but only if it's within 5 ft from the point of entrance into the building.
(c) Any metal structure that is effectively grounded.
(d) a or b

Answer: _____   Section: _____._____

41.   The metal frame of a building where one of the four *Code*-prescribed methods of making an earth connection has been met may serve as part of the grounding electrode system.

(a) True   (b) False

Answer: _____   Section: _____._____

42.   There must be no more than _____ disconnects installed for each service or for each set of service-entrance conductors as permitted in 230.2 and 230.40.

(a) two   (b) four   (c) six   (d) none of these

Answer: _____   Section: _____._____

43.   To prevent water from entering service equipment, service-entrance conductors must _____.

(a) be connected to service-drop conductors below the level of the service head
(b) have drip loops formed on the service-entrance conductors
(c) a or b
(d) a and b

Answer: _____   Section: _____._____

44.   When driving a ground rod electrode, if rock bottom is encountered, the rod must be driven at an angle not to exceed 45 degrees. Where rock bottom is encountered when driving at an angle up to 45 degrees, the electrode is permitted to be buried in a trench that is at least _____ deep.

(a) 4 ft   (b) 30 in.   (c) 8 ft   (d) 18 in.

Answer: _____   Section: _____._____

45.   When service-entrance conductors exceed 1,100 kcmil for copper, the required grounded conductor for the service must be sized not less than _____ percent of the area of the largest ungrounded service-entrance (phase) conductor.

(a) 15   (b) 19   (c) 12 1/2   (d) 25

Answer: _____   Section: _____._____

46.   When supplying a grounded system at a separate building or structure, if the equipment grounding conductor is run with the supply conductors and connected to the building disconnecting means, there must be no connection made between the grounded conductor and the equipment grounding conductor at the separate building.

(a) True   (b) False

Answer: _____   Section: _____._____

47. Where a main bonding jumper is a screw only, the screw must be identified with _____ that must be visible with the screw installed.

    (a) a silver or white finish   (b) an etched ground symbol   (c) a green tag   (d) a green finish

    Answer: _____   Section: _____._____

48. Where exposed to _____, service conductors must be mounted on insulators or on insulating supports attached to racks, brackets, or other approved means. Where not exposed to the weather, the conductors must be mounted on glass or porcelain knobs.

    (a) a corrosive environment   (b) the weather   (c) the general public   (d) any inspector

    Answer: _____   Section: _____._____

49. Where the service overcurrent devices are locked or sealed or are not readily accessible to the _____, branch-circuit overcurrent devices must be installed on the load side, must be mounted in a readily accessible location, and must be of lower ampere rating than the service overcurrent device.

    (a) inspector   (b) electrician   (c) occupant   (d) all of these

    Answer: _____   Section: _____._____

50. Wiring methods permitted for service conductors include _____.

    (a) rigid metal conduit   (b) electrical metallic tubing   (c) rigid nonmetallic conduit   (d) all of these

    Answer: _____   Section: _____._____

1. Armored cable is limited or not permitted _____.

    (a) in damp or wet locations   (b) where subject to physical damage
    (c) where exposed to corrosive fumes or vapors   (d) all of these

    Answer: _____   Section: _____._____

2. Armored cable used for the connection of recessed luminaires or equipment within an accessible ceiling does not need to be secured for lengths up to _____.

    (a) 2 ft   (b) 3 ft   (c) 4 ft   (d) 6 ft

    Answer: _____   Section: _____._____

3. Article 604 contains all requirements for the installation of manufactured wiring systems, no other *Code* articles will apply.

    (a) True   (b) False

    Answer: _____   Section: _____._____

4. At carnivals, circuses, and similar events, electrical service equipment must not be installed in a location that is accessible to unqualified persons, unless the equipment is _____.

    (a) lockable   (b) operating at under 600V   (c) weatherproof   (d) arc-fault protected

    Answer: _____   Section: _____._____

5. At least _____ 125V, single-phase, duplex receptacle(s) must be provided in each machine room and machinery space.

    (a) one   (b) two   (c) three   (d) four

    Answer: _____   Section: _____._____

6. Attachment plugs, cord connectors, and flanged-surface devices, must be listed with the manufacturer's name or identification and voltage and ampere ratings.

    (a) True   (b) False

    Answer: _____   Section: _____._____

7. Audio cables installed exposed on the surface of ceilings and sidewalls must be supported by the structural components of the building in such a manner that the cable will not be damaged by normal building use. Such cables must be supported by _____ designed and installed so as not to damage the cable.

    (a) straps   (b) staples   (c) hangers   (d) any of these

    Answer: _____   Section: _____._____

8.   Automatic transfer switches on legally required standby systems must be electrically operated and _____ held.

      (a) electrically   (b) mechanically   (c) gravity   (d) any of these

      Answer: _____   Section: _____._____

9.   Ballasts, transformers, and electronic power supplies for electric signs must be located where accessible and must be securely fastened in place. Where they are not installed in the sign, a working space at least _____ must be provided.

      (a) 3 ft high, 3 ft wide by 3 ft deep   (b) 4 ft high, 3 ft wide by 3 ft deep
      (c) 6 ft high, 3 ft wide by 3 ft deep   (d) none of these

      Answer: _____   Section: _____._____

10.   Bare aluminum or copper-clad aluminum grounding conductors must not be used where in direct contact with masonry, the earth, or where subject to corrosive conditions. Where used outside, aluminum or copper-clad aluminum grounding electrode conductors must not be terminated within _____ of the earth.

      (a) 6 in.   (b) 12 in.   (c) 15 in.   (d) 18 in.

      Answer: _____   Section: _____._____

11.   Bends in ITC cable must be made _____.

      (a) so as not to exceed 45 degrees   (b) so as not to damage the cable
      (c) not less than 5 times the diameter of the cable   (d) using listed bending tools

      Answer: _____   Section: _____._____

12.   Bends made in UF cable must be made so that the cable will not be damaged. The radius of the curve of the inner edge of any bend during or after installation must not be less than _____ the diameter of the cable.

      (a) 5 times   (b) 7 times   (c) 10 times   (d) 125% of

      Answer: _____   Section: _____._____

13.   Boxes and fittings must be _____ where installed in a Class III, Division 1 or 2 hazardous (classified) location.

      (a) explosionproof   (b) dust-ignitionproof   (c) dusttight   (d) weatherproof

      Answer: _____   Section: _____._____

14.   Boxes and fittings used for taps, joints, or terminal connections must be _____ where installed in a Class II, Division 1 hazardous (classified) location.

      (a) explosionproof   (b) identified for Class II locations (dust-ignitionproof)
      (c) dusttight   (d) weatherproof

      Answer: _____   Section: _____._____

15.   Boxes can be supported from a multiconductor cord or cable, provided the conductors are protected from _____.

      (a) strain   (b) temperature   (c) sunlight   (d) abrasion

      Answer: _____   Section: _____._____

16. Boxes, enclosures, fittings, and joints are not required to be explosionproof in a Class I, Division 2 location. However, if arcs or sparks (such as from make-and-break contacts) can result from equipment being utilized, that equipment must be installed in an explosionproof enclosure meeting the requirements for Class I, Division 1 locations.

    (a) True   (b) False

    Answer: _____   Section: _____._____

17. Branch-circuit conductors for data-processing equipment must have an ampacity not less than _____ of the total connected load.

    (a) 80 percent   (b) 100 percent   (c) 125 percent   (d) the sum

    Answer: _____   Section: _____._____

18. Branch-circuit conductors supplying a single motor-compressor must have an ampacity not less than _____ percent of either the motor-compressor rated-load current or the branch-circuit selection current, whichever is greater.

    (a) 125   (b) 100   (c) 250   (d) 80

    Answer: _____   Section: _____._____

19. Branch-circuit conductors that supply a continuous load, or any combination of continuous and non-continuous loads, must have an ampacity of not less than 125 percent of the continuous load, plus 100 percent of the noncontinuous load.

    (a) True   (b) False

    Answer: _____   Section: _____._____

20. Cable or nonmetallic raceway-type wiring methods installed in a groove, to be covered by wallboard, siding, paneling, carpeting, or similar finish must be protected by 1/16 in. thick _____ or by not less than 1 1/4 in. of free space for the full length of the groove. A thinner plate that provides equal or better protection may be used if listed and marked.

    (a) steel plate   (b) steel sleeve   (c) PVC bushing   (d) a or b

    Answer: _____   Section: _____._____

21. Cable splices or terminations in power-limited fire alarm systems must be made in listed _____ or utilization equipment.

    (a) fittings   (b) boxes or enclosures   (c) fire alarm devices   (d) all of these

    Answer: _____   Section: _____._____

22. Cable trays and their associated fittings must be _____ for the intended use.

    (a) listed   (b) approved   (c) identified   (d) none of these

    Answer: _____   Section: _____._____

23. Cable trays must be _____ except as permitted by 392.6(G).

    (a) exposed   (b) accessible   (c) concealed   (d) a and b

    Answer: _____   Section: _____._____

24. Cable wiring methods must not be used as a means of support for _____.

    (a) other cables   (b) raceways   (c) non electrical equipment (d) a, b, or c

    Answer: _____   Section: _____._____

25. Capable of being removed or exposed without damaging the building structure or finish, or not permanently closed in by the structure or finish of the building defines _____.

    (a) accessible (equipment)   (b) accessible (wiring methods)
    (c) accessible, readily   (d) all of these

    Answer: _____   Section: _____._____

26. Circuit breakers and fuses must be readily accessible and they must be installed so the center of the grip of the operating handle of the fuse switch or circuit breaker, when in its highest position, isn't more than _____ above the floor or working platform.

    (a) 6 ft 7 in.   (b) 2 ft   (c) 5 ft   (d) 4 ft 6 in.

    Answer: _____   Section: _____._____

27. Circuit breakers must clearly indicate whether they are in the open "off" or closed "on" position. Where the circuit breaker handles are operated vertically the "up" position of the handle must be the _____.

    (a) "on" position   (b) "off" position   (c) tripped position   (d) any of these

    Answer: _____   Section: _____._____

28. Circuit breakers rated at _____ amperes or less and _____ volts or less must have the ampere rating molded, stamped, etched, or similarly marked into their handles or escutcheon areas.

    (a) 100, 600   (b) 600, 100   (c) 1,000, 6,000   (d) 6,000, 1,000

    Answer: _____   Section: _____._____

29. Circuits used only for the operation of fire alarms, other protective signaling systems, or the supply to fire pump equipment are permitted to be connected on the _____ of the service overcurrent protection device where separately provided with overcurrent protection.

    (a) base   (b) load side   (c) supply side   (d) top

    Answer: _____   Section: _____._____

30. Class 1 and nonpower-limited fire alarm circuits can occupy the same cable, enclosure, or raceway, provided all conductors are insulated for the maximum voltage of any conductor.

    (a) True   (b) False

    Answer: _____   Section: _____._____

31. Class 1 power-limited circuits must be supplied from a source having a rated output of not more than 30V. If the voltage rating were 25V, the maximum VA of the circuit would be _____.

    (a) 750 VA   (b) 700 VA   (c) 1,000 VA   (d) 1,200 VA

    Answer: _____   Section: _____._____

32. Class 2 and Class 3 plenum cables listed as suitable for use in ducts, plenums, and other spaces used for environmental air are _____.

    (a) CL2P and CL3P   (b) CL2R and CL3R   (c) CL2 and CL3   (d) PLCT

    Answer: _____   Section: _____._____

33. Coaxial cables used for CATV systems must not be strapped, taped, or attached by any means to the exterior of any _____ as a means of support.

(a) conduit
(b) raceway
(c) raceway-type mast intended for overhead spans of such cables
(d) a or b

Answer: _____ Section: _____._____

34. Communications wiring such as telephone, antenna, and CATV wiring within a building is not required to comply with the installation requirements of Chapters 1 through 7, except where it is specifically referenced therein.

(a) True   (b) False

Answer: _____ Section: _____._____

35. Composite optical fiber cables contain optical fibers and current-carrying electrical conductors. They are permitted to contain noncurrent-carrying conductive members such as metallic _____. Composite optical fiber cables are classified as electrical cables in accordance with the type of electrical conductors.

(a) strength members   (b) vapor barriers   (c) none of these   (d) a and b

Answer: _____ Section: _____._____

36. Concrete-encased electrodes of _____ are not required to be part of the grounding electrode system where the steel reinforcing bars or rods aren't accessible for use without disturbing the concrete.

(a) hazardous locations   (b) health care facilities
(c) existing buildings or structures   (d) agricultural buildings with equipotential planes

Answer: _____ Section: _____._____

37. Conductors and cables of intrinsically safe circuits not in raceways or cable trays must be separated by at least _____ and secured from conductors and cables of any nonintrinsically safe circuits.

(a) 6 in.   (b) 2 in.   (c) 18 in.   (d) 12 in.

Answer: _____ Section: _____._____

38. Conductors for an appliance circuit supplying more than one appliance or appliance receptacle in an installation operating at less than 50V must not be smaller than _____ AWG copper or equivalent.

(a) 18   (b) 14   (c) 12   (d) 10

Answer: _____ Section: _____._____

39. Conductors in metal raceways and enclosures must be so arranged as to avoid heating the surrounding metal by alternating-current induction. To accomplish this, the _____ conductor(s) must be grouped together.

(a) phase   (b) grounded   (c) ungrounded   (d) all of these

Answer: _____ Section: _____._____

40. Conductors installed in conduit exposed to direct sunlight in close proximity to rooftops have been shown, under certain conditions, to experience an increase in temperature of _____°F above ambient temperature.

    (a) 70   (b) 10   (c) 30   (d) 40

    Answer: _____   Section: _____._____

41. Conductors larger than that for which the wireway is designed may be installed in any wireway.

    (a) True   (b) False

    Answer: _____   Section: _____._____

42. Conductors must have their ampacity determined using the _____ column of Table 310.16 for circuits rated 100A or less or marked for 14 AWG through 1 AWG conductors, unless the equipment terminals are listed for use with higher temperature rated conductors.

    (a) 60°C   (b) 75°C   (c) 30°C   (d) 90°C

    Answer: _____   Section: _____._____

43. Conductors smaller than 1/0 AWG can be connected in parallel to supply control power, provided _____.

    (a) they are all contained within the same raceway or cable
    (b) each parallel conductor has an ampacity sufficient to carry the entire load
    (c) the circuit overcurrent protection device rating does not exceed the ampacity of any individual parallel conductor
    (d) all of these

    Answer: _____   Section: _____._____

44. Conduits, cable trays, and open wiring used for intrinsically safe systems must be identified with permanently affixed labels with the wording "Intrinsic Safety Wiring." The labels must be visible after installation and the spacing between labels must not exceed _____ ft.

    (a) 3   (b) 10   (c) 25   (d) 50

    Answer: _____   Section: _____._____

45. Connection of conductors to terminal parts must ensure a thoroughly good connection without damaging the conductors and must be made by means of _____.

    (a) solder lugs   (b) pressure connectors   (c) splices to flexible leads   (d) any of these

    Answer: _____   Section: _____._____

46. Constant-voltage generators must be protected from overloads by _____ or other acceptable overcurrent protective means suitable for the conditions of use.

    (a) inherent design   (b) circuit breakers   (c) fuses   (d) any of these

    Answer: _____   Section: _____._____

47. Continuous duty is defined as _____.

   (a) when the load is expected to continue for three hours or more
   (b) operation at a substantially constant load for an indefinite length of time
   (c) operation at loads and for intervals of time, both of which may be subject to wide variations
   (d) operation at which the load may be subject to maximum current for six hours or more

   Answer: _____   Section: _____._____

48. Cord connectors for carnivals, circuses, and fairs can be laid on the ground when the connectors are _____ for a wet location, but they must not be placed in audience traffic paths or within areas accessible to the public unless guarded.

   (a) listed   (b) labeled   (c) approved   (d) all of these

   Answer: _____   Section: _____._____

49. Cord-and-Plug connected equipment must be grounded by means of _____.

   (a) an equipment grounding conductor in the cable assembly   (b) a separate flexible wire or strap
   (c) either a or b   (d) none of these

   Answer: _____   Section: _____._____

50. Each _____ service conductor must have overload protection.

   (a) overhead   (b) underground   (c) ungrounded   (d) none of these

   Answer: _____   Section: _____._____

Unit 4
NEC Review Quiz
Articles 250 through 310

(• Indicates that 75% or fewer exam takers get the question correct)

Article 250 Grounding and Bonding (continued)

1. The connection (attachment) of the grounding electrode conductor to a grounding electrode must _____.

   (a) be accessible   (b) be made in a manner that will ensure a permanent and effective grounding path
   (c) a and b   (d) none of these

   Answer: _____   Section: _____._____

2. The grounding conductor connection to the grounding electrode must be made by _____.

   (a) listed lugs   (b) exothermic welding   (c) listed pressure connectors   (d) any of these

   Answer: _____   Section: _____._____

3. A metal elbow that is installed in an underground installation of rigid nonmetallic conduit and is isolated from possible contact by a minimum cover _____ to any part of the elbow, is not required to be grounded.

   (a) of 6 in.   (b) of 12 in.   (c) of 18 in.   (d) as specified in Table
   300.5

   Answer: _____   Section: _____._____

4. Metal enclosures and raceways for conductors added to existing installations of _____, which do not provide an equipment ground are not required to be grounded if they are less than 25 ft long, they are free from probable contact with grounded conductive material, and are guarded against contact by persons.

   (a) nonmetallic-sheathed cable   (b) open wiring   (c) knob-and-tube wiring   (d) all of these

   Answer: _____   Section: _____._____

5. Bonding must be provided where necessary to ensure _____ and the capacity to conduct safely any fault current likely to be imposed.

   (a) electrical continuity   (b) fiduciary responsibility   (c) listing requirements   (d) electrical demand

   Answer: _____   Section: _____._____

6.   Service equipment, service raceways, and service conductor enclosures must be bonded _____.

(a) to the grounded service conductor
(b) by threaded raceways into enclosures, couplings, hubs, conduit bodies, etc.
(c) by listed bonding devices with bonding jumpers
(d) any of these

Answer: _____   Section: _____._____

7.   Service metal raceways and metal clad cables are considered effectively bonded when using threadless couplings and connectors that are _____.

(a) nonmetallic   (b) made up tight
(c) sealed   (d) these are never allowed for bonding

Answer: _____   Section: _____._____

8.   An accessible means external to enclosures for connecting intersystem _____ conductors must be provided at the service equipment and at the disconnecting means.

(a) bonding   (b) grounding   (c) secondary   (d) a and b

Answer: _____   Section: _____._____

9.   When bonding enclosures, metal raceways, frames, fittings, and other metal noncurrent-carrying parts, any nonconductive paint, enamel, or similar coating must be removed at _____.

(a) contact surfaces   (b) threads   (c) contact points   (d) all of these

Answer: _____   Section: _____._____

10. For circuits over 250 volts-to-ground (277/480V), electrical continuity can be maintained between a box or enclosure where no oversized, concentric, or eccentric knockouts are encountered, and a metal conduit by _____.

(a) threadless fittings for cables with metal sheath
(b) double locknuts on threaded conduit (one inside and one outside the box or enclosure)
(c) fittings that have shoulders that seat firmly against the box with a locknut on the inside or listed fittings identified for the purpose.
(d) all of these

Answer: _____   Section: _____._____

11. Regardless of the voltage of the electrical system, the electrical continuity of non-current carrying metal parts of equipment, raceways, and other enclosures in any hazardous (classified) location as defined in Article 500 must be ensured by any of the methods specified in 250.92(B)(2) through (B)(4). One or more of these _____ methods must be used whether or not supplementary equipment grounding conductors are installed.

(a) grounded   (b) securing   (c) sealing   (d) bonding

Answer: _____   Section: _____._____

12. Equipment bonding jumpers on the supply side of the service must be no smaller than the sizes shown in _____.

(a) Table 250.66   (b) Table 250.122   (c) Table 310.16   (d) Table 310.15(B)(6)

Answer: _____   Section: _____._____

13. A service is supplied by three metal raceways. Each raceway contains 600 kcmil ungrounded (phase) conductors. Determine the size of the service bonding jumper for each raceway.

    (a) 1/0 AWG   (b) 2/0 AWG   (c) 225 kcmil   (d) 500 kcmil

    Answer: _____   Section: _____._____

14. What is the minimum size copper bonding jumper for a service raceway containing 4/0 THHN aluminum conductors?

    (a) 6 AWG aluminum   (b) 3 AWG copper   (c) 4 AWG aluminum   (d) 4 AWG copper

    Answer: _____   Section: _____._____

15. The equipment bonding jumper can be installed on the outside of a raceway providing the length of the run is not more than _____ and the bonding jumper is routed with the raceway.

    (a) 12 in.   (b) 24 in.   (c) 36 in.   (d) 72 in.

    Answer: _____   Section: _____._____

16. The metal water-piping system(s) must be bonded to the _____.

    (a) grounded conductor at the service
    (b) service equipment enclosure
    (c) equipment grounding bar or bus at any panelboard within the building
    (d) a or b

    Answer: _____   Section: _____._____

17. A building or structure that is supplied by a feeder must have the interior metal water-piping system bonded with a conductor sized from _____.

    (a) Table 250.66   (b) Table 250.122   (c) Table 310.16   (d) none of these

    Answer: _____   Section: _____._____

18. Exposed structural metal that is interconnected to form a steel building frame, that is not intentionally grounded and is likely to become energized, must be bonded to:

    (a) The service equipment enclosure.
    (b) The grounded conductor at the service.
    (c) The grounding electrode conductor where of sufficient size.
    (d) any of these

    Answer: _____   Section: _____._____

19. Lightning protection system ground terminals _____ be bonded to the building grounding electrode system.

    (a) must   (b) must not   (c) can   (d) none of these

    Answer: _____   Section: _____._____

20. Exposed non-current-carrying metal parts of fixed equipment likely to become energized must be grounded where _____.

    (a) within 8 ft vertically or 5 ft horizontally of ground or grounded metal objects
    (b) located in wet or damp locations and not isolated
    (c) in electrical contact with metal
    (d) any of these

    Answer: _____   Section: _____._____

21. Electrical equipment permanently mounted on skids, and the skids, must be grounded with an equipment bonding jumper sized as required by _____.

    (a) 250.50   (b) 250.66   (c) 250.122   (d) 310.15

    Answer: _____   Section: _____._____

22. An equipment grounding conductor run with, or enclosing, the circuit conductors must be _____ or metal raceway as listed in 250.118.

    (a) a copper conductor   (b) an aluminum conductor
    (c) a copper-clad aluminum conductor   (d) any of these

    Answer: _____   Section: _____._____

23. For flexible metal conduit (FMC) and liquidtight flexible metal conduit (LFMC), an equipment grounding conductor is required regardless of the size of the overcurrent protection if the FMC or LFMC is installed for the reason of _____.

    (a) physical protection   (b) flexibility
    (c) protection from moisture   (d) communications systems

    Answer: _____   Section: _____._____

24. Liquidtight flexible metal conduit (LFMC) in 3/4 through 1 1/4 in. trade sizes can be used as the equipment grounding conductor if the length in any ground return path does not exceed 6 ft and the circuit conductors contained in the conduit are protected by overcurrent devices rated at _____ or less when the conduit is not installed for flexibility.

    (a) 15A   (b) 20A   (c) 30A   (d) 60A

    Answer: _____   Section: _____._____

25. Conductors with insulation that is _____ cannot be used for ungrounded or grounded conductors.

    (a) green   (b) green with one or more yellow stripes
    (c) a or b   (d) white

    Answer: _____   Section: _____._____

26. Equipment grounding conductors for feeder taps must be sized in accordance with _____ based on the ampere rating of the circuit protection device ahead of the feeder, but in no case is it required to be larger than the circuit conductors.

    (a) Table 250.66   (b) Table 250.94   (c) Table 250.122   (d) Table 220.19

    Answer: _____   Section: _____._____

27. The equipment grounding conductor must not be smaller than shown in Table 250.122, but it must not be required to be larger than the circuit conductors supplying the equipment.

    (a) True   (b) False

    Answer: _____   Section: _____._____

28. When a single equipment grounding conductor is used for multiple circuits in the same raceway or cable, the single equipment grounding conductor must be sized according to _____.

    (a) the combined rating of all the overcurrent protection devices
    (b) the largest overcurrent protection device of the multiple circuits
    (c) the combined rating of all the loads
    (d) any of these

    Answer: _____   Section: _____._____

29. The terminal of a wiring device for the connection of the equipment grounding conductor must be identified by a green-colored, _____.

    (a) not readily removable terminal screw with a hexagonal head
    (b) hexagonal, not readily removable terminal nut
    (c) pressure wire connector
    (d) any of these

    Answer: _____   Section: _____._____

30. When considering whether equipment is effectively grounded, the structural metal frame of a building is permitted to be used as the required equipment grounding conductor for ac equipment.

    (a) True   (b) False

    Answer: _____   Section: _____._____

31. Ranges and clothes dryers for existing branch circuit installations that were installed with the frame grounded by the grounded circuit conductor are allowed to continue this practice if all conditions of the exception to 250.140 are met.

    (a) True   (b) False

    Answer: _____   Section: _____._____

32. A grounded circuit conductor must not be used for grounding non-current-carrying metal parts of equipment on the load side of _____.

    (a) the service disconnecting means
    (b) the separately derived system disconnecting means
    (c) overcurrent protection devices for separately derived systems not having a main disconnecting means
    (d) all of these

    Answer: _____   Section: _____._____

33. An _____ must be used to connect the grounding terminal of a grounding-type receptacle to a grounded box.

    (a) equipment bonding jumper   (b) equipment grounding jumper
    (c) a or b   (d) a and b

    Answer: _____   Section: _____._____

34. An equipment bonding jumper must be used to connect the grounding terminal of a grounding-type receptacle to a grounded box. Where the box is surface-mounted, direct metal-to-metal contact between the device yoke and the box can be permitted to ground the receptacle to the box.

    (a) True   (b) False

    Answer: _____   Section: _____._____

35. Receptacle yokes designed and _____ as self-grounding are permitted to establish the bonding path between the device yoke and a grounded outlet box.

    (a) approved   (b) advertised   (c) listed   (d) installed

    Answer: _____   Section: _____._____

36. Contact devices or yokes designed and listed as self-grounding are permitted in conjunction with the supporting screws to establish the grounding circuit between the device yoke and flush-type boxes.

    (a) True   (b) False

    Answer: _____   Section: _____._____

37. Where circuit conductors are spliced within a box, or terminated on equipment within or supported by a box, any equipment grounding conductors associated with those circuit conductors must be spliced or joined within the box or to the box with devices suitable for the use.

    (a) True   (b) False

    Answer: _____   Section: _____._____

38. When equipment grounding conductor(s) are installed in a metal box, an electrical connection is required between the equipment grounding conductor and the metal box enclosure by means of a _____.

    (a) grounding screw   (b) soldered connection   (c) listed grounding device   (d) a or c

    Answer: _____   Section: _____._____

39. The secondary circuits of current and potential instrument transformers must be grounded where the primary windings are connected to circuits of _____ or more to ground and, where on switchboards, must be grounded irrespective of voltage.

    (a) 300V   (b) 600V   (c) 1,000V   (d) 150V

    Answer: _____   Section: _____._____

40. The grounding conductor for secondary circuits of instrument transformers and for instrument cases must not be smaller than _____ AWG copper.

    (a) 18   (b) 16   (c) 14   (d) 12

    Answer: _____   Section: _____._____

Article 280 Surge Arresters

This article covers general requirements, installation requirements, and connection requirements for surge arresters installed on the line side of service equipment.

41. Line and ground-connecting conductors for a surge arrester must not be smaller than _____ AWG copper.

(a) 14   (b) 12   (c) 10   (d) 8

Answer: _____   Section: _____._____

Article 285 Transient Voltage Surge Suppressors (TVSSs)

This article covers general requirements, installation requirements, and connection requirements for transient voltage surge suppressors (TVSSs) permanently installed on the load side of service equipment. It doesn't apply to cord-and-plug connected units, such as "computer power strips."

42. Article 285 covers surge arresters.

(a) True   (b) False

Answer: _____   Section: _____._____

43. A TVSS is listed to limit transient voltages by diverting or limiting surge current.

(a) True   (b) False

Answer: _____   Section: _____._____

44. TVSSs must be marked with their short-circuit current rating, and they must not be installed where the available fault current is in excess of that rating.

(a) True   (b) False

Answer: _____   Section: _____._____

45. A TVSS can be connected anywhere on the premises wiring system.

(a) True   (b) False

Answer: _____   Section: _____._____

Chapter 3 Wiring Methods and Materials

Article 300 Wiring Methods

Article 300 contains the general requirements for all wiring methods included in the *NEC*, except for signaling and communications systems, which are covered in Chapters 7 and 8.

46. Unless specified elsewhere in the *Code*, Chapter 3 must be used for voltages of _____.

(a) 600 volts-to-ground or less   (b) 300V between conductors or less
(c) 600V, nominal, or less   (d) 600V RMS

Answer: _____   Section: _____._____

47. All conductors of a circuit, including the grounded and equipment grounding conductors, must be contained within the same _____.

(a) raceway   (b) cable   (c) trench   (d) all of these

Answer: _____   Section: _____._____

48. In both exposed and concealed locations, where a cable or nonmetallic raceway-type wiring method is installed through bored holes in joists, rafters, or wood members, holes must be bored so that the edge of the hole is _____ the nearest edge of the wood member.

(a) not less than 1 1/4 in. from   (b) immediately adjacent to
(c) not less than 1/ 16 in. from   (d) 90°away from

Answer: _____   Section: _____._____

49. Cables laid in wood notches require protection against nails or screws by using a steel plate at least _____ thick, installed before the building finish is applied. A thinner plate that provides equal or better protection may be used if listed and marked.

(a) 1/16 in.   (b) 1/8 in.   (c) 1/2 in.   (d) none of these

Answer: _____   Section: _____._____

50. Where NM cable passes through factory or field openings in metal members, it must be protected by _____ bushings or _____ grommets that cover metal edges. The protection fitting must be securely fastened in the opening prior to the installation of the cable.

(a) approved   (b) identified   (c) listed   (d) none of these

Answer: _____   Section: _____._____

51. Wiring methods installed behind panels that allow access, such as the space above a dropped ceiling, are required to be _____ according to their applicable Articles.

(a) supported   (b) painted   (c) in a metal raceway   (d) all of these

Answer: _____   Section: _____._____

52. When unable to maintain the minimum required distance from the edge of a wood framing member when installing a cable or nonmetallic raceway parallel to framing members, the cable or raceway must be protected from penetration by screws or nails by a steel plate or bushing at least _____ and of appropriate length and width to cover the area of the wiring. A thinner plate that provides equal or better protection may be used if listed and marked.

(a) 1/4 in. thick   (b) 1/8 in. thick   (c) 1/16 in. thick   (d) 24 gauge

Answer: _____   Section: _____._____

53. Where underground conductors and cables emerge from underground, they must be protected by enclosures or raceways to a point _____ above finished grade. In no case can the protection be required to exceed 18 in. below grade.

(a) 3 ft   (b) 6 ft   (c) 8 ft   (d) 10 ft

Answer: _____   Section: _____._____

54. What is the minimum cover requirement in inches for direct burial UF cable installed outdoors that supplies power to a 120V, 30A circuit?

   (a) 6 in.   (b) 12 in.   (c) 18 in.   (d) 24 in.

   Answer: _____   Section: _____._____

55. •When installing raceways underground in rigid nonmetallic conduit and other approved raceways, there must be a minimum of _____ of cover.

   (a) 6 in.   (b) 12 in.   (c) 18 in.   (d) 22 in.

   Answer: _____   Section: _____._____

56. UF cable used with a 24V landscape lighting system is permitted to have a minimum cover of _____.

   (a) 6 in.   (b) 12 in.   (c) 18 in.   (d) 24 in.

   Answer: _____   Section: _____._____

57. Direct-buried conductors or cables can be spliced or tapped without the use of splice boxes when the splice or tap is made in accordance with 110.14(B).

   (a) True   (b) False

   Answer: _____   Section: _____._____

58. Conduits or raceways through which moisture may contact live parts must be _____ at either or both ends.

   (a) sealed   (b) plugged   (c) bushed   (d) a or b

   Answer: _____   Section: _____._____

59. All conductors of the same circuit are required to be _____.

   (a) in the same raceway or cable   (b) in close proximity in the same trench
   (c) the same size   (d) a or b

   Answer: _____   Section: _____._____

60. Cables or raceways installed using directional boring equipment must be _____ for this purpose.

   (a) marked   (b) listed   (c) labeled   (d) approved

   Answer: _____   Section: _____._____

61. Which of the following metal parts must be protected from corrosion both inside and out?

   (a) Ferrous metal raceways   (b) Metal elbows   (c) Boxes   (d) all of these

   Answer: _____   Section: _____._____

62. Metal raceways, boxes, fittings, supports, and support hardware can be installed in concrete or in direct contact with the earth or other areas subject to severe corrosive influences, where _____ approved for the conditions, or where provided with corrosion protection approved for the purpose.

   (a) the soil is   (b) made of material   (c) the qualified installer is   (d) none of these

   Answer: _____   Section: _____._____

63. Nonmetallic raceways, cable trays, cablebus, auxiliary gutters, boxes, cables with a nonmetallic outer jacket and internal metal armor or jacket, cable sheathing, cabinets, elbows, couplings, nipples, fittings, supports and support hardware must be made of material _____.

(a) listed for the condition   (b) approved for the condition   (c) both a and b   (d) either a or b

Answer: _____   Section: _____._____

64. Nonmetallic raceways, cable trays, cablebus, auxiliary gutters, boxes, and cables with a nonmetallic outer jacket must be made of material approved for the condition and where exposed to chemicals, the materials or coatings must be _____.

(a) listed as inherently resistant to chemicals   (b) identified for the specific chemical reagent
(c) both a and b   (d) either a or b

Answer: _____   Section: _____._____

65. In general, areas where _____ are handled and stored may present severe corrosive conditions, particularly when wet or damp.

(a) laboratory chemicals and acids   (b) acids and alkali chemicals
(c) acids and water   (d) chemicals and water

Answer: _____   Section: _____._____

66. Raceways must be provided with expansion fittings where necessary to compensate for thermal expansion and contraction.

(a) True   (b) False

Answer: _____   Section: _____._____

67. •Metal raceways, cable armor, and other metal enclosures for conductors must be _____ joined together to form a continuous electrical conductor.

(a) electrically   (b) permanently   (c) metallically   (d) none of these

Answer: _____   Section: _____._____

68. Where independent support wires of a ceiling assembly are used to support raceways, cable assemblies, or boxes above a ceiling, they must be secured at both ends. Cables and raceways must _____.

(a) be identified for this purpose   (b) not be supported by ceiling grids
(c) not contain conductors larger than 14 AWG   (d) be identified by painting them orange

Answer: _____   Section: _____._____

69. The independent support wires for wiring in a fire-rated ceiling assembly must be distinguishable from fire-rated suspended-ceiling framing support wires by _____.

(a) color   (b) tagging   (c) other effective means   (d) any of these

Answer: _____   Section: _____._____

70. Raceways are allowed to be used as a means of support when the raceway contains electrical power supply conductors for electrically controlled equipment and the raceway is used to support Class 2 circuit conductors or cables that connect to the same equipment.

(a) True   (b) False

Answer: _____   Section: _____._____

71. Metal or nonmetallic raceways, cable armors, and cable sheaths _____ between cabinets, boxes, fittings or other enclosures or outlets.

    (a) can be attached with electrical tape
    (c) must be continuous

    (b) are allowed gaps for expansion
    (d) none of these

    Answer: _____   Section: _____._____

72. In multiwire circuits, the continuity of the _____ conductor must not be dependent upon the device connections.

    (a) ungrounded   (b) grounded   (c) grounding   (d) a and b

    Answer: _____   Section: _____._____

73. When the opening to an outlet, junction, or switch point is less than 8 in. in any dimension, each conductor must be long enough to extend at least _____ outside the opening of the enclosure.

    (a) 0 in.   (b) 3 in.   (c) 6 in.   (d) 12 in.

    Answer: _____   Section: _____._____

74. A box or conduit body is not required where cables enter or exit from conduit or tubing that is used to provide cable support or protection against physical damage. A fitting must be provided on the end(s) of the conduit or tubing to _____.

    (a) allow for the future connection of a box
    (c) protect the cable from abrasion

    (b) be used for a future pull point
    (d) allow the coupling of another section of conduit

    Answer: _____   Section: _____._____

75. Splices and taps are permitted in cabinets or cutout boxes if the conductors, splices, and taps do not fill the wiring space at any cross-section to more than _____ percent.

    (a) 20   (b) 40   (c) 60   (d) 75

    Answer: _____   Section: _____._____

76. A bushing is permitted in lieu of a box or terminal where conductors emerge from a raceway and enter or terminate at equipment, such as open switchboards, unenclosed control equipment, or similar equipment.

    (a) True   (b) False

    Answer: _____   Section: _____._____

77. The number of conductors permitted in a raceway must be limited to _____.

    (a) permit heat to dissipate
    (c) prevent damage to insulation during removal of conductors

    (b) prevent damage to insulation during installation
    (d) all of these

    Answer: _____   Section: _____._____

78. Prewired raceway assemblies are permitted only where specifically permitted in the *Code* for the applicable wiring method.

    (a) True   (b) False

    Answer: _____   Section: _____._____

79. Metal raceways must not be _____ by welding to the raceway unless specifically designed to be, or otherwise specifically permitted to be, by the *Code*.

    (a) supported   (b) terminated   (c) connected   (d) all of these

    Answer: _____   Section: _____._____

80. A vertical run of 4/0 AWG copper must be supported at intervals not exceeding _____.

    (a) 80 ft   (b) 100 ft   (c) 120 ft   (d) 40 ft

    Answer: _____   Section: _____._____

81. _____ is a nonferrous, nonmagnetic metal that has no heating due to inductive hysteresis heating.

    (a) Steel   (b) Iron   (c) Aluminum   (d) all of these

    Answer: _____   Section: _____._____

82. Openings around electrical penetrations through fire-resistant-rated walls, partitions, floors, or ceilings must _____ to maintain the fire resistance rating.

    (a) be documented   (b) not be allowed
    (c) be firestopped using approved methods   (d) be enlarged

    Answer: _____   Section: _____._____

83. Equipment and devices are permitted within ducts or plenum chambers used to transport environmental air only if necessary for their direct action upon, or sensing of, the _____.

    (a) contained air   (b) air quality   (c) air temperature   (d) none of these

    Answer: _____   Section: _____._____

84. One wiring method that is permitted in ducts or plenums used for environmental air is _____.

    (a) flexible metal conduit of any length   (b) electrical metallic tubing
    (c) armored cable (Type AC)   (d) nonmetallic-sheathed cable

    Answer: _____   Section: _____._____

85. The space above a hung ceiling used for environmental air handling purposes is an example of _____ and the wiring limitations of _____ apply.

    (a) a plenum, 300.22(B)   (b) other spaces, 300.22(C)   (c) a duct, 300.22(B)   (d) none of these

    Answer: _____   Section: _____._____

86. Electric wiring in the air-handling area beneath raised floors for data-processing systems is permitted in accordance with Article 645.

    (a) True   (b) False

    Answer: _____   Section: _____._____

Article 310 Conductors for General Wiring

This article contains the general requirements for conductors, such as insulation markings, ampacity ratings, and conductor use. Article 310 doesn't apply to conductors that are part of cable assemblies, flexible cords, fixture wires, or conductors that are an integral part of equipment [90.6, 300.1(B)].

87. Conductors must be insulated except where specifically allowed by the *NEC* to be bare, such as for equipment grounding or bonding purposes.

    (a) True   (b) False

    Answer: _____   Section: _____._____

88. In general, the minimum size phase, neutral, or grounded conductor permitted for use in parallel installations is _____ AWG.

    (a) 10   (b) 1   (c) 1/0   (d) 4

    Answer: _____   Section: _____._____

89. When conductors are run in parallel, the currents should be evenly divided between the individual parallel conductors so that each conductor is evenly heated. This is accomplished by ensuring that each of the conductors within a parallel set has the same _____ and all conductors terminate in the same manner.

    (a) length   (b) material   (c) cross-sectional area   (d) all of these

    Answer: _____   Section: _____._____

90. It is not the intent of 310.4 to require that conductors of one phase, neutral, or grounded circuit conductor be the same as those of another phase, neutral, or grounded circuit conductor to achieve _____.

    (a) polarity   (b) balance   (c) grounding   (d) none of these

    Answer: _____   Section: _____._____

91. The minimum size conductor permitted in any building for branch circuits under 600V is _____ AWG.

    (a) 14   (b) 12   (c) 10   (d) 8

    Answer: _____   Section: _____._____

92. •Insulated conductors used in wet locations must be _____.

    (a) moisture-impervious metal-sheathed   (b) RHW, TW, THW, THHW, THWN, XHHW
    (c) listed for wet locations   (d) any of these

    Answer: _____   Section: _____._____

93. Where conductors of different insulation are associated together, the limiting temperature of any conductor must not be exceeded.

    (a) True   (b) False

    Answer: _____   Section: _____._____

94. There are four principal determinants of conductor operating temperature, one of which is _____ generated internally in the conductor as the result of load current flow.

    (a) friction   (b) magnetism   (c) heat   (d) none of these

    Answer: _____   Section: _____._____

95.   Letters used to designate the number of conductors within a cable are _____.

(a) D - Two insulated conductors laid parallel   (b) M - Two or more insulated conductors twisted spirally
(c) T - Two or more insulated conductors twisted in parallel   (d) a and b

Answer: _____   Section: _____._____

96.   TFE-insulated conductors are manufactured in sizes from 14 through _____ AWG.

(a) 2   (b) 1   (c) 2/0   (d) 4/0

Answer: _____   Section: _____._____

97.   Lettering on conductor insulation indicates its intended condition of use. THWN is rated _____.

(a) 75°C   (b) for wet locations   (c) a and b   (d) not enough information

Answer: _____   Section: _____._____

98.   The ampacities listed in the Tables of Article 310 are based on temperature alone and do not take _____ into consideration.

(a) continuous loads   (b) voltage drop   (c) insulation   (d) wet locations

Answer: _____   Section: _____._____

99.   Where six current-carrying conductors are run in the same conduit or cable, the ampacity of each conductor must be adjusted to a factor of _____ percent of its value.

(a) 90   (b) 60   (c) 40   (d) 80

Answer: _____   Section: _____._____

100.   Conductor derating factors do not apply to conductors in nipples having a length not exceeding _____

(a) 12 in.   (b) 24 in.   (c) 36 in.   (d) 48 in.

Answer: _____   Section: _____._____

Unit 4
NEC Practice Quiz
Articles 250 through 310

(• Indicates that 75% or fewer exam takers get the question correct)

1. When an underground metal water-piping system is used as a grounding electrode, effective bonding must be provided around insulated joints and around any equipment that is likely to be disconnected for repairs or replacement. Bonding conductors must be of _____ to permit removal of such equipment while retaining the integrity of the bond.

   (a) stranded wire   (b) flexible conduit   (c) sufficient length   (d) none of these

   Answer: _____   Section: _____ . _____

2. •Cases or frames of instrument transformers are not required to be grounded _____.

   (a) when accessible to qualified persons only
   (b) for current transformers where the primary is not over 150 volts-to-ground and that are used exclusively to supply current to meters
   (c) for potential transformers where the primary is less than 150 volts-to-ground
   (d) a or b

   Answer: _____   Section: _____ . _____

3. •Circuit conductors that operate at 277V (with 600V insulation) may occupy the same enclosure or raceway with 48V dc conductors that have an insulation rating of 300V.

   (a) True   (b) False

   Answer: _____   Section: _____ . _____

4. •What is the minimum cover requirement in inches for UF cable supplying power to a 120V, 15A GFCI-protected circuit outdoors under a driveway of a one-family dwelling?

   (a) 12 in.   (b) 24in.   (c) 16 in.   (d) 6 in.

   Answer: _____   Section: _____ . _____

5. •Where circuit conductors are spliced within a box, or terminated on equipment within or supported by a box, any equipment grounding conductors associated with those circuit conductors must be spliced or joined in the box or to the box with devices suitable for the use. This does not apply to insulated equipment grounding conductors for isolated ground receptacles for electronic equipment.

   (a) True   (b) False

   Answer: _____   Section: _____ . _____

6. •Wiring methods permitted in the hung ceiling area used for environmental air include _____.

(a) electrical metallic tubing
(b) flexible metal conduit of any length
(c) rigid metal conduit without an overall nonmetallic covering
(d) all of these

Answer: _____   Section: _____._____

7. A 100 ft vertical run of 4/0 AWG copper requires the conductors to be supported at _____ locations.

(a) 4   (b) 5   (c) 2   (d) none of these

Answer: _____   Section: _____._____

8. A grounding-type receptacle can replace a nongrounding-type receptacle at an outlet box that does not contain an equipment grounding conductor if the equipment grounding conductor is connected to the _____.

(a) grounding electrode system as described in 250.50
(b) grounding electrode conductor
(c) equipment grounding terminal bar within the enclosure where the branch circuit for the receptacle originates
(d) any of these

Answer: _____   Section: _____._____

9. A TVSS device must be listed.

(a) True   (b) False

Answer: _____   Section: _____._____

10. An equipment bonding jumper for a grounding-type receptacle must be installed between the receptacle and a flush-mounted outlet box, even when the contact device is listed as self-grounding.

(a) True   (b) False

Answer: _____   Section: _____._____

11. Backfill used for underground wiring must not _____.

(a) damage the wiring method   (b) prevent compaction of the fill
(c) contribute to the corrosion of the raceway (d) all of these

Answer: _____   Section: _____._____

12. Bonding jumpers must be used around _____ knockouts that are punched or otherwise formed so as to impair the electrical connection to ground. Standard locknuts or bushings cannot be the sole means for this bonding.

(a) concentric   (b) eccentric   (c) field-punched   (d) a or b

Answer: _____   Section: _____._____

13. Ceiling-support wires used for the support of electrical raceways and cables within nonfire rated assemblies are required to be distinguishable from the suspended-ceiling framing support wires.

(a) True   (b) False

Answer: _____   Section: _____._____

14. Conductors in raceways must be _____ between outlets, boxes, devices, and so forth.

(a) continuous   (b) installed   (c) copper   (d) in conduit

Answer: _____   Section: _____._____

15. Direct buried conductors, cables, or raceways, which are subject to movement by settlement or frost, must be arranged to prevent damage to the _____ or to equipment connected to the raceways.

(a) siding of the building mounted on   (b) landscaping around the cable or raceway
(c) the enclosed conductors   (d) expansion fitting

Answer: _____   Section: _____._____

16. Each current-carrying conductor of a paralleled set of conductors must be counted as a current-carrying conductor for the purpose of applying the adjustment factors of 310.15(B)(2)(a).

(a) True   (b) False

Answer: _____   Section: _____._____

17. Electrical installations in hollow spaces, vertical shafts, and ventilation or air-handling ducts must be made so that the possible spread of fire or products of combustion will not be _____.

(a) substantially increased   (b) allowed   (c) inherent   (d) possible

Answer: _____   Section: _____._____

18. Equipment bonding jumpers must be of copper or other corrosion-resistant material. A bonding jumper must be a _____ or similar suitable conductor.

(a) wire   (b) bus   (c) screw   (d) any of these

Answer: _____   Section: _____._____

19. Fittings and connectors must be used only with the specific wiring methods for which they are designed and listed.

(a) True   (b) False

Answer: _____   Section: _____._____

20. In both exposed and concealed locations, where a cable or nonmetallic raceway-type wiring method is installed parallel to framing members such as joists, rafters, or studs or furring strips, the nearest outside surface of the cable or raceway must be _____ the nearest edge of the framing member where nails or screws are likely to penetrate.

(a) not less than 1 1/4 in. from   (b) immediately adjacent to
(c) not less than 1/16 in. from   (d) 90°away from

Answer: _____   Section: _____._____

21. Liquidtight flexible metal conduit (LFMC) up to 1/2 in. trade size can be used as the equipment grounding conductor if the length in any ground return path does not exceed 6 ft and the circuit conductors contained in the conduit are protected by overcurrent devices rated at _____ or less when the conduit is not installed for flexibility.

(a) 15A   (b) 20A   (c) 30A   (d) 60A

Answer: _____   Section: _____._____

22.　Metal enclosures and raceways for other than service conductors must be grounded except as permitted by 250.112(I).

(a) True　　　　　　　　　　　　(b) False

Answer: _____　　Section: _____._____

23.　Metal gas piping can be considered bonded by the circuit's equipment grounding conductor of the circuit that is likely to energize the piping.

(a) True　　　　　　　　　　　　(b) False

Answer: _____　　Section: _____._____

24.　Metal raceways, enclosures, frames, and other noncurrent-carrying metal parts of electric equipment installed on a building equipped with a lightning protection system may require spacing from the lightning protection conductors, typically 6 ft through air or ___ through dense materials, such as concrete, brick, wood, etc.

(a) 2 ft　　　　　　　(b) 3 ft　　　　　　　(c) 4 ft　　　　　　　(d) 6 ft

Answer: _____　　Section: _____._____

25.　Metric designators and trade sizes for conduit, tubing, and associated fittings and accessories are designated in Table _____.

(a) 250.66　　　　　　(b) 250.122　　　　　　(c) 300.1(C)　　　　　　(d) 310.16

Answer: _____　　Section: _____._____

26.　Nonmetallic raceways, cable trays, cablebus, auxiliary gutters, boxes, and cables with a nonmetallic outer jacket must be made of material approved for the condition and where exposed to sunlight, the materials must be _____.

(a) listed as sunlight resistant　　(b) identified as sunlight resistant
(c) both a and b　　　　　　　　(d) either a or b

Answer: _____　　Section: _____._____

27.　Raceways must be _____ between outlet, junction, or splicing points prior to the installation of conductors.

(a) installed complete　　　(b) tested for ground faults　　(c) a minimum of 80 percent completed　　(d) none of these

Answer: _____　　Section: _____._____

28.　Raceways, cable assemblies, boxes, cabinets, and fittings must be securely fastened in place. Support wires and associated fittings that provide secure support and that are installed in addition to the ceiling grid support wires are permitted as the sole support.

(a) True　　　　　　　　　　　　(b) False

Answer: _____　　Section: _____._____

29.　Solid dielectric insulated conductors operated above 2,000V in permanent installations must have _____ insulation and must be shielded.

(a) ozone-resistant　　　　(b) asbestos　　　　(c) high-temperature　　　　(d) perfluoro-alkoxy

Answer: _____　　Section: _____._____

30.　The _____ is defined as the area between the top of direct-burial cable and the finished grade.

(a) notch　　　　　　(b) cover　　　　　　(c) gap　　　　　　(d) none of these

Answer: _____　　Section: _____._____

31. The _____ rating of a conductor is the maximum temperature, at any location along its length, which the conductor can withstand over a prolonged period of time without serious degradation.

    (a) ambient   (b) temperature   (c) maximum withstand   (d) short-circuit

    Answer: _____   Section: _____._____

32. The conductor between a surge arrester and the line and the grounding connection must not be smaller than _____ AWG copper for installations operating at 1 kV or more.

    (a) 4   (b) 6   (c) 8   (d) 2

    Answer: _____   Section: _____._____

33. The equipment bonding jumper on the supply side of services (service raceway) must be sized according to the _____.

    (a) calculated load   (b) service-entrance conductor size
    (c) service-drop size   (d) load to be served

    Answer: _____   Section: _____._____

34. The general rule for equipment bonding jumpers installed on the outside of a raceway or enclosure is that they are not permitted to be longer than 6 ft, but an equipment bonding jumper can be longer than 6 ft at outside pole locations for the purpose of bonding or grounding isolated sections of metal raceways or elbows installed in exposed risers of metal conduit or other metal raceways.

    (a) True   (b) False

    Answer: _____   Section: _____._____

35. The grounded circuit conductor is permitted to ground non-current-carrying metal parts of equipment, raceways, and other enclosures at the supply side or within the enclosure of the ac service-disconnecting means.

    (a) True   (b) False

    Answer: _____   Section: _____._____

36. The noncurrent-carrying metal parts of service equipment, such as _____, must be effectively bonded together.

    (a) service raceways, cable trays, or service cable armor
    (b) service equipment enclosures containing service conductors, including meter fittings, boxes, or the like, interposed in the service raceway or armor
    (c) the metallic raceway or armor enclosing a grounding electrode conductor
    (d) all of these

    Answer: _____   Section: _____._____

37. THW insulation has a _____ rating when installed within electric-discharge lighting equipment, such as through fluorescent luminaires.

    (a) 60°C   (b) 75°C   (c) 90°C   (d) none of these

    Answer: _____   Section: _____._____

38. Type AC cable can be installed in ducts or plenums that are used for environmental air.

    (a) True   (b) False

    Answer: _____   Section: _____._____

39. When ungrounded conductors are increased in size, the equipment grounding conductor is not required to be increased because it is not a current-carrying conductor.

(a) True   (b) False

Answer: _____   Section: _____._____

40. Where _____ conductors are run in separate raceways or cables, the same number of conductors must be used in each raceway or cable.

(a) parallel   (b) control   (c) communication   (d) aluminum

Answer: _____   Section: _____._____

41. Where a metal box is surface-mounted, direct metal-to-metal contact between the device yoke and the box is permitted to ground the receptacle to the box. Unless the receptacle is listed as _____, at least one of the insulating retaining washers must be removed from the receptacle to ensure direct metal-to-metal contact between the device yoke and metal outlet box.

(a) self-grounding   (b) weatherproof   (c) metal contact sufficient   (d) isolated grounding

Answer: _____   Section: _____._____

42. Where accessible only to qualified persons, a box or conduit body is not required for conductors in _____ when installed in accordance with applicable *Code* provisions.

(a) manholes   (b) handhole enclosures   (c) a or b   (d) elevator pits

Answer: _____   Section: _____._____

43. Where an equipment grounding conductor consists of a raceway, cable tray, cable armor, cablebus framework, or cable sheath, it must be installed _____.

(a) in accordance with applicable *Code* provisions
(b) using fittings for joints and terminations approved for the use
(c) with all connections, joints, and fittings made tight using suitable tools
(d) all of these

Answer: _____   Section: _____._____

44. Where corrosion protection is necessary and the conduit is threaded in the field, the threads must be coated with a(n) _____, electrically conductive, corrosion-resistance compound.

(a) marked   (b) listed   (c) labeled   (d) approved

Answer: _____   Section: _____._____

45. Where installed in raceways, conductors _____ AWG and larger must be stranded.

(a) 10   (b) 6   (c) 8   (d) 4

Answer: _____   Section: _____._____

46. Where NM cables pass through cut or drilled slots or holes in metal members, the cable needs to be protected by _____ securely covering all metal edges fastened in the opening prior to installation of the cable.

(a) listed bushings   (b) listed grommets   (c) plates   (d) a or b

Answer: _____   Section: _____._____

47. Where portions of a cable raceway or sleeve are subjected to different temperatures and where condensation is known to be a problem, as in cold storage areas of buildings or where passing from the interior to the exterior of a building, the _____ must be filled with an approved material to prevent the circulation of warm air to a colder section of the raceway or sleeve.

    (a) raceways   (b) sleeve   (c) a or b   (d) none of these

    Answer: _____ Section: _____._____

48. Where required to reduce electric noise for electronic equipment, electrical continuity of the metal raceway is not required and the metal raceway can terminate to a(n) _____ nonmetallic fitting(s) or spacer on the electronic equipment.

    (a) listed   (b) labeled   (c) identified   (d) marked

    Answer: _____ Section: _____._____

49. Which conductor has an insulation temperature rating of 90°C?

    (a) RH   (b) RHW   (c) THHN   (d) TW

    Answer: _____ Section: _____._____

50. Which of the following appliances installed in residential occupancies need not be grounded?

    (a) Toaster   (b) Aquarium   (c) Dishwasher   (d) Refrigerator

    Answer: _____ Section: _____._____

1. Each dispensing device must be provided with a means to remove all external voltage sources, including feedback, during periods of maintenance and service of the dispensing equipment. The disconnecting means must be either inside or adjacent to the dispensing device.

   (a) True   (b) False

   Answer: _____   Section: _____._____

2. Each doorway leading into a transformer vault from the building interior must be provided with a tight-fitting door having a minimum fire rating of _____ hours.

   (a) 2   (b) 4   (c) 5   (d) 3

   Answer: _____   Section: _____._____

3. Each length of HDPE must be clearly and durably marked not less than every _____ ft, as required in 110.21.

   (a) 10   (b) 3   (c) 5   (d) 20

   Answer: _____   Section: _____._____

4. Each service disconnecting means must be permanently _____ to identify it as a service disconnect.

   (a) identified   (b) positioned   (c) marked   (d) none of these

   Answer: _____   Section: _____._____

5. Electrical systems that are grounded, including transformers and generators, must be connected to the _____ for the purpose of limiting the voltage imposed by lightning, line surges, or unintentional contact with higher voltage lines.

   (a) ground   (b) earth   (c) electrical supply source   (d) none of these

   Answer: _____   Section: _____._____

6. Electrical wiring and equipment located at or serving motor fuel dispensing equipment in marinas or boatyards must be in accordance with Article 514, in addition to the requirements of Article 555. All electrical wiring for_____ must be installed on the side of the wharf, pier, or dock opposite from the liquid piping system.

   (a) power   (b) lighting   (c) dispensing equipment   (d) all of these

   Answer: _____   Section: _____._____

7. Electrical wiring within the cavity of a fire-rated floor-ceiling or roof-ceiling assembly cannot be supported by the ceiling assembly or ceiling support wires. An independent means of support must be provided which _____.

    (a) is permitted to be attached to the ceiling assembly   (b) cannot be attached to the ceiling assembly
    (c) can be nonmetallic material   (d) none of these

    Answer: _____   Section: _____._____

8. Electronic organs or other electronic musical instruments are included in the scope of equipment and wiring covered by Article 640.

    (a) True   (b) False

    Answer: _____   Section: _____._____

9. Emergency lighting and/or emergency power in a building or group of buildings must be available within the time period required for the application, but not to exceed _____ seconds.

    (a) 5   (b) 10   (c) 30   (d) 60

    Answer: _____   Section: _____._____

10. Emergency systems may also provide power for such functions as ventilation where essential to maintain life, fire detection and alarm systems, elevators, fire pumps, public safety communications systems, industrial processes where current interruption would produce serious _____, and similar functions.

    (a) production slowdowns   (b) life, safety, or health hazards
    (c) a and b   (d) a or b

    Answer: _____   Section: _____._____

11. EMT must not be used where _____.

    (a) subject to severe physical damage   (b) protected from corrosion only by enamel
    (c) used for the support of luminaires   (d) any of these

    Answer: _____   Section: _____._____

12. Enclosures and fittings installed in areas of agricultural buildings where excessive dust may be present must be designed to minimize the entrance of dust and must have no openings through which dust can enter the enclosure. Only dust-ignitionproof enclosures and fittings can be used for this purpose.

    (a) True   (b) False

    Answer: _____   Section: _____._____

13. Enclosures for overcurrent protection devices must be mounted in a _____ position unless that is shown to be impracticable.

    (a) vertical   (b) horizontal   (c) vertical or horizontal   (d) there are no requirements

    Answer: _____   Section: _____._____

14. ENT and fittings can be _____, provided fittings identified for this purpose are used.

    (a) encased in poured concrete
    (b) embedded in a concrete slab on grade where the tubing is placed on sand or approved screenings
    (c) either a or b
    (d) none of these

    Answer: _____   Section: _____._____

15. ENT must be securely fastened in place every _____.

    (a) 12 in.   (b) 18 in.   (c) 24 in.   (d) 36 in.

    Answer: _____   Section: _____._____

16. ENT must not be used where exposed to the direct rays of the sun, unless identified as _____.

    (a) high-temperature rated   (b) sunlight resistant   (c) schedule 80   (d) never can be

    Answer: _____   Section: _____._____

17. Equipment bonding jumpers are not required for receptacles listed as self-grounding that have mounting screws to provide the grounding continuity between the metal yoke and the flush box.

    (a) True   (b) False

    Answer: _____   Section: _____._____

18. Equipment grounding conductors must be the same size as the circuit conductors for _____ circuits.

    (a) 15A   (b) 20A   (c) 30A   (d) all of these

    Answer: _____   Section: _____._____

19. Equipment is required to be identified not only for the class of location but also for the explosive, combustible, or ignitible properties of the specific _____ that will be present.

    (a) gas or vapor   (b) dust   (c) fiber or flyings   (d) all of these

    Answer: _____   Section: _____._____

20. Equipment listed by a qualified electrical testing laboratory is not required to have the factory-installed _____ wiring inspected at the time of installation except to detect alterations or damage.

    (a) external   (b) associated   (c) internal   (d) all of these

    Answer: _____   Section: _____._____

21. Examples of assembly occupancies include, but are not limited to _____.

    (a) restaurants   (b) conference rooms   (c) pool rooms   (d) all of these

    Answer: _____   Section: _____._____

22. Exposed CATV cables must be secured by straps, staples, hangers, or similar fittings designed and installed so as not to damage the cable.

    (a) True   (b) False

    Answer: _____   Section: _____._____

23. Exposed Class 1, 2, and 3 cables must be supported by straps, staples, hangers, or similar fittings designed and installed so as not to damage the cable.

    (a) True   (b) False

    Answer: _____   Section: _____._____

24. Exposed communications cables must be secured by straps, staples, hangers, or similar fittings designed and installed so as not to damage the cable.

    (a) True   (b) False

    Answer: _____   Section: _____._____

25. Exposed vertical risers of IMC for industrial machinery or fixed equipment can be supported at intervals not exceeding _____ if the conduit is made up with threaded couplings, firmly supported at the top and bottom of the riser, and no other means of support is available.

    (a) 10 ft   (b) 12 ft   (c) 15 ft   (d) 20 ft

    Answer: _____   Section: _____._____

26. Exposed vertical risers of RMC for industrial machinery or fixed equipment can be supported at intervals not exceeding _____ if the conduit is made up with threaded couplings, firmly supported at the top and bottom of the riser, and no other means of support is available.

    (a) 6 ft   (b) 10 ft   (c) 20 ft   (d) none of these

    Answer: _____   Section: _____._____

27. Feeder and branch-circuit conductors installed for sensitive electronic equipment systems must be identified _____ by color, marking, tagging, or other effective means, and the means of identification must be posted at each branch-circuit panelboard and at the disconnecting means for the building.

    (a) at splices   (b) at terminations   (c) only on the blueprints   (d) a and b

    Answer: _____   Section: _____._____

28. Feeder conductors to the mobile home must consist of _____.

    (a) a listed cord   (b) a permanently installed feeder consisting of 4 color coded, insulated conductors
    (c) either a or b   (d) none of these

    Answer: _____   Section: _____._____

29. Feeders for temporary installations may be within cable assemblies or within multiconductor cords or cables identified for hard usage or extra-hard usage. Type NM and Type NMC cables are permitted to be used in any dwelling, building, or structure not more than 3 floors high for temporary feeders.

    (a) True   (b) False

    Answer: _____   Section: _____._____

30. Field-installed skeleton tubing and outline lighting consisting of listed luminaires are not required to be listed when installed in conformance with the *Code*.

    (a) True   (b) False

    Answer: _____   Section: _____._____

31. Flexible cords and cables must be connected to devices and to fittings so that tension will not be transmitted to joints or terminal screws. This must be accomplished by _____.

    (a) knotting the cord   (b) winding the cord with tape
    (c) fittings designed for the purpose   (d) any of these

    Answer: _____   Section: _____._____

32. Flexible cords and flexible cables used for temporary wiring must _____.

    (a) be protected from accidental damage   (b) be protected where passing through doorways
    (c) avoid sharp corners and projections   (d) all of these

    Answer: _____   Section: _____._____

33. Flexible cords immersed in or exposed to water in a fountain must be _____.

    (a) of the hard-service type   (b) marked water resistant   (c) encased in at least 2 in. of concrete   (d) a and b

    Answer: _____   Section: _____._____

34. Flexible cords must not be used as a substitute for _____ wiring unless specifically permitted in 400.7.

    (a) temporary   (b) fixed   (c) overhead   (d) none of these

    Answer: _____   Section: _____._____

35. Flexible metal conduit can be used as the equipment grounding conductor if the length in any ground return path does not exceed 6 ft and the circuit conductors contained in the conduit are protected by overcurrent devices rated at _____ or less.

    (a) 15A   (b) 20A   (c) 30A   (d) 60A

    Answer: _____   Section: _____._____

36. FMC must be supported and secured _____.

    (a) at intervals not exceeding 4 1/2 ft   (b) within 8 in. on each side of a box where fished
    (c) where fished   (d) at intervals not exceeding 6 ft at motor terminals

    Answer: _____   Section: _____._____

37. For a cabinet or cutout box constructed of sheet steel, the metal must not be thinner than _____ uncoated.

    (a) 0.53 in.   (b) 0.035 in.   (c) 0.053 in.   (d) 1.35 in.

    Answer: _____   Section: _____._____

38. For a cover mounted receptacle, direct metal-to-metal contact of the receptacle yoke and the metal cover is always considered to be sufficiently bonded and no equipment bonding jumper is required.

    (a) True   (b) False

    Answer: _____   Section: _____._____

39. For a grounded system, an unspliced _____ must be used to connect the equipment grounding conductor(s) and the service disconnect enclosure to the grounded conductor of the system within the enclosure for each service disconnect.

    (a) grounding electrode   (b) main bonding jumper
    (c) bus bar only   (d) insulated copper conductor only

    Answer: _____   Section: _____._____

40. For a single separately derived system, the grounding electrode conductor connects the grounding electrode to the grounded conductor of the derived system at the same point on the separately derived system where the _____ is installed.

    (a) metering equipment   (b) transfer switch   (c) bonding jumper   (d) largest circuit breaker

    Answer: _____   Section: _____._____

41. For a transformer rated 600V, nominal, or less, if the primary overcurrent protection device is sized at 250 percent of the primary current, what size secondary overcurrent protection device is required if the secondary current is 42A?

    (a) 40A   (b) 70A   (c) 60A   (d) 90A

    Answer: _____   Section: _____._____

42. For electrical equipment supplementary electrodes:

    (a) A bond to the grounding electrode system is not required.
    (b) The bonding jumper to the supplementary electrode can be any size.
    (c) The 25 ohm resistance requirement of 250.56 does not apply.
    (d) All of the above are true

    Answer: _____   Section: _____._____

43. For grounded systems, non-current-carrying conductive materials enclosing electrical conductors or equipment, or forming part of such equipment, must be connected together and to the _____ in a manner that establishes an effective ground-fault current path.

    (a) ground   (b) earth   (c) electrical supply source   (d) none of these

    Answer: _____   Section: _____._____

44. For pendants used in an aircraft hanger, not installed in a Class I location, cords are not required to include a separate equipment grounding conductor.

    (a) True   (b) False

    Answer: _____   Section: _____._____

45. For permanently connected appliances rated over _____ or 1/8 hp, the branch-circuit switch or circuit breaker is permitted to serve as the disconnecting means where the switch or circuit breaker is within sight from the appliance or is capable of being locked in the open position with a permanently installed locking provision.

    (a) 200 VA   (b) 300 VA   (c) 400 VA   (d) 500 VA

    Answer: _____   Section: _____._____

46. For ungrounded systems, noncurrent-carrying conductive materials enclosing electrical conductors or equipment, or forming part of such equipment, must be connected to earth in a manner that will limit the voltage imposed by lightning or unintentional contact with higher-voltage lines.

    (a) True   (b) False

    Answer: _____   Section: _____._____

47. Fuses are required to be marked with _____.

    (a) ampere and voltage rating
    (b) interrupting rating where other than 10,000A
    (c) the name or trademark of the manufacturer
    (d) all of these

    Answer: _____   Section: _____._____

48. General-purpose optical fiber cables listed as suitable for general-purpose use, with the exception of risers and plenums are Types _____.

    (a) OFNP and OFCP   (b) OFNR and OFCR   (c) OFNG and OFCG   (d) OFN and OFC

    Answer: _____   Section: _____._____

49. GFCI protection for personnel must be provided for electrically-heated floors in _____ locations.

    (a) bathroom   (b) hydromassage bathtub   (c) kitchen   (d) a and b

    Answer: _____   Section: _____._____

50. GFCI protection is required for all 15 and 20A, 125V single-phase receptacles located within an arc measurement of 6 ft from the dwelling unit _____.

    (a) laundry sink   (b) utility sink   (c) wet bar sink   (d) all of these

    Answer: _____   Section: _____._____

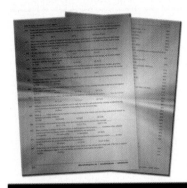

(• Indicates that 75% or fewer exam takers get the question correct)

Article 310 Conductors for General Wiring (continued)

1. •When bare grounding conductors are allowed, their ampacities are limited to _____.

    (a) 60°C   (b) 75°C
    (c) 90°C   (d) those permitted for the insulated conductors of the same size

    Answer: _____   Section: _____._____

2. On a 3-phase, 4-wire, wye circuit, where the major portion of the load consists of electrical discharge lighting, data-processing equipment, or other harmonic current inducting loads, the grounded conductor must be counted when applying 310.15(B)(2) adjustment factors.

    (a) True   (b) False

    Answer: _____   Section: _____._____

3. Service and feeder conductors may be sized using Table 310.15(B)(6) for_____.

    (a) any kind of service under 400 amps
    (b) only multifamily dwelling services
    (c) only 120/240 volt, 3-wire, 1-phase services for individual dwelling units
    (d) commercial services only

    Answer: _____   Section: _____._____

4. In designing circuits, the current-carrying capacity of conductors should be corrected for heat at room temperatures above _____.

    (a) 30°F   (b) 86°F   (c) 94°F   (d) 75°F

    Answer: _____   Section: _____._____

5. The ampacity of a single insulated 1/0 THHN copper conductor in free air is _____.

    (a) 260A   (b) 300A   (c) 185A   (d) 215A

    Answer: _____   Section: _____._____

6. As used in the *Code*, thermal resistivity refers to the heat _____ capability through a substance by conduction.

    (a) assimilation   (b) generation   (c) transfer   (d) dissipation

    Answer: _____   Section: _____._____

7.   Table 310.70 provides the ampacities of insulated single aluminum conductors isolated in air. If the conductor size is 8 AWG, MV-90, and the voltage range is 2,001 through 5,000, then the ampacity is _____.

   (a) 64A   (b) 85A   (c) 115A   (d) 150A

   Answer: _____   Section: _____._____

Article 312 Cabinets, Cutout Boxes, and Meter Socket Enclosures

Article 312 covers the installation and construction specifications for cabinets, cutout boxes, and meter socket enclosures.

8.   Cabinets or cutout boxes installed in wet locations must be _____.

   (a) waterproof   (b) raintight   (c) weatherproof   (d) watertight

   Answer: _____   Section: _____._____

9.   Where raceways or cables enter above the level of uninsulated live parts of an enclosure in a wet location, a(n) _____ must be used.

   (a) fitting listed for wet locations   (b) explosion proof seal-off
   (c) fitting listed for damp locations   (d) insulated fitting

   Answer: _____   Section: _____._____

10. Plaster, drywall, or plasterboard surfaces that are broken or incomplete must be repaired so there will be no gaps or open spaces greater than _____ at the edge of a cabinet or cutout box employing a flush-type cover.

   (a) 1/4 in   (b) 1/2 in   (c) 1/8 in   (d) 1/16 in

   Answer: _____   Section: _____._____

11. Each cable entering a cutout box _____.

   (a) must be secured to the cutout box   (b) can be sleeved through a chase
   (c) must have a maximum of two cables per connector (d) all of these

   Answer: _____   Section: _____._____

12. A switch enclosure (cabinet) must not be used as a junction box, except where adequate space is provided so that the conductors don't fill the wiring space at any cross-section to more than 40 percent of the cross-sectional area of the space, and so that _____ don't fill the wiring space at any cross-section to more than 75 percent of the cross-sectional area of the space.

   (a) splices   (b) taps   (c) conductors   (d) all of these

   Answer: _____   Section: _____._____

Article 314 Outlet, Device, Pull and Junction Boxes, Conduit Bodies, and Handhole Enclosures

Article 314 contains installation requirements for outlet boxes, pull and junction boxes, as well as conduit bodies, and handhole enclosures.

13. Round boxes must not be used where conduits or connectors requiring the use of locknuts or bushings are to be connected to the side of the box.

   (a) True   (b) False

   Answer: _____   Section: _____._____

14.   Metallic boxes are required to be _____.

    (a) metric   (b) installed   (c) grounded   (d) all of these

    Answer: _____   Section: _____._____

15.   Short-radius conduit bodies such as capped elbows, and service-entrance elbows that enclose conductors 6 AWG and smaller are intended to enable the installation of the raceway and the contained conductors and must not contain _____.

    (a) splices   (b) taps   (c) devices   (d) any of these

    Answer: _____   Section: _____._____

16.   According to the *NEC*, the volume of a 3 x 2 x 2 in. device box is _____

    (a) 12 cu in.   (b) 14 cu in.   (c) 10 cu in.   (d) 8 cu in.

    Answer: _____   Section: _____._____

17.   When counting the number of conductors in a box, a conductor running through the box with an unbroken loop not less than twice the minimum length required for free conductors in 300.14 is counted as _____ conductor(s).

    (a) one   (b) two   (c) zero   (d) none of these

    Answer: _____   Section: _____._____

18.   When determining the number of conductors in a box, and one or more factory or field-supplied internal cable clamps are present in the box, a double volume allowance for the clamps, in accordance with Table 314.16(B), must be made based on the largest conductor present in the box.

    (a) True   (b) False

    Answer: _____   Section: _____._____

19.   Each yoke or strap containing one or more devices or equipment counts as _____ conductor(s), based on the largest conductor that terminates on that device.

    (a) 1   (b) 2   (c) 3   (d) none

    Answer: _____   Section: _____._____

20.   When a box contains three equipment grounding conductors that originated outside the box, the three grounding conductors are counted as _____ conductor(s) when determining the number of conductors in a box for box fill calculations.

    (a) 3   (b) 6   (c) 1   (d) 0

    Answer: _____   Section: _____._____

21.   Splices and taps can be made in conduit bodies that are durably and legibly marked by the manufacturer with their volume and the maximum number of conductors as computed in accordance with Table 314.16(B)

    (a) True   (b) False

    Answer: _____   Section: _____._____

22.   •In noncombustible walls or ceilings, the front edge of a box, plaster ring, extension ring, or listed extender may be set back not more than _____ from the finished surface.

    (a) 3/8 in.   (b) 1/8 in.   (c) 1/2 in.   (d) 1/4 in.

    Answer: _____   Section: _____._____

23. Plaster, drywall, or plasterboard surfaces that are broken or incomplete around boxes employing a flush-type cover or faceplate must be repaired so there will be no gaps or open spaces larger than _____ at the edge of the box.

    (a) 1/4 in.   (b) 1/2 in.   (c) 1/8 in.   (d) 1/16 in.

    Answer: _____   Section: _____._____

24. •Only a _____ wiring method can be used for a surface extension from a cover, and the wiring method must include an equipment grounding conductor.

    (a) solid   (b) flexible   (c) rigid   (d) cord

    Answer: _____   Section: _____._____

25. Nails or screws can fasten boxes to structural members of a building using brackets on the outside of the enclosure, or they can pass through the interior within _____ of the back or ends of the enclosure. Screws are not permitted to pass through the box unless exposed threads in the box are protected using approved means to avoid abrasions of conductor insulation.

    (a) 1/8 in   (b) 1/16 in   (c) 1/4 in   (d) 1/2 in

    Answer: _____   Section: _____._____

26. When mounting an enclosure in a finished surface, the enclosure must be _____ secured to the surface by clamps, anchors, or fittings identified for the application.

    (a) temporarily   (b) partially   (c) never   (d) rigidly

    Answer: _____   Section: _____._____

27. Outlet boxes can be secured to independent support wires, which are taut and secured at both ends, if the box is supported to the independent support wires using methods identified for the purpose.

    (a) True   (b) False

    Answer: _____   Section: _____._____

28. •Enclosures not over 100 cu in. that have threaded entries that support luminaires or contain devices are considered adequately supported where two or more conduits are threaded wrenchtight into the enclosure where each conduit is supported within _____ of the enclosure.

    (a) 12 in.   (b) 18 in.   (c) 24 in.   (d) 30 in.

    Answer: _____   Section: _____._____

29. •The minimum size box that is to contain a flush device must not be less than _____ deep.

    (a) 15/16 in.   (b) 8/15 in.   (c) 1 in.   (d) 1 1/2 in.

    Answer: _____   Section: _____._____

30. Outlet boxes used at luminaire or lamp holder outlets must be _____.

    (a) designed for the purpose   (b) metal only
    (c) plastic only   (d) mounted using bar hangers only

    Answer: _____   Section: _____._____

31. Luminaires must be supported independently of the outlet box where the weight exceeds _____

    (a) 60 lbs   (b) 50 lbs   (c) 40 lbs   (d) 30 lbs

    Answer: _____   Section: _____._____

32. When installing floor boxes, boxes _____ must be used.

    (a) made only of metal   (b) listed specifically for this application
    (c) fed by metal raceways only   (d) fed by nonmetallic cable only

    Answer: _____   Section: _____._____

33. Listed outlet boxes, or outlet box systems that are identified for the purpose are permitted to support ceiling-suspended fans that weigh more than 35 lbs but no more than _____ if the allowable weight is marked on the box.

    (a) 50 lbs   (b) 60 lbs   (c) 70 lbs   (d) none of these

    Answer: _____   Section: _____._____

34. Pull boxes or junction boxes that have any dimension over _____ must have all conductors cabled or racked in an approved manner.

    (a) 3 ft   (b) 6 ft   (c) 9 ft   (d) 12 ft

    Answer: _____   Section: _____._____

35. Listed boxes designed for underground installation can be directly buried when covered by _____ if their location is identified and accessible.

    (a) concrete   (b) gravel
    (c) noncohesive granulated soil   (d) b or c

    Answer: _____   Section: _____._____

36. Handhole enclosures must be sized in accordance with 314.28(A) for conductors operating at 600V and below. For handhole enclosures without bottoms, the measurement to the removable cover is taken from the _____.

    (a) end of the conduit or cable assembly   (b) lowest point in the hole
    (c) leveling marks provided   (d) highest possible ground water level

    Answer: _____   Section: _____._____

37. Where handhole enclosures without bottoms are installed, all enclosed conductors and any splices or terminations, if present, must be listed as _____.

    (a) suitable for wet locations   (b) suitable for damp locations
    (c) handhole ready   (d) general duty

    Answer: _____   Section: _____._____

38. Handhole enclosure covers must require the use of tools to open, or they must weigh over _____. Metal covers and other exposed conductive surfaces must be bonded to an effective ground-fault current path.

    (a) 45 lbs   (b) 100 lbs   (c) 70 lbs   (d) 200 lbs

    Answer: _____   Section: _____._____

39. Metal boxes over _____ in size must be constructed so as to be of ample strength and rigidity. Sheet steel must not be less than 0.053 in. thick.

    (a) 50 cu in.   (b) 75 cu in.   (c) 100 cu in.   (d) 125 cu in.

    Answer: _____   Section: _____._____

40. For systems over 600V, the length of a pull box for a straight pull must not be less than _____ entering the box.

    (a) 18 times the diameter of the largest raceway
    (b) 48 times the diameter of the largest raceway
    (c) 48 times the outside diameter of the largest shielded conductor or cable
    (d) 36 times the largest conductor

    Answer: _____   Section: _____._____

41. •For angle or U-pulls, the distance between the shielded conductor entry (for systems over 600V, nominal) and the opposite wall of the box must not be less than _____ times the outside diameter of the largest cable or conductor.

    (a) 6   (b) 12   (c) 24   (d) 36

    Answer: _____   Section: _____._____

Article 320 Armored Cable (Type AC)

Armored cable is an assembly of insulated conductors, 14 AWG through 1 AWG, that are individually wrapped with waxed paper. The conductors are contained within a flexible spiral metal (steel or aluminum) sheath that interlocks at the edges. Armored cable looks like flexible metal conduit. Many electricians call this metal cable BX®.

42. •The use of Type AC cable is permitted in _____ installations.

    (a) wet   (b) cable tray   (c) exposed   (d) b and c

    Answer: _____   Section: _____._____

43. Exposed runs of Type AC cable must closely follow the surface of the building finish or of running boards. Exposed runs are also permitted to be installed on the underside of joists where supported at each joist and located so as not to be subject to physical damage.

    (a) True   (b) False

    Answer: _____   Section: _____._____

44. Where run across the top of floor joists, or within 7 ft of floor or floor joists, across the face of rafters or studding in attics and roof spaces that are accessible by permanent stairs or ladders, Type AC cable must be protected by substantial guard strips that are _____.

    (a) at least as high as the cable   (b) constructed of metal   (c) made for the cable   (d) none of these

    Answer: _____   Section: _____._____

45. When armored cable is run parallel to the sides of rafters, studs, or floor joists in an accessible attic, the cable must be protected with running boards.

    (a) True   (b) False

    Answer: _____   Section: _____._____

46. Type AC cable must be supported and secured at intervals not exceeding 4 1/2 ft and the cable must be secured within _____ of every outlet box, cabinet, conduit body, or other armored cable termination.

    (a) 4 in.   (b) 8 in.   (c) 9 in.   (d) 12 in.

    Answer: _____   Section: _____._____

47. At all Type AC cable terminations, a(n) _____ must be provided.

    (a) fitting (or box design) that protects the wires from abrasion
    (b) insulating bushing between the conductors and the cable armor
    (c) both a and b
    (d) none of these

    Answer: _____   Section: _____._____

48. Type AC cable must provide _____ for equipment grounding as required by Article 250.

    (a) an adequate path
    (b) a green terminal on all Type AC fittings
    (c) a solid copper insulated green conductor in all Type AC cables
    (d) a bonding locknut on all Type AC fittings

    Answer: _____   Section: _____._____

Article 322 Flat Cable Assemblies (Type FC)

This article covers the use, installation, and construction specifications for flat cable assemblies, Type FC.

49. Flat cable assemblies are suitable to supply tap devices for _____ loads. The rating of the branch circuit must not exceed 30A.

    (a) lighting   (b) small appliance   (c) small power   (d) all of these

    Answer: _____   Section: _____._____

50. Flat cable assemblies must not be installed _____.

    (a) where subject to corrosive vapors unless suitable for the application
    (b) in hoistways
    (c) in any hazardous (classified) location
    (d) all of these

    Answer: _____   Section: _____._____

51. Tap devices used in Type FC assemblies must be rated at not less than _____ or more than 300 volts-to-ground, and they must be color coded in accordance with the requirements of 322.120(C).

    (a) 20A   (b) 15A   (c) 30A   (d) 40A

    Answer: _____   Section: _____._____

52. Flat cable assemblies must have conductors of _____ AWG special stranded copper wires.

    (a) 14   (b) 12   (c) 10   (d) all of these

    Answer: _____   Section: _____._____

Article 324 Flat Conductor Cable (Type FCC)

This article covers a field-installed wiring system for branch circuits incorporating Type FCC cable and associated accessories as defined by the article. The wiring system is designed for installation under carpet squares.

53. Type FCC cable consists of _____ copper conductors placed edge-to-edge and separated and enclosed within an insulating assembly.

(a) 3 or more square   (b) 2 or more round   (c) 3 or more flat   (d) 2 or more flat

Answer: _____   Section: _____._____

54. The maximum voltage permitted between ungrounded conductors of flat conductor cable systems is _____.

(a) 600V   (b) 300V   (c) 250V   (d) 150V

Answer: _____   Section: _____._____

55. Use of Type FCC cable systems are permitted on wall surfaces in _____.

(a) surface metal raceways   (b) cable trays   (c) busways   (d) any of these

Answer: _____   Section: _____._____

56. Floor-mounted flat conductor cable and fittings must be covered with carpet squares no larger than _____.

(a) 36 sq in. area   (b) 36 inches square   (c) 30 sq in. area   (d) 24 inches square

Answer: _____   Section: _____._____

57. No more than _____ layers of flat conductor cable can cross at any one point.

(a) 2   (b) 3   (c) 4   (d) none of these

Answer: _____   Section: _____._____

58. The top shield installed over all floor-mounted Type FCC cable must completely _____ all cable runs, corners, connectors, and ends.

(a) cover   (b) encase   (c) protect   (d) none of these

Answer: _____   Section: _____._____

59. Each Type FCC transition assembly must incorporate means for _____.

(a) facilitating the entry of the Type FCC cable into the assembly
(b) connecting the Type FCC cable to the grounded conductors
(c) electrically connecting the assembly to the metal cable shields and equipment grounding conductors
(d) all of these

Answer: _____   Section: _____._____

60. Type FCC cable must be clearly and durably marked _____.

(a) on the top side at intervals not exceeding 30 in.
(b) on both sides at intervals not exceeding 24 in.
(c) with conductor material, maximum temperature, and ampacity
(d) b and c

Answer: _____   Section: _____._____

Article 328 Medium Voltage Cable (Type MV)

This article covers the use, installation, and construction specifications for medium voltage cable, Type MV.

61. Type MV cable is defined as a single or multiconductor solid dielectric insulated cable rated _____ V or higher.

    (a) 601　　　　　　　　(b) 1,001　　　　　　　　(c) 2,001　　　　　　　　(d) 6,001

    Answer: _____　　Section: _____._____

Article 330 Metal-Clad Cable (Type MC)

Metal-clad cable encloses one or more insulated conductors in a metal sheath of either corrugated or smooth copper or aluminum tubing, or spiral interlocked steel or aluminum. The physical characteristics of type MC cable make it a versatile wiring method that is permitted in almost any location and for almost any application. The most common type of MC cable is the interlocking type, which looks similar to armored cable or flexible metal conduit.

62. Type MC cable installed through, or parallel to, framing members must be protected against physical damage from penetration by screws or nails by 1 1/4 in. separation or protected by a suitable metal plate.

    (a) True　　　　　　　　(b) False

    Answer: _____　　Section: _____._____

63. Type MC cable installed in accessible attics or roof spaces must comply with the same requirements as given for AC cable in 320.24. This includes the installation of guard strips to protect the cable when run across the top of floor joists within _____ of the nearest edge of the scuttle hole or attic entrance if the space is not accessible by permanent stairs or ladders.

    (a) 6 ft　　　　　　　　(b) 7 ft　　　　　　　　(c) 1 1/4 in.　　　　　　　　(d) 18 in.

    Answer: _____　　Section: _____._____

64. Bends made in interlocked or corrugated sheath metal clad cable must maintain a bending radius of at least _____ the external diameter of the metallic sheath.

    (a) 5 times　　　　　　　　(b) 7 times　　　　　　　　(c) 10 times　　　　　　　　(d) 125% of

    Answer: _____　　Section: _____._____

65. Type MC cable containing four or fewer conductors, sized no larger than 10 AWG, must be secured within _____ of every box, cabinet, fitting, or other cable termination.

    (a) 8 in.　　　　　　　　(b) 18 in.　　　　　　　　(c) 12 in.　　　　　　　　(d) 24 in.

    Answer: _____　　Section: _____._____

66. Fittings used for connecting Type MC cable to boxes, cabinets, or other equipment must _____.

    (a) be nonmetallic only　　　　　　　　　　(b) be listed and identified for such use
    (c) be listed and identified as weatherproof　　(d) include anti-shorting bushings (red heads)

    Answer: _____　　Section: _____._____

67. Where MC cable is used for equipment grounding it must comply with 250.118(10) which allows the metallic sheath alone of interlocked metal tape-type MC cable to be used as an equipment grounding conductor.

    (a) True　　　　　　　　(b) False

    Answer: _____　　Section: _____._____

Article 332 Mineral-Insulated, Metal-Sheathed Cable (Type MI)

This article covers the use, installation, and construction specifications for mineral-insulated, metal-sheathed cable, Type MI.

68. The outer sheath of Type MI cable is made of _____.

(a) aluminum   (b) steel alloy   (c) copper   (d) b or c

Answer: _____   Section: _____._____

69. Bends in Type MI cable must be made so that the cable will not be _____.

(a) damaged   (b) shortened   (c) a and b   (d) none of these

Answer: _____   Section: _____._____

70. The radius of the inner edge of any bend in Type MI cable must not be less than _____ times the external diameter of the metallic sheath for any cable having a diameter greater than 3/4 in., but not more than 1 in.

(a) 6   (b) 3   (c) 8   (d) 10

Answer: _____   Section: _____._____

71. Where single-conductor Type MI cables are used, all ungrounded (phase) conductors and, when used, the _____ conductor, must be grouped together to minimize induced voltage on the metal sheath.

(a) larger   (b) grounded neutral   (c) grounding   (d) largest

Answer: _____   Section: _____._____

72. Type MI cable conductors must be made of _____, nickel, or nickel-coated copper with a resistance corresponding to standard AWG and kcmil sizes.

(a) solid copper   (b) solid or stranded copper   (c) stranded copper   (d) solid copper or aluminum

Answer: _____   Section: _____._____

73. The conductor insulation of Type MI cable must be a highly-compressed refractory mineral that will provide proper _____ for all conductors.

(a) covering   (b) spacing   (c) resistance   (d) none of these

Answer: _____   Section: _____._____

Article 334 Nonmetallic-Sheathed Cable (Types NM and NMC)

Nonmetallic-sheathed cable encloses two, three, or four insulated conductors, 14 AWG through 2 AWG, within a nonmetallic outer jacket. Because this cable is nonmetallic, it contains a separate equipment grounding conductor. Nonmetallic-sheathed cable is a common wiring method used for residential and commercial branch circuits. Most electricians call this plastic cable Romex®.

74. Types NM and NMC nonmetallic-sheathed cables can be used in _____.

(a) one-family dwellings   (b) multifamily dwellings   (c) other structures   (d) all of these

Answer: _____   Section: _____._____

75. Type NM cable can be installed in multifamily dwellings of Types III, IV, and V construction except as prohibited in 334.12.

    (a) True   (b) False

    Answer: _____   Section: _____._____

76. Type NM cable must not be used _____.

    (a) in commercial buildings   (b) in the air void of masonry block not subject to excessive moisture
    (c) for exposed work   (d) embedded in poured cement, concrete, or aggregate

    Answer: _____   Section: _____._____

77. When installed in _____, nonmetallic-sheathed cable must be protected from physical damage where necessary by RMC, IMC, Schedule 80 rigid nonmetallic conduit, EMT, guard strips, or other means.

    (a) hazardous locations of commercial garages   (b) exposed work
    (c) service entrance applications   (d) motion picture studios

    Answer: _____   Section: _____._____

78. NM cable on a wall of an unfinished basement is permitted to be installed in a listed raceway. A _____ must be installed at the point where the cable enters the raceway. Metal conduit and tubing and metal outlet boxes must be grounded.

    (a) nonmetallic bushing or adapter   (b) sealing fitting
    (c) bonding bushing   (d) junction box

    Answer: _____   Section: _____._____

79. Nonmetallic-sheathed cable installed in accessible attics or roof spaces must comply with the same requirements as given for AC cable in 320.24. This includes the installation of _____ to protect the cable when run across the top of floor joists if the space is accessible by permanent stairs or ladders.

    (a) GFCI protection   (b) Arc-fault protection   (c) rigid metal conduit   (d) guard strips

    Answer: _____   Section: _____._____

80. Bends made in nonmetallic-sheathed cable must be made so that the cable will not be damaged. The radius of the curve of the inner edge of any bend during or after installation must not be less than _____ the external diameter of the cable.

    (a) 5 times   (b) 7 times   (c) 10 times   (d) 12 times

    Answer: _____   Section: _____._____

81. Flat two-conductor Type NM cables cannot be stapled on edge.

    (a) True   (b) False

    Answer: _____   Section: _____._____

82. Type NM cables run horizontally through framing are considered supported and secured where such support does not exceed 4 1/2 ft intervals and the Type NM cable is securely fastened in place within 12 in. of each box, cabinet, or conduit body.

    (a) True   (b) False

    Answer: _____   Section: _____._____

83. Switch, outlet, and tap devices of insulating material can be used without boxes in exposed cable wiring of Type NM or Type NMC cable.

(a) True   (b) False

Answer: _____   Section: _____._____

84. Where more than two NM cables containing two or more current-carrying conductors are bundled together and pass through wood framing that is to be fire- or draft-stopped using thermal insulation or sealing foam, the allowable ampacity of each conductor is _____.

(a) no more than 20A   (b) adjusted in accordance with 310.15(B)(2)(a)
(c) limited to 30A   (d) calculated by an engineer

Answer: _____   Section: _____._____

85. •The difference in the construction specifications between Type NM cable and Type NMC cable is that Type NMC cable is _____which Type NM is not.

(a) corrosion-resistant   (b) flame-retardant   (c) fungus-resistant   (d) a and c

Answer: _____   Section: _____._____

Article 336 Power and Control Tray Cable (Type TC)

Power and control cable tray is a factory assembly of two or more insulated conductors under a nonmetallic sheath for installation in cable trays, in raceways, or where supported by a messenger wire.

86. Type TC tray cable must not be installed _____.

(a) where it will be exposed to physical damage   (b) outside of a raceway or cable tray system
(c) direct buried unless identified for such use   (d) all of these

Answer: _____   Section: _____._____

Article 338 Service-Entrance Cable (Types SE and USE)

Service-entrance cable can be a single-conductor or multiconductor assembly within an overall nonmetallic covering. This cable is used primarily for services not over 600V, but is also permitted for feeders and branch circuits.

87. Type USE cable used for service laterals can emerge from the ground outside at termination in meter bases or other enclosures where protected in accordance with 300.5(D).

(a) True   (b) False

Answer: _____   Section: _____._____

88. Type SE service-entrance cables are permitted for use for branch circuits or feeders where the insulated conductors are used for circuit wiring and the uninsulated conductor is used only for _____ purposes.

(a) grounded neutral connection   (b) equipment grounding
(c) remote control and signaling   (d) none of these

Answer: _____   Section: _____._____

89. Bends made in USE and SE cable must be made so that the cable will not be damaged. The radius of the curve of the inner edge of any bend during or after installation must not be less than _____ the diameter of the cable.

    (a) 5 times   (b) 7 times   (c) 10 times   (d) 125% of

    Answer: _____   Section: _____._____

Article 340 Underground Feeder and Branch-Circuit Cable (Type UF)

Underground feeder cable is a moisture-, fungus-, and corrosion-resistant cable suitable for direct burial in the earth, and it comes in sizes 14 AWG through 4/0 AWG [340.104]. Multiconductor UF cable is covered in molded plastic that encapsulates the insulated conductors.

90. Type UF cable must not be used where subject to physical damage. When this cable is subject to physical damage, it must be protected by a suitable method as described in 300.5.

    (a) True   (b) False

    Answer: _____   Section: _____._____

91. Underground Feeder and branch circuit (Type UF) cable is allowed to be used in commercial garages.

    (a) True   (b) False

    Answer: _____   Section: _____._____

92. Type UF cable must not be used _____.

    (a) in any hazardous (classified) location
    (b) embedded in poured cement, concrete, or aggregate
    (c) where exposed to direct rays of the sun, unless identified as sunlight-resistant
    (d) all of these

    Answer: _____   Section: _____._____

93. The ampacity of Type UF cables must be that of _____ in accordance with 310.15.

    (a) 90°C conductors   (b) 75°C conductors   (c) 60°C conductors   (d) none of these

    Answer: _____   Section: _____._____

94. The overall covering of Type UF cable must be _____.

    (a) flame retardant   (b) moisture, fungus, and corrosion resistant
    (c) suitable for direct burial in the earth   (d) all of these

    Answer: _____   Section: _____._____

Article 342 Intermediate Metal Conduit (Type IMC)

Intermediate metal conduit is a circular metal raceway with the same outside diameter as rigid metal conduit. The wall thickness of intermediate metal conduit is less than that of rigid metal conduit, so it has a greater interior cross-sectional area. Intermediate metal conduit is lighter and less expensive than rigid metal conduit, but it's permitted in all the same locations as rigid metal conduit. Intermediate metal conduit also uses a different steel alloy, which makes it stronger than rigid metal conduit, even though the walls are thinner.

95.   Materials such as straps, bolts, screws, etc. that are associated with the installation of IMC in wet locations are required to be
      _____.

      (a) weatherproof   (b) weathertight   (c) corrosion-resistant   (d) none of these

      Answer: _____   Section: _____._____

96.   Trade Size 1 IMC raceway containing three or more conductors must not exceed _____ percent conductor fill.

      (a) 53   (b) 31   (c) 40   (d) 60

      Answer: _____   Section: _____._____

97.   A run of IMC must not contain more than the equivalent of _____ quarter bends including all offsets between pull points such as
      conduit bodies and boxes.

      (a) 1   (b) 2   (c) 3   (d) 4

      Answer: _____   Section: _____._____

98.   Trade Size 1 IMC must be supported every _____ .

      (a) 8 ft   (b) 10 ft   (c) 12 ft   (d) 14 ft

      Answer: _____   Section: _____._____

99.   Horizontal runs of IMC supported by openings through framing members at intervals not exceeding 10 ft and securely fastened
      within 3 ft of terminations is permitted.

      (a) True   (b) False

      Answer: _____   Section: _____._____

100. Threadless couplings and connectors must not be used on threaded IMC ends unless the fittings are listed for the purpose.

      (a) True   (b) False

      Answer: _____   Section: _____._____

Unit 5
NEC Practice Quiz
Articles 310 through 342

(• Indicates that 75% or fewer exam takers get the question correct)

1. In a balanced 120/208V, 4-wire, 3-phase system, the grounded conductor will carry _____ amperes if the loads supplied are linear loads and no harmonic currents are present.

    (a) full load   (b) zero   (c) fault-current   (d) none of these

    Answer: _____   Section: _____._____

2. •Nonmetallic boxes are permitted for use with _____.

    (a) flexible nonmetallic conduit   (b) liquidtight nonmetallic conduit
    (c) nonmetallic cables and raceways   (d) all of these

    Answer: _____   Section: _____._____

3. •Type USE or SE cable must have a minimum of _____ conductors (including the uninsulated one) in order for one of the conductors to be uninsulated.

    (a) one   (b) two   (c) three   (d) four

    Answer: _____   Section: _____._____

4. •What is the total volume, in cubic inches, for box fill calculations for two internal cable clamps, six 12 THHN conductors, and one single-pole switch?

    (a) 2.00 cu in.   (b) 4.50 cu in.   (c) 14.50 cu in.   (d) 20.25 cu in.

    Answer: _____   Section: _____._____

5. A luminaire that weighs more than 50 lbs is permitted to be supported by an outlet box or fitting that is designed and listed for the weight of the luminaire.

    (a) True   (b) False

    Answer: _____   Section: _____._____

6. A wood brace that is used for mounting a box must have a cross-section not less than nominal _____.

    (a) 1 x 2 in   (b) 2 x 2 in   (c) 2 x 3 in   (d) 2 x 4 in

    Answer: _____   Section: _____._____

7. All bare Type FCC cable ends must _____.

    (a) be sealed   (b) be insulated   (c) use listed insulating ends   (d) all of these

    Answer: _____   Section: _____._____

8. All boxes and conduit bodies, covers, extension rings, plaster rings, and the like must be durably and legibly marked with the manufacturer's name or trademark.

   (a) True   (b) False

   Answer: _____   Section: _____._____

9. Boxes, conduit bodies, and fittings installed in wet locations do not need to be listed for use in wet locations.

   (a) True   (b) False

   Answer: _____   Section: _____._____

10. Cables with entirely nonmetallic sheaths are permitted to enter the top of a surface-mounted enclosure through one or more non-flexible raceways not less than 18 in. or more than _____ ft in length if all of the required conditions are met.

    (a) 3   (b) 10   (c) 25   (d) 100

    Answer: _____   Section: _____._____

11. Enclosures not over _____ in size, having threaded entries and that do not contain a device(s) or support a luminaire(s) or other equipment, is considered to be adequately supported where two or more conduits are threaded wrenchtight into the enclosure and each conduit secured within 3 ft.

    (a) 50 cu in.   (b) 75 cu in.   (c) 100 cu in.   (d) 125 cu in.

    Answer: _____   Section: _____._____

12. Equipment grounding conductor(s), and not more than _____ fixture wires (smaller than 14 AWG) can be omitted from the calculations where they enter the box from a domed luminaire or similar canopy and terminate within that box.

    (a) 2   (b) 3   (c) 4   (d) none of these

    Answer: _____   Section: _____._____

13. Flat cable assemblies must consist of _____ conductors.

    (a) 2   (b) 3   (c) 4   (d) any of these

    Answer: _____   Section: _____._____

14. Flat cable assemblies must not be installed outdoors or in wet or damp locations unless _____ for the use.

    (a) special permission is granted   (b) approved
    (c) identified   (d) none of these

    Answer: _____   Section: _____._____

15. For conductors rated 2,001V to 35,000V, thermal resistively is the reciprocal of thermal conductivity, is designated Rho, and is expressed in units of _____.

    (a) °F-cm/volt   (b) °F-cm/watt   (c) °C-cm/volt   (d) °C-cm/watt

    Answer: _____   Section: _____._____

16. For individual dwelling units of _____ dwellings, Table 310.15(B)(6) can be used to size 3-wire, 1-phase, 120/240V service or feeder conductors that serve as the main power feeder.

    (a) one-family   (b) two-family   (c) multifamily   (d) any of these

    Answer: _____   Section: _____._____

17. Handhole enclosure covers must have an identifying _____ that prominently identifies the function of the enclosure, such as "electric."

    (a) mark   (b) logo   (c) a or b   (d) manual

    Answer: _____   Section: _____._____

18. Handhole enclosures must be designed and installed to withstand _____.

    (a) 3,000 lbs   (b) 6,000 lbs   (c) all loads likely to be imposed   (d) 600 lbs

    Answer: _____   Section: _____._____

19. IMC must be firmly fastened within _____ of each outlet box, junction box, device box, fitting, cabinet, or other conduit termination.

    (a) 12 in.   (b) 18 in.   (c) 2 ft   (d) 3 ft

    Answer: _____   Section: _____._____

20. In completed installations, each outlet box must have a _____.

    (a) cover   (b) faceplate   (c) canopy   (d) any of these

    Answer: _____   Section: _____._____

21. In walls constructed of wood or other _____ material, electrical cabinets must be flush with the finished surface or project therefrom.

    (a) nonconductive   (b) porous   (c) fibrous   (d) combustible

    Answer: _____   Section: _____._____

22. Metal shields for flat conductor cable must be electrically continuous to the _____.

    (a) floor   (b) cable
    (c) equipment grounding conductor   (d) none of these

    Answer: _____   Section: _____._____

23. Nonmetallic-sheathed cable installed in accessible attics or roof spaces must comply with the same requirements as given for AC cable in 320.24. This includes the installation of guard strips to protect the cable when run across the top of floor joists within _____ of the nearest edge of the scuttle hole or attic entrance if the space is not accessible by permanent stairs or ladders.

    (a) 6 ft   (b) 7 ft   (c) 1 1/4 in.   (d) 18 in.

    Answer: _____   Section: _____._____

24. Sections of Type NM cable protected from physical damage by a raceway are not required to be _____ within the raceway.

    (a) covered   (b) insulated   (c) secured   (d) unspliced

    Answer: _____   Section: _____._____

25. Smooth-sheath Type MC cable with an external diameter of not greater than 1 in. must have a bending radius of not more than _____ times the cable external diameter.

    (a) 5   (b) 10   (c) 12   (d) 13

    Answer: _____   Section: _____._____

26.   Surface extensions from a flush-mounted box must be made by mounting and mechanically securing an extension ring over the flush box.

(a) True   (b) False

Answer: _____   Section: _____._____

27.   Table 310.71 provides ampacities of an insulated three-conductor copper cable isolated in air, based on conductor temperature of 90°C (194°F) and ambient air temperature of 40°C (104°F). If the conductor size is 4/0 AWG, MV-105, and the voltage range is 2,001 through 5,000, then the ampacity is _____.

(a) 250A   (b) 285A   (c) 320A   (d) 325A

Answer: _____   Section: _____._____

28.   The ampacity of Type NM cable must be that of 60°C conductors, as listed in 310.15. However, the 90°C rating can be used for ampacity derating purposes provided the final derated ampacity does not exceed that of a _____ rated conductor.

(a) 120°C   (b) 60°C   (c) 90°C   (d) none of these

Answer: _____   Section: _____._____

29.   The distance between a shielded cable or conductor entry and its exit from the box must be not less than _____ times the outside diameter of that cable or conductor on a system of over 600V.

(a) 16   (b) 18   (c) 36   (d) 40

Answer: _____   Section: _____._____

30.   The maximum size of conductors in Underground Feeder (Type UF) cable is _____ AWG.

(a) 14   (b) 10   (c) 1/0   (d) 4/0

Answer: _____   Section: _____._____

31.   The metallic sheath of metal-clad cable must be continuous and _____.

(a) flame-retardant   (b) weatherproof   (c) close fitting   (d) all of these

Answer: _____   Section: _____._____

32.   The radius of the curve of the inner edge of any bend must not be less than _____ for AC cable.

(a) five times the largest conductor within the cable   (b) three times the diameter of the cable
(c) five times the diameter of the cable   (d) six times the outside diameter of the conductors

Answer: _____   Section: _____._____

33.   The radius of the inner edge of any bend in Type MI cable must not be less than five times the external diameter of the metallic sheath for cable not more than _____ in external diameter.

(a) 1/2 in.   (b) 3/4 in.   (c) 5/8 in.   (d) 1 1/2 in.

Answer: _____   Section: _____._____

34.   Threadless couplings approved for use with IMC in wet locations must be _____.

(a) rainproof   (b) listed for wet locations   (c) moistureproof   (d) concrete-tight

Answer: _____   Section: _____._____

35. Type AC cable installed through, or parallel to, framing members must be protected against physical damage from penetration by screws or nails.

    (a) True   (b) False

    Answer: _____   Section: _____._____

36. Type FCC systems are permitted both for general-purpose and appliance branch circuits; they are not permitted for individual branch circuits.

    (a) True   (b) False

    Answer: _____   Section: _____._____

37. Type MC cable can be unsupported where it is:

    (a) Fished between concealed access points in finished buildings or structures and support is impracticable.
    (b) Not more than 2 ft in length at terminals where flexibility is necessary.
    (c) Not more than 6 ft from the last point of support within an accessible ceiling for the connection of luminaires.
    (d) a or c

    Answer: _____   Section: _____._____

38. Type MC cable must not be used where exposed to the following destructive corrosive condition(s), unless the metallic sheath is suitable for the condition(s) or is protected by material suitable for the condition(s):

    (a) Direct burial in the earth   (b) In concrete   (c) In cinder fill   (d) all of these

    Answer: _____   Section: _____._____

39. Type NM cable can be installed as open runs in dropped or suspended ceilings in other than one- and two-family and multifamily dwellings.

    (a) True   (b) False

    Answer: _____   Section: _____._____

40. Type NM cable must be _____.

    (a) marked   (b) approved   (c) identified   (d) listed

    Answer: _____   Section: _____._____

41. Type SE service entrance cable is permitted for use as _____ in wiring systems where all of the circuit conductors of the cable are of the rubber-covered or thermoplastic type.

    (a) branch circuits   (b) feeders   (c) a or b   (d) neither a or b

    Answer: _____   Section: _____._____

42. Type TC cable can be used _____.

    (a) for power and lighting circuits   (b) in cable trays in hazardous locations
    (c) in Class 1 control circuits   (d) all of these

    Answer: _____   Section: _____._____

43. Type UF cable must not be used in _____.

(a) motion picture studios   (b) storage battery rooms   (c) hoistways   (d) all of these

Answer: _____   Section: _____._____

44. Use of Type FCC systems in damp locations _____.

(a) are restricted   (b) are permitted
(c) are permitted provided the system is encased in concrete   (d) must be approved by special permission

Answer: _____   Section: _____._____

45. When NM cable is used with nonmetallic boxes no larger than 2 1/4 x 4 in., securing the cable to the box is not required if the cable is fastened within _____ of that box.

(a) 6 in.   (b) 8 in.   (c) 10 in.   (d) 12 in.

Answer: _____   Section: _____._____

46. When sizing a pull box in a straight run which contains conductors of 4 AWG or larger, the length of the box must not be less than _____ for systems not over 600V.

(a) 8 times the diameter of the largest raceway
(b) 6 times the diameter of the largest raceway
(c) 48 times the outside diameter of the largest shielded conductor
(d) 36 times the largest conductor

Answer: _____   Section: _____._____

47. When Type AC cable is installed in thermal insulation, it must have conductors that are rated at 90°C. The ampacity of the cable in this application is _____.

(a) based on 90°C column   (b) as labeled by the manufacturer
(c) based on the 60°C column   (d) none of these

Answer: _____   Section: _____._____

48. Where practicable, contact of dissimilar metals must be avoided anywhere in an IMC raceway installation to prevent _____.

(a) corrosion   (b) galvanic action   (c) shorts   (d) none of these

Answer: _____   Section: _____._____

49. Where Type MI cable terminates, a (n) _____ must be installed immediately after stripping to prevent the entrance of moisture into the insulation.

(a) bushing   (b) connector   (c) flexible fitting   (d) end seal fitting

Answer: _____   Section: _____._____

50. Where Type NMC cable is run at angles with joists in unfinished basements, it is permissible to secure cables not smaller than _____ conductors directly to the lower edges of the joist.

(a) two, 6 AWG   (b) three, 8 AWG   (c) three, 10 AWG   (d) a or b

Answer: _____   Section: _____._____

1. Grounded conductors _____ and larger must be identified by a continuous white or gray outer finish along their entire length, by three continuous white stripes along their entire length, or by distinctive white or gray markings such as tape, paint, or other effective means at their terminations.

   (a) 10 AWG   (b) 8 AWG   (c) 6 AWG   (d) 4 AWG

   Answer: _____   Section: _____._____

2. Grounding and bonding conductors cannot be connected by _____.

   (a) pressure connections   (b) solder   (c) lugs   (d) approved clamps

   Answer: _____   Section: _____._____

3. Grounding electrodes that are driven rods require a minimum of _____ in contact with the soil.

   (a) 10 ft   (b) 8 ft   (c) 6 ft   (d) 12 ft

   Answer: _____   Section: _____._____

4. Grounding-type attachment plugs must be used only with a cord having a(n) _____ conductor.

   (a) equipment grounding   (b) isolated   (c) computer circuit   (d) insulated

   Answer: _____   Section: _____._____

5. Hazards often occur because of _____.

   (a) overloading of wiring systems by methods or usage not in conformity with this *Code*
   (b) initial wiring not providing for increases in the use of electricity
   (c) a and b
   (d) none of these

   Answer: _____   Section: _____._____

6. HDPE is allowed only in trade sizes _____.

   (a) 3/4 to 4   (b) 1/2 to 4   (c) 1 to 5   (d) 1 to 3

   Answer: _____   Section: _____._____

7. HDPE is permitted to be installed _____.

   (a) where subject to chemicals for which the conduit is listed   (b) in cinder fill
   (c) in direct burial installations in earth or concrete   (d) all of these

   Answer: _____   Section: _____._____

8. How many 12 XHHW conductors, not counting a bare ground wire, are allowed in trade size 3/8 FMC (maximum of 6 ft) with outside fittings?

    (a) 4   (b) 3   (c) 2   (d) 5

    Answer: _____   Section: _____._____

9. Hydromassage bathtubs and their associated electrical components must be GFCI protected.

    (a) True   (b) False

    Answer: _____   Section: _____._____

10. If required by the authority having jurisdiction, a diagram showing feeder details must be provided _____ of the feeders.

    (a) after the installation   (b) prior to the installation   (c) before the final inspection   (d) diagrams are not required

    Answer: _____   Section: _____._____

11. If the motor disconnecting means is a motor-circuit switch, it must be rated in _____.

    (a) horsepower   (b) watts   (c) amperes   (d) locked-rotor current

    Answer: _____   Section: _____._____

12. IMC can be installed in or under cinder fill subject to permanent moisture _____.

    (a) where the conduit is not less than 18 in. under the fill
    (b) when protected on all sides by 2 in. of noncinder concrete
    (c) where protected by corrosion protection judged suitable for the condition
    (d) any of these

    Answer: _____   Section: _____._____

13. In a Class II, Division 1 location, switches, circuit breakers, motor controllers, and fuses, including pushbuttons, relays, and similar devices that are intended to interrupt current during normal operation or that are installed where combustible dusts of an electrically conductive nature may be present, are required to be provided with identified _____ enclosures.

    (a) explosionproof   (b) dust-ignitionproof   (c) dusttight   (d) weatherproof

    Answer: _____   Section: _____._____

14. In a Class III hazardous (classified) location, pendant luminaires suspended by stems longer than _____ ft must be provided with a fitting or flexible connector approved for the location.

    (a) 1   (b) 2   (c) 3   (d) 4

    Answer: _____   Section: _____._____

15. In a dwelling unit, illumination on the exterior side of outdoor entrances or exits that have grade-level access can be controlled by _____.

    (a) home automation devices   (b) motion sensors   (c) photocells   (d) any of these

    Answer: _____   Section: _____._____

16. In a multiple-occupancy building, each occupant must have access to his or her own _____.

    (a) disconnecting means
    (b) building drops
    (c) building-entrance assembly
    (d) lateral conductors

    Answer: _____   Section: _____._____

17. In areas used for patient care, the grounding terminals of all receptacles and all noncurrent-carrying conductive surfaces of fixed electric equipment _____ must be grounded by an insulated copper equipment grounding conductor.

    (a) operating at over 100V
    (b) likely to become energized
    (c) subject to personal contact
    (d) all of these

    Answer: _____   Section: _____._____

18. In assembly occupancies, NM cable, type AC cable, electrical nonmetallic tubing, and rigid nonmetallic conduit are permitted to be installed in those portions of the building that is not required to be of _____ construction by the applicable building code.

    (a) Class I, Division 1   (b) fire-rated   (c) occupancy-rated   (d) above-ground

    Answer: _____   Section: _____._____

19. In Class I, Division 1 and 2 locations, locknut-bushing and double-locknut types of fittings are depended on for bonding purposes.

    (a) True   (b) False

    Answer: _____   Section: _____._____

20. In Class I, Division 1 and 2 locations, receptacles and attachment plugs must be of the type providing for _____ a flexible cord and must be identified for the location.

    (a) sealing compound around
    (b) quick connection to
    (c) connection to the grounding conductor of
    (d) none of these

    Answer: _____   Section: _____._____

21. In Class II, Division 1 locations, motors, generators, or other rotating electric machinery must be _____.

    (a) identified for Class II, Division 1 locations
    (b) totally enclosed pipe-ventilated, and meet the temperature limitations of 502.5
    (c) general duty
    (d) a or b

    Answer: _____   Section: _____._____

22. In Class II, Division 1 locations, receptacles and attachment plugs must be of the type providing for connection to the grounding conductor of the flexible cord and must be identified _____.

    (a) as explosionproof   (b) for Class II locations   (c) with laminated tags   (d) for general duty

    Answer: _____   Section: _____._____

23. In Class III, Divisions 1 and 2, _____ used as or in conjunction with control equipment for motors, generators, and appliances must be provided with dusttight enclosures complying with the temperature limitations in 504.5.

    (a) transformers   (b) impedance coils   (c) resistors   (d) all of these

    Answer: _____   Section: _____._____

24. In dwelling units, the voltage between conductors that supply the terminals of _____ must not exceed 120V, nominal.

    (a) luminaires
    (b) cord-and-plug connected loads of 1,440 VA, nominal, or less
    (c) cord-and-plug connected loads of more than 1/4 hp
    (d) a and b

    Answer: _____   Section: _____._____

25. In dwelling units, when determining the spacing of general-use receptacles, _____ on exterior walls are not considered wall space.

    (a) fixed panels   (b) fixed glass   (c) sliding panels   (d) all of these

    Answer: _____   Section: _____._____

26. In general, branch-circuit conductors to individual appliances must not be sized _____ than required by the appliance markings or instructions.

    (a) larger   (b) smaller

    Answer: _____   Section: _____._____

27. In information technology equipment rooms, a single disconnecting means is permitted to control _____.

    (a) only the HVAC systems to the room
    (b) only the power to electronic computer/data-processing equipment
    (c) the electronic computer/data-processing equipment and the building supply
    (d) the HVAC systems to the room and power to electronic computer/data-processing equipment

    Answer: _____   Section: _____._____

28. In marinas or boatyards, the *NEC* requires a(n) _____ disconnecting means, which allows individual boats to be isolated from their supply circuit.

    (a) accessible   (b) readily accessible   (c) remote   (d) any of these

    Answer: _____   Section: _____._____

29. In one- and two-family dwellings, the grounding conductor for CATV must be as short as practicable, not to exceed _____ in length.

    (a) 5 ft   (b) 8 ft   (c) 10 ft   (d) 20 ft

    Answer: _____   Section: _____._____

30. In one- and two-family dwellings, the primary protector grounding conductor for communications systems must be as short as practicable, not to exceed _____ in length.

    (a) 5 ft   (b) 8 ft   (c) 10 ft   (d) 20 ft

    Answer: _____   Section: _____._____

31.   In order for equipment and materials to receive approval _____.

(a) the equipment and material must always be listed by UL
(b) the authority having jurisdiction must decide on approval
(c) the authority having jurisdiction can never approve non-listed items
(d) the local electrical distributor must decide on approval

Answer: _____   Section: _____._____

32.   In order to use the optional method for calculating a service to a school, the school must be equipped with _____.

(a) cooking facilities   (b) electric space heating   (c) air-conditioning   (d) b or c

Answer: _____   Section: _____._____

33.   In walls or ceilings constructed of wood or other combustible surface material, boxes, plaster rings, extension rings, or listed extenders must _____.

(a) be flush with the surface   (b) project from the surface
(c) a or b   (d) be set back no more than 1/4 in

Answer: _____   Section: _____._____

34.   Individual unit equipment for legally required standby illumination must be permanently fixed in place. Flexible cord-and-plug connection is permitted, provided the cord does not exceed _____ in length.

(a) 3 ft   (b) 18 in.   (c) 6 ft   (d) 12 in.

Answer: _____   Section: _____._____

35.   Indoor antenna and lead-in conductors for radio and television receiving equipment must be separated by at least _____ from conductors of any electric light, power, or Class 1 circuit conductors.

(a) 6 ft   (b) 2 in.   (c) 12 in.   (d) 18 in.

Answer: _____   Section: _____._____

36.   Insulated conductors and cables exposed to the direct rays of the sun must be _____.

(a) covered with insulating material that is listed or listed and marked sunlight resistant
(b) listed and marked sunlight resistant
(c) listed for sunlight resistance
(d) any of these

Answer: _____   Section: _____._____

37.   It is permitted to base the _____ rating of a range receptacle on a single range demand load specified in Table 220.19.

(a) circuit   (b) voltage   (c) ampere   (d) resistance

Answer: _____   Section: _____._____

38.   Legally required standby system equipment must be suitable for _____ at its line terminals.

(a) the maximum available fault current   (b) the maximum overload current only
(c) the minimum fault current   (d) a one hour rating

Answer: _____   Section: _____._____

39. Lighting outlets can be controlled by occupancy sensors equipped with a _____ that will allow the sensor to function as a wall switch.

    (a) manual override   (b) photo cell
    (c) GFCI device   (d) selenium controlled rectifier (SCR)

    Answer: _____   Section: _____._____

40. Lighting systems operating at 30V or less need not be listed for the purpose.

    (a) True   (b) False

    Answer: _____   Section: _____._____

41. Listed plenum signaling raceways and _____ cable for Class 1, Class 2, and Class 3 circuits are permitted to be installed in other spaces used for environmental air as described in 300.22(C).

    (a) Type CL2P   (b) Type CL3P   (c) a or b   (d) none of these

    Answer: _____   Section: _____._____

42. Listed spa and hot tub packaged units installed indoors, rated 20A or less, are permitted to be cord-and-plug connected.

    (a) True   (b) False

    Answer: _____   Section: _____._____

43. Locations in which combustible dust is in the air under normal operating conditions in quantities sufficient to produce explosive or ignitible mixtures are classified as _____.

    (a) Class I, Division 2   (b) Class II, Division 1   (c) Class II, Division 2   (d) Class III, Division 1

    Answer: _____   Section: _____._____

44. Luminaires and ceiling fans located over or within 5 ft, measured horizontally, from the inside walls of an indoor spa or hot tub must have a mounting height of not less than _____ above the maximum water level when GFCI protection is NOT provided.

    (a) 4.7 ft   (b) 5 ft   (c) 7 ft 6 in.   (d) 12 ft

    Answer: _____   Section: _____._____

45. Luminaires are permitted to be installed in a commercial cooking hood where specific conditions are met, including the requirement that the luminaire be identified for use within a _____ cooking hood.

    (a) nonresidential   (b) commercial   (c) multifamily   (d) all of these

    Answer: _____   Section: _____._____

46. Luminaires containing a metal halide lamp, other than a thick-glass parabolic reflector lamp (PAR), must be provided with a containment barrier that encloses the lamp, or the luminaire must be provided with a physical means that only allows the use of a(n) _____.

    (a) Type "O" lamp   (b) Type PAR lamp   (c) a or b   (d) inert gas

    Answer: _____   Section: _____._____

47. Luminaires installed in a fountain must _____

   (a) be capable of being removed from the water for relamping or normal maintenance
   (b) not be permanently embedded into the fountain structure
   (c) a and b
   (d) a or b

   Answer: _____   Section: _____._____

48. Manufactured wiring systems constructed with Type MC cable must be supported and secured at intervals not exceeding _____.

   (a) 3 ft   (b) 4 1/2 ft   (c) 6 ft   (d) none of these

   Answer: _____   Section: _____._____

49. Masts and metal structures supporting antennas must be grounded in accordance with the requirements of Article 250.

   (a) True   (b) False

   Answer: _____   Section: _____._____

50. Materials such as straps, bolts, etc., associated with the installation of RMC in a wet location are required to be _____.

   (a) weatherproof   (b) weathertight   (c) corrosion-resistant   (d) none of these

   Answer: _____   Section: _____._____

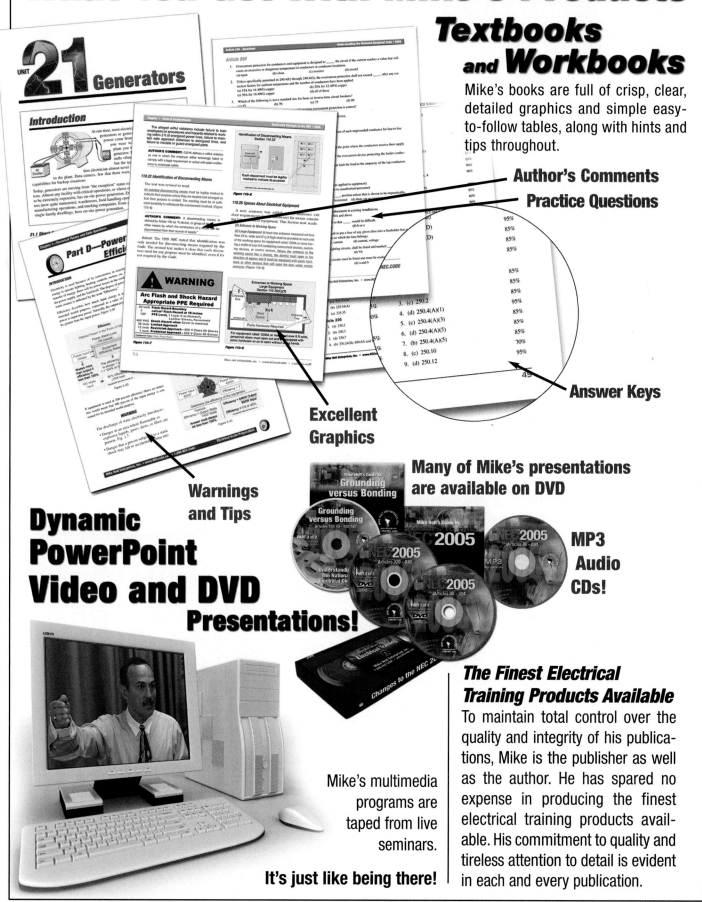

What You Get With Mike's Products

Textbooks and Workbooks

Mike's books are full of crisp, clear, detailed graphics and simple easy-to-follow tables, along with hints and tips throughout.

Author's Comments

Practice Questions

Answer Keys

Excellent Graphics

Warnings and Tips

Dynamic PowerPoint Video and DVD Presentations!

Many of Mike's presentations are available on DVD

MP3 Audio CDs!

Mike's multimedia programs are taped from live seminars.

It's just like being there!

The Finest Electrical Training Products Available

To maintain total control over the quality and integrity of his publications, Mike is the publisher as well as the author. He has spared no expense in producing the finest electrical training products available. His commitment to quality and tireless attention to detail is evident in each and every publication.

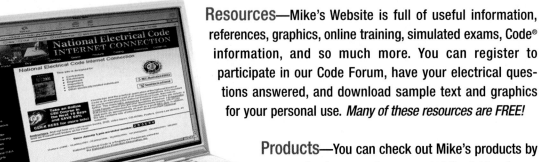

www.NECcode.com

The Most Informative Electrical Resource on the Web Today!

Resources—Mike's Website is full of useful information, references, graphics, online training, simulated exams, Code® information, and so much more. You can register to participate in our Code Forum, have your electrical questions answered, and download sample text and graphics for your personal use. *Many of these resources are FREE!*

Products—You can check out Mike's products by viewing sample pages and the table of contents for his most popular books before purchasing using the Website's online secure shopping cart.

FREE online tools, designed to help you succeed!

- Arc Blast Calculator
- Electrical Formulas (Chart)
- Electrical Instructor's Training Materials
- Fault-Current Calculator
- Graphics and Video Downloads
- Journeyman Simulated Online Exam

- Low-Voltage Book
- Master/Contractor Simulated Online Exam
- NEC® Quiz
- Newsletter
- Online Training Course
- Product Catalog

- Technical Calculators
- Touch Voltage Calculator
- TVSS Manual
- Video Clips
- Wiring and Raceway Chart And Much More!

For an entire listing of the FREE resources available online, just click on the FREE STUFF link at www.NECcode.com

Interactive Online Training

Interactive Online Training is available. Many states are now accepting online testing for Continuing Education credits. Go online today and see if your state is on the list and *view selected chapters for FREE*. Don't get frustrated trying to find a local class or miss valuable time at work if your state accepts this convenient solution. Try an online quiz and see just how quick and easy it is to meet your Continuing Education requirements. FREE Online Simulated Journeyman and Master/Contractor exams are also available. Discover your strengths and weaknesses before you take your exam.

Unit 6
NEC Review Quiz
Articles 342 through 386

(• Indicates that 75% or fewer exam takers get the question correct)

Article 342 Intermediate Metal Conduit (Type IMC) (continued)

1. Where intermediate metal conduit enters a box, fitting, or other enclosure, _____ must be provided to protect the wire from abrasion.

    (a) a bushing   (b) duct seal   (c) electrical tape   (d) seal off fittings

    Answer: _____   Section: _____._____

Article 344 Rigid Metal Conduit (Type RMC)

Rigid metal conduit is similar to intermediate metal conduit, except the wall thickness is greater, so it has a smaller interior cross-sectional area. Rigid metal conduit is heavier than intermediate metal conduit and it's permitted to be installed in any location, just like intermediate metal conduit.

2. RMC can be installed in or under cinder fill subject to permanent moisture when protected on all sides by a layer of noncinder concrete not less than _____ thick.

    (a) 2 in.   (b) 4 in.   (c) 6 in.   (d) 18 in.

    Answer: _____   Section: _____._____

3. Aluminum fittings and enclosures can be used with _____ conduit where not subject to severe corrosive influences.

    (a) steel rigid metal   (b) aluminum rigid metal
    (c) PVC-coated rigid conduit only   (d) a and b

    Answer: _____   Section: _____._____

4. The minimum radius of a field bend on 1 1/4 in. RMC is _____.

    (a) 7 in.   (b) 8 in.   (c) 14 in.   (d) 10 in.

    Answer: _____   Section: _____._____

5. When rigid metal conduit is threaded in the field, a standard die with _____ must be used.

    (a) 3/4 in. taper per foot   (b) 1 in. taper per foot   (c) 1/16 in. taper per foot   (d) no taper

    Answer: _____   Section: _____._____

6. Straight runs of 1 in. RMC using threaded couplings may be secured at intervals not exceeding _____.

   (a) 5 ft   (b) 10 ft   (c) 12 ft   (d) 14 ft

   Answer: _____   Section: _____._____

7. Horizontal runs of RMC supported by openings through _____ at intervals not exceeding 10 ft and securely fastened within 3 ft of termination points are permitted.

   (a) walls   (b) trusses   (c) rafters   (d) framing members

   Answer: _____   Section: _____._____

8. Threadless couplings and connectors used with RMC and installed in wet locations must be _____.

   (a) listed for wet locations   (b) listed for damp location   (c) nonabsorbent   (d) weatherproof

   Answer: _____   Section: _____._____

9. Where rigid metal conduit enters a box, fitting, or other enclosure, a bushing must be provided to protect the wire from abrasion unless the design of the box, fitting, or enclosure is such as to afford equivalent protection.

   (a) True   (b) False

   Answer: _____   Section: _____._____

10. The standard length of RMC as shipped must _____.

   (a) be in lengths of 10 ft   (b) include a coupling on each length
   (c) be threaded on each end   (d) all of these

   Answer: _____   Section: _____._____

Article 348 Flexible Metal Conduit (Type FMC)

Flexible metal conduit is a raceway of circular cross section made of a helically wound, interlocked metal strip of either steel or aluminum. It's commonly called "Greenfield" or "Flex."

11. FMC cannot be installed _____.

   (a) underground   (b) embedded in poured concrete
   (c) where subject to physical damage   (d) all of these

   Answer: _____   Section: _____._____

12. The largest size THHN conductor permitted in trade size 3/8 FMC is _____ AWG.

   (a) 12   (b) 16   (c) 14   (d) 10

   Answer: _____   Section: _____._____

13. Bends in flexible metal conduit must be made so that the conduit is not damaged and the internal diameter of the conduit is _____. The radius of the curve to the centerline of any bend must not be less than shown in Table 2, Chapter 9 using the column for "Other Bends."

   (a) larger than 3/8 in   (b) not effectively reduced   (c) increased   (d) larger than 1 in

   Answer: _____   Section: _____._____

14.   All cut ends of flexible metal conduit must be trimmed or otherwise finished to remove rough edges, except where fittings _____.

(a) are the crimp-on type   (b) thread into the convolutions
(c) contain insulated throats   (d) are listed for grounding

Answer: _____   Section: _____._____

15.   Unsupported lengths of flexible metal conduit are allowed at terminals where flexibility is required but must not exceed _____.

(a) 3 ft for trade sizes 1/2 in. through 1 1/4 in   (b) 4 ft for trade sizes 1 1/2 in. through 2 in
(c) 5 ft for trade size 2 1/2 in. and larger   (d) all of these

Answer: _____   Section: _____._____

16.   In a concealed FMC installation, _____ connectors must not be used.

(a) straight   (b) angle   (c) grounding-type   (d) none of these

Answer: _____   Section: _____._____

Article 350 Liquidtight Flexible Metal Conduit (Type LFMC)

Liquidtight flexible metal conduit is a listed raceway of circular cross section with an outer liquidtight, nonmetallic, sunlight-resistant jacket over an inner flexible metal core, with associated couplings, connectors, and fittings. It's listed for the installation of electric conductors. Liquidtight flexible metal conduit is commonly called Sealtite® or simply "liquidtight." Liquidtight flexible metal conduit is of similar construction to flexible metal conduit but has an outer thermoplastic covering.

17.   The use of listed and marked LFMC is permitted for _____.

(a) direct burial where listed and marked for the purpose   (b) exposed work
(c) concealed work   (d) all of these

Answer: _____   Section: _____._____

18.   The maximum number of 14 THHN conductors permitted in trade size 3/8 LFMC with outside fittings is _____.

(a) 4   (b) 7   (c) 5   (d) 6

Answer: _____   Section: _____._____

19.   When LFMC is used as a fixed raceway, it must be secured within _____ in. on each side of the box and must be supported and secured at intervals not exceeding _____ ft.

(a) 12, 4 1/2   (b) 18, 3   (c) 12, 3   (d) 18, 4

Answer: _____   Section: _____._____

20.   Horizontal runs of liquidtight flexible metal conduit supported by openings through framing members at intervals not greater than _____ and securely fastened within 12 in. of termination points are permitted.

(a) 1.4 ft   (b) 12 in.   (c) 4 1/2 ft   (d) 6 ft

Answer: _____   Section: _____._____

21.   When LFMC is used to connect equipment requiring flexibility, a separate _____ conductor must be installed.

(a) main bonding jumper   (b) grounded   (c) equipment grounding   (d) none of these

Answer: _____   Section: _____._____

Article 352 Rigid Nonmetallic Conduit (Type RNC)

Rigid nonmetallic conduit is a listed nonmetallic raceway of circular cross section with integral or associated couplings, connectors, and fittings. It's listed for the installation of electrical conductors. Typically, it's constructed of polyvinyl chloride (PVC).

22. Extreme _____ may cause rigid nonmetallic conduit to become brittle, and therefore more susceptible to damage from physical contact.

    (a) sunlight   (b) corrosive conditions   (c) heat   (d) cold

    Answer: _____   Section: _____._____

23. Rigid nonmetallic conduit is permitted for exposed work in buildings _____, where not subject to physical damage and if identified for such use.

    (a) three floors and less   (b) twelve floors and less   (c) six floors and less   (d) without height limits

    Answer: _____   Section: _____._____

24. Among the uses that are NOT permitted for rigid nonmetallic conduit, RNC must not be used _____.

    (a) in hazardous (classified) locations
    (b) for the support of luminaires or other equipment
    (c) where subject to physical damage unless identified for such use
    (d) all of these

    Answer: _____   Section: _____._____

25. Bends in rigid nonmetallic conduit must be made so that the conduit is not damaged and the internal diameter of the conduit is not effectively reduced. Field bends must be made only _____.

    (a) by hand forming the bend   (b) with bending equipment identified for the purpose
    (c) with a truck exhaust pipe   (d) by use of an open flame torch

    Answer: _____   Section: _____._____

26. When installing rigid nonmetallic conduit, _____.

    (a) all cut ends must be trimmed inside and outside to remove rough edges
    (b) there must be a support within 2 ft of each box and cabinet
    (c) all joints must be made by an approved method
    (d) a and c

    Answer: _____   Section: _____._____

27. Trade Size 1 rigid nonmetallic conduit must be supported every _____, unless otherwise listed.

    (a) 2 ft   (b) 3 ft   (c) 4 ft   (d) 6 ft

    Answer: _____   Section: _____._____

28. Where rigid nonmetallic conduit enters a box, fitting, or other enclosure, a bushing or adapter must be provided to protect the wire from abrasion unless the design of the box, fitting, or enclosure is such as to afford equivalent protection.

    (a) True   (b) False

    Answer: _____   Section: _____._____

29. An equipment grounding conductor is not required in rigid nonmetallic conduit if the grounded conductor is used to ground equipment as permitted in 250.142.

    (a) True   (b) False

    Answer: _____   Section: _____._____

Article 353 High-Density Polyethylene Conduit (Type HDPE)

This article covers the use, installation, and construction specifications for high density polyethylene (HDPE) conduit and associated fittings. It's lightweight and durable. It resists decomposition, oxidation, and hostile elements that cause damage to other materials. HDPE is mechanically and chemically resistant to a host of environmental conditions. Uses include communication, data, cable television, and general-purpose raceways.

30. High-Density Polyethylene Conduit (HDPE) can be manufactured _____.

    (a) in discrete lengths   (b) in continuous lengths from a reel
    (c) only in 20 ft. lengths   (d) either a or b

    Answer: _____   Section: _____._____

31. There is never a case where HDPE can be installed in a hazardous location.

    (a) True   (b) False

    Answer: _____   Section: _____._____

32. HDPE is not permitted where it will be subject to ambient temperatures in excess of _____.

    (a) 50°C   (b) 60°C   (c) 75°C   (d) 90°C

    Answer: _____   Section: _____._____

33. Bends made in HDPE must be made _____.

    (a) in a manner that will not damage the raceway
    (b) so as not to significantly reduce the internal diameter of the raceway
    (c) only with mechanical bending tools
    (d) a and b

    Answer: _____   Section: _____._____

34. The cut ends of HDPE must be _____ to avoid rough edges.

    (a) filed on the inside   (b) trimmed inside and outside
    (c) cut only with a hack saw   (d) all of these

    Answer: _____   Section: _____._____

35. Any joints between lengths of HDPE must be made using _____.

    (a) expansion fittings   (b) an approved method   (c) a listed method   (d) none of these

    Answer: _____   Section: _____._____

36. HDPE must be resistant to _____.

    (a) moisture   (b) corrosive chemical atmospheres
    (c) impact and crushing   (d) all of these

    Answer: _____   Section: _____._____

Article 354 Nonmetallic Underground Conduit with Conductors (Type NUCC)

Nonmetallic underground conduit with conductors is a factory assembly of conductors or cables inside a nonmetallic, smooth wall conduit with a circular cross section. It can also be supplied on reels without damage or distortion and is of sufficient strength to withstand abuse, such as impact or crushing when handled and installed, without damage to conduit or conductors.

37. NUCC and its associated fittings must be _____.

    (a) listed   (b) approved   (c) identified   (d) none of these

    Answer: _____   Section: _____._____

38. NUCC must not be used _____.

    (a) in exposed locations   (b) inside buildings
    (c) in hazardous (classified) locations   (d) all of these

    Answer: _____   Section: _____._____

39. Bends in nonmetallic underground conduit with conductors (NUCC) must be _____ so that the conduit will not be damaged and the internal diameter of the conduit will not be effectively reduced.

    (a) manually made   (b) made only with approved benders
    (c) made with rigid metal conduit bending shoes (d) made using an open flame torch

    Answer: _____   Section: _____._____

40. In order to _____ NUCC, the conduit must be trimmed away from the conductors or cables using an approved method that will not damage the conductor or cable insulation or jacket.

    (a) facilitate installing   (b) enhance the appearance of the installation of
    (c) terminate   (d) provide safety to the persons installing

    Answer: _____   Section: _____._____

41. All joints between nonmetallic underground conduit with conductors (NUCC), fittings, and boxes must be made by _____.

    (a) a qualified person   (b) set screw fittings   (c) an approved method   (d) exothermic welding

    Answer: _____   Section: _____._____

Article 356 Liquidtight Flexible Nonmetallic Conduit (Type LFNC)

Liquidtight flexible nonmetallic conduit is a listed raceway of circular cross section with an outer liquidtight, nonmetallic, sunlight-resistant jacket over an inner flexible core, with associated couplings, connectors, and fittings. It's listed for the installation of electric conductors. LFNC is available in three types:

- Type LFNC-A (orange). A smooth seamless inner core and cover bonded together. One or more reinforcement layers are inserted between the core and covers.
- Type LFNC-B (gray). A smooth inner surface with integral reinforcement within the conduit wall.
- Type LFNC-C (black). A corrugated internal and external surface without integral reinforcement within the conduit wall.

42.   Type LFNC-B can be installed in lengths longer than _____ where secured in accordance with 356.30.

(a) 2 ft   (b) 3 ft   (c) 6 ft   (d) 10 ft

Answer: _____   Section: _____._____

43.   The number of conductors allowed in LFNC must not exceed that permitted by the percentage fill specified in _____.

(a) Table 1, Chapter 9   (b) Table 250.66   (c) Table 310.16   (d) 240.6

Answer: _____   Section: _____._____

44.   Bends in LFNC must _____ between pull points.

(a) not be made   (b) not be limited in degrees
(c) be limited to not more than 360 degrees (d) be limited to 180 degrees

Answer: _____   Section: _____._____

45.   Where flexibility is necessary, securing LFNC is not required for lengths less than _____ at terminals.

(a) 2 ft   (b) 3 ft   (c) 4 ft   (d) 6 ft

Answer: _____   Section: _____._____

Article 358 Electrical Metallic Tubing (Type EMT)

Electrical metallic tubing is a listed metallic tubing of circular cross section raceway listed for the installation of electrical conductors. Compared to rigid metal conduit and intermediate metal conduit, electrical metallic tubing is relatively easy to bend, cut, and ream. Because it isn't threaded, all connectors and couplings are of the threadless type.

46.   When EMT is installed in wet locations, all support, bolts, straps, screws, and so forth must be _____.

(a) of corrosion-resistant materials   (b) protected against corrosion
(c) a or b   (d) nonmetallic materials only

Answer: _____   Section: _____._____

47.   The minimum and maximum size of EMT is _____, except for special installations.

(a) 5/16 and 3 in.   (b) 3/8 and 4 in.   (c) 1/2 and 3 in.   (d) 1/2 and 4 in.

Answer: _____   Section: _____._____

48.   EMT must not be threaded.

(a) True   (b) False

Answer: _____   Section: _____._____

49.   Fastening of unbroken lengths of EMT conduit can be increased to a distance of _____ from the termination point where the structural members do not readily permit fastening within 3 ft.

(a) 10 ft   (b) 5 ft   (c) 4 ft   (d) 25 ft

Answer: _____   Section: _____._____

50. Couplings and connectors used with EMT must be made up _____.

    (a) of metal   (b) in accordance with industry standards
    (c) tight   (d) none of these

    Answer: _____   Section: _____._____

Article 360 FMT (Type FMT)

This article covers the use, installation, and construction specifications for FMT (FMT) and associated fittings. Which is a raceway that is circular in cross section, flexible, metallic, and liquidtight without a nonmetallic jacket.

51. The maximum size FMT permitted is _____

    (a) 3/8 in.   (b) 1/2 in.   (c) 3/4 in.   (d) 1 in.

    Answer: _____   Section: _____._____

Article 362 Electrical Nonmetallic Tubing (Type ENT)

Electrical nonmetallic tubing is a pliable, corrugated, circular raceway made of PVC. It's often called "Smurf Pipe" or "Smurf Tube," because it originally came out at the height of popularity of the children's cartoon characters "the Smurfs," and was available only in blue.

52. ENT is composed of a material that is resistant to moisture, chemical atmospheres, and is _____.

    (a) flexible   (b) flame-retardant   (c) fireproof   (d) flammable

    Answer: _____   Section: _____._____

53. When a building is supplied with a(n) _____ fire sprinkler system, ENT can be installed exposed or concealed in buildings of any height.

    (a) listed   (b) identified   (c) NFPA 13-2002 approved   (d) none of these

    Answer: _____   Section: _____._____

54. When a building is supplied with an approved fire sprinkler system, ENT is permitted to be installed above any suspended ceiling.

    (a) True   (b) False

    Answer: _____   Section: _____._____

55. ENT is not permitted in hazardous (classified) locations, except for intrinsically safe applications.

    (a) True   (b) False

    Answer: _____   Section: _____._____

56. ENT is not permitted in places of assembly unless it is encased in at least _____ of concrete.

    (a) 1 in.   (b) 2 in.   (c) 3 in.   (d) 4 in.

    Answer: _____   Section: _____._____

57. The number of conductors allowed in ENT must not exceed that permitted by the percentage fill specified in _____.

    (a) Table 1, Chapter 9   (b) Table 250.66   (c) Table 310.16   (d) 240.6

    Answer: _____   Section: _____._____

58. All cut ends of ENT must be trimmed inside and _____ to remove rough edges.

    (a) outside   (b) tapered   (c) filed   (d) beveled

    Answer: _____   Section: _____._____

59. Bushings or adapters are required at ENT terminations to protect the conductors from abrasion, unless the box, fitting, or enclosure design provides equivalent protection.

    (a) True   (b) False

    Answer: _____   Section: _____._____

60. Where equipment grounding is required by Article 250 for ENT installations, a separate equipment grounding conductor must _____.

    (a) be run outside the raceway using solid copper wire   (b) be installed in the raceway
    (c) be obtained using a separate driven ground rod   (d) not be required

    Answer: _____   Section: _____._____

Article 366 Auxiliary Gutters

This article covers the use, installation, and construction requirements of metal auxiliary gutters and nonmetallic auxiliary gutters and associated fittings. Which are enclosures with hinged or removable covers for housing and protecting electric wires, cable, and busbars in which conductors are laid in place after the wireway has been installed as a complete system.

61. An auxiliary gutter is permitted to contain _____.

    (a) conductors   (b) overcurrent devices   (c) busways   (d) none of these

    Answer: _____   Section: _____._____

62. When conductor ampacity adjustment factors of 310.15(B)(2)(a) are used, an auxiliary gutter must not contain more than _____ at any cross section. Also, conductors are not permitted to fill more than 20 percent of the cross sectional area.

    (a) 25 conductors   (b) 40 current-carrying conductors
    (c) 20 conductors   (d) no limit on the number of conductors

    Answer: _____   Section: _____._____

63. The maximum ampere rating of a 4 in. x 1/2 in. busbar that is 4 ft long and installed in an auxiliary gutter is _____.

    (a) 500A   (b) 750A   (c) 650A   (d) 2,000A

    Answer: _____   Section: _____._____

64. Auxiliary gutters must be constructed and installed so that adequate _____ continuity of the complete system is secured.

    (a) mechanical   (b) electrical   (c) a or b   (d) a and b

    Answer: _____   Section: _____._____

Article 368 Busways

This article covers service-entrance, feeder, and branch-circuit busways and associated fittings. Which is a grounded metal enclosure containing factory-mounted, bare or insulated conductors, which are usually copper or aluminum bars, rods, or tubes.

65. It is permissible to extend busways vertically through dry floors if totally enclosed (unventilated) where passing through, and for a minimum distance of _____ above the floor to provide adequate protection from physical damage.

    (a) 6 ft   (b) 6 1/2 ft   (c) 8 ft   (d) 10 ft

    Answer: _____   Section: _____._____

66. Busways must not be installed _____.

    (a) where subject to severe physical damage
    (b) outdoors or in wet or damp locations unless identified for such use
    (c) in hoistways
    (d) all of these

    Answer: _____   Section: _____._____

67. Busways must be securely supported, unless otherwise designed and marked as such, at intervals not to exceed _____.

    (a) 10 ft   (b) 5 ft   (c) 3 ft   (d) 8 ft

    Answer: _____   Section: _____._____

68. When busway enclosures for voltage levels exceeding 600V terminate at machines cooled by flammable gas, _____ or other means must be provided to prevent accumulation of flammable gas within the bus enclosures.

    (a) seal-off bushings   (b) baffles   (c) a or b   (d) none of these

    Answer: _____   Section: _____._____

Article 370 Cablebus

This article covers the use and installation requirements of cablebus and associated fittings. Which is an assembly of insulated conductors with fittings and conductor terminations in a completely enclosed, ventilated protective metal housing. Cablebus is ordinarily assembled at the point of installation from the components furnished or specified by the manufacturer in accordance with instructions for the specific job.

69. The cablebus assembly is designed to carry _____ current and to withstand the magnetic forces of such current.

    (a) service   (b) load   (c) fault   (d) grounded

    Answer: _____   Section: _____._____

70. Cablebus framework that is _____ is permitted as the equipment grounding conductor for branch circuits and feeders.

    (a) bonded   (b) welded   (c) protected   (d) galvanized

    Answer: _____   Section: _____._____

71. The individual conductors in a cablebus must be supported at intervals not greater than _____ for vertical runs.

    (a) 1/2 ft   (b) 1 ft   (c) 1 1/2 ft   (d) 2 ft

    Answer: _____   Section: _____._____

72. Each section of cablebus must be marked with the manufacturer's name or trade designation and the minimum diameter, number, voltage rating, and ampacity of the conductors to be installed. Markings must be so located as to be visible after installation.

(a) True   (b) False

Answer: _____   Section: _____._____

Article 372 Cellular Concrete Floor Raceways

This article covers cellular concrete floor raceways, the hollow spaces in floors constructed of precast cellular concrete slabs, together with suitable metal fittings designed to provide access to the floor cells.

73. A transverse metal raceway for electrical conductors, providing access to predetermined cells of precast cellular concrete floors, which permits installation of electrical conductors from a distribution center to the floor cells, is usually known as a(n) _____.

(a) cell   (b) header   (c) open-bottom raceway   (d) none of these

Answer: _____   Section: _____._____

74. Connections from cellular concrete floor raceway headers to cabinets must be made by means of _____.

(a) listed metal raceways   (b) PVC raceways   (c) listed fittings   (d) a and c

Answer: _____   Section: _____._____

75. In cellular concrete floor raceways, a grounding conductor must connect the insert receptacle to a _____.

(a) negative ground connection provided in the raceway   (b) negative ground connection provided on the header
(c) positive ground connection provided on the header   (d) grounded terminal located within the insert

Answer: _____   Section: _____._____

Article 374 Cellular Metal Floor Raceways

This article covers the use and installation requirements for cellular metal floor raceways. Which is approved as enclosures for electric conductors.

76. A _____ is defined as a single, enclosed tubular space in a cellular metal floor member, the axis of which is parallel to the axis of the metal floor member.

(a) cellular metal floor raceway   (b) cell   (c) header   (d) none of these

Answer: _____   Section: _____._____

77. Loop wiring _____ in a cellular metal raceway.

(a) is not permitted   (b) is not considered a splice or tap
(c) is considered a splice or tap when used   (d) none of these

Answer: _____   Section: _____._____

78. Inserts for cellular metal floor raceways must be leveled to the floor grade and sealed against the entrance of _____.

(a) concrete   (b) water   (c) moisture   (d) all of these

Answer: _____   Section: _____._____

Article 376 Metal Wireways

This article covers the use, installation, and construction specifications for metal wireways and associated fittings. A metal wireway is a sheet metal trough with hinged or removable covers for housing and protecting electric wires and cable, in which conductors are placed after the wireway has been installed as a complete system.

79. Metal wireways can be installed either exposed or concealed under all conditions.

    (a) True   (b) False

    Answer: _____   Section: _____._____

80. Wireways are permitted to pass transversely through a wall _____. Access to the conductors must be maintained on both sides of the wall.

    (a) if the length passing through the wall is unbroken   (b) if the wall is not fire rated
    (c) in hazardous locations   (d) if the wall is fire rated

    Answer: _____   Section: _____._____

81. The sum of the cross-sectional areas of all contained conductors at any cross section of a metal wireway must not exceed _____.

    (a) 50 percent   (b) 20 percent   (c) 25 percent   (d) 80 percent

    Answer: _____   Section: _____._____

82. Where insulated conductors are deflected within a metallic wireway, the wireway must be sized to meet the bending requirements corresponding to one wire per terminal in Table 312.6(A).

    (a) True   (b) False

    Answer: _____   Section: _____._____

83. Wireways must be supported where run horizontally at each end and at intervals not to exceed _____, or for individual lengths longer than _____ at each end or joint, unless listed for other support intervals.

    (a) 5 ft   (b) 10 ft   (c) 3 ft   (d) 6 ft

    Answer: _____   Section: _____._____

84. Splices and taps are permitted within a metal wireway provided they are accessible. The conductors, including splices and taps, must not fill the wireway to more than _____ percent of its area at that point.

    (a) 25   (b) 80   (c) 125   (d) 75

    Answer: _____   Section: _____._____

85. In addition to the wiring space requirement in 376.56(A), the power distribution block must be installed in a metal wireway not smaller than that specified _____.

    (a) by the wireway manufacturer   (b) by the manufacturer of the power distribution block
    (c) both a and b   (d) either a or b

    Answer: _____   Section: _____._____

86. Extensions from wireways by raceway or cable wiring methods are not permitted.

    (a) True   (b) False

    Answer: _____   Section: _____._____

Article 378 Nonmetallic Wireways

A nonmetallic wireway is a flame-retardant trough with hinged or removable covers for housing and protecting electric wires and cable, in which conductors are placed after the wireway has been installed as a complete system.

87. Nonmetallic wireways can pass transversely through a wall _____.

    (a) if the length through the wall is unbroken
    (c) in hazardous locations
    (b) if the wall is not fire rated
    (d) if the wall is fire rated

    Answer: _____   Section: _____._____

88. The derating factors in 310.15(B)(2)(a) apply to a nonmetallic wireway.

    (a) True   (b) False

    Answer: _____   Section: _____._____

89. Nonmetallic wireways must be supported where run horizontally at each end and at intervals not to exceed _____ and at each end or joint, unless listed for other support intervals.

    (a) 5 ft   (b) 10 ft   (c) 3 ft   (d) 6 ft

    Answer: _____   Section: _____._____

90. Expansion fittings for nonmetallic wireways must be provided to compensate for thermal expansion and contraction, where the length change is expected to be _____ or greater in a straight run.

    (a) 1/4 in.   (b) 1/2 in.   (c) 6 in.   (d) 1/16 in.

    Answer: _____   Section: _____._____

91. Where equipment grounding is required by Article 250 for nonmetallic wireway installations, a separate equipment grounding conductor must _____.

    (a) be run outside the raceway using solid copper wire
    (c) be obtained using a separate driven ground rod
    (b) be installed in the raceway
    (d) not be required

    Answer: _____   Section: _____._____

Article 380 Multioutlet Assemblies

A multioutlet assembly is a surface, flush, or freestanding raceway designed to hold conductors and receptacles. It's assembled in the field or at the factory.

92. A multioutlet assembly cannot be installed _____.

    (a) in concealed locations
    (c) where subject to corrosive vapors
    (b) where subject to severe physical damage
    (d) all of these

    Answer: _____   Section: _____._____

Article 382 Nonmetallic Extensions

This article covers the use, installation, and construction specifications for nonmetallic extensions. A nonmetallic extension is an assembly of two insulated conductors within a nonmetallic jacket or an extruded thermoplastic covering. The classification includes surface extensions intended for mounting directly on the surface of walls or ceilings.

93. Nonmetallic surface extensions are permitted in _____ when occupied for residential or office purposes.

(a) buildings not over three stories high
(b) buildings over four stories high
(c) all buildings
(d) none of these

Answer: _____   Section: _____._____

94. Each run of nonmetallic extension must terminate in a fitting that covers the _____.

(a) device   (b) box   (c) end of the extension   (d) end of the assembly

Answer: _____   Section: _____._____

Article 384 Strut-Type Channel Raceways

Strut-type channel raceway is a metallic raceway intended to be mounted to the surface or suspended with associated accessories, in which conductors are placed after the raceway has been installed as a complete system.

95. A strut-type channel raceway can be installed _____.

(a) where exposed
(b) as a power pole
(c) unbroken through walls, partitions, and floors
(d) all of these

Answer: _____   Section: _____._____

96. The ampacity adjustment factors of 310.15(B)(2)(a) do not apply to conductors installed in strut-type channel raceways where _____.

(a) the cross-sectional area of the raceway is at least 4 sq in
(b) the number of current-carrying conductors do not exceed 30
(c) the sum of the cross-sectional areas of all contained conductors does not exceed 20 percent of the interior cross-sectional area of the strut-type channel raceways
(d) all of these

Answer: _____   Section: _____._____

97. Splices and taps are permitted within a strut-type channel raceway provided they are accessible. The conductors, including splices and taps, must not fill the raceway to more than _____ percent of its area at that point.

(a) 25   (b) 80   (c) 125   (d) 75

Answer: _____   Section: _____._____

Article 386 Surface Metal Raceways

A surface metal raceway is a metallic raceway intended to be mounted to the surface with associated accessories, in which conductors are placed after the raceway has been installed as a complete system.

98. It is permissible to run unbroken lengths of surface metal raceways through dry _____.

(a) walls   (b) partitions   (c) floors   (d) all of these

Answer: _____   Section: _____._____

99. In general, the voltage limitation between conductors in a surface metal raceway must not exceed _____ unless the metal has a thickness of not less than 0.040 in., nominal.

(a) 300V   (b) 150V   (c) 600V   (d) 1,000V

Answer: _____   Section: _____._____

100. •The maximum number of conductors permitted in any surface raceway must be _____.

(a) no more than 30 percent of the inside diameter   (b) no greater than the number for which it was designed
(c) no more than 75 percent of the cross-sectional area   (d) that which is permitted in the Table 312.6(A)

Answer: _____   Section: _____._____

Unit 6
NEC Practice Quiz
Articles 344 through 386

(• Indicates that 75% or fewer exam takers get the question correct)

1. RMC can be installed in concrete, in direct contact with the earth, or in areas subject to severe corrosive influences when protected by _____ and judged suitable for the condition.

    (a) ceramic   (b) corrosion protection   (c) backfill   (d) a natural barrier

    Answer: _____   Section: _____._____

2. •A cablebus system must include approved fittings for dead ends.

    (a) True   (b) False

    Answer: _____   Section: _____._____

3. •LFMC smaller than _____ must not be used, except as permitted in 348.20(A).

    (a) 3/8 in.   (b) 1/2 in.   (c) 1 1/2 in.   (d) 1 1/4 in.

    Answer: _____   Section: _____._____

4. A junction box used with a cellular metal floor raceway must be _____.

    (a) level with the floor grade   (b) sealed against the entrance of water or concrete
    (c) metal and electrically continuous with the raceway   (d) all of these

    Answer: _____   Section: _____._____

5. A multioutlet assembly can be installed in _____.

    (a) dry locations   (b) wet locations   (c) a and b   (d) none of these

    Answer: _____   Section: _____._____

6. A run of EMT between outlet boxes must not exceed _____ offsets close to the box.

    (a) 360° plus   (b) 360° total including   (c) four quarter bends plus   (d) 180° total including

    Answer: _____   Section: _____._____

7. A strut-type channel raceway cannot be installed _____.

    (a) in concealed locations   (b) where subject to corrosive vapors if protected solely by enamel
    (c) a or b   (d) none of these

    Answer: _____   Section: _____._____

8.   All joints between lengths of ENT, and between ENT and couplings, fittings, and boxes must be made by _____.

      (a) a qualified person   (b) set screw fittings   (c) an approved method   (d) exothermic welding

      Answer: _____   Section: _____._____

9.   Bends in flexible metal conduit must _____ between pull points.

      (a) not be made   (b) not be limited in degrees
      (c) be limited to not more than 360 degrees   (d) be limited to 180 degrees

      Answer: _____   Section: _____._____

10.   Bends in LFNC must be made so that the conduit will not be damaged and the internal diameter of the conduit will not be effec-
      tively reduced. Bends are permitted to be made only _____.

      (a) manually without auxiliary equipment   (b) with bending equipment identified for the purpose
      (c) with any kind of conduit bending tool that will work   (d) by use of an open flame torch

      Answer: _____   Section: _____._____

11.   Bends in nonmetallic underground conduit with conductors (NUCC) must _____ between termination points.

      (a) not be made   (b) not be limited in degrees
      (c) be limited to not more than 360 degrees   (d) be limited to 180 degrees

      Answer: _____   Section: _____._____

12.   Bends in rigid nonmetallic conduit must _____ between pull points.

      (a) not be made   (b) not be limited in degrees
      (c) be limited to not more than 360 degrees   (d) be limited to 180 degrees

      Answer: _____   Section: _____._____

13.   Bends made in HDPE must not exceed _____ degrees between pull points.

      (a) 180   (b) 270   (c) 360   (d) 480

      Answer: _____   Section: _____._____

14.   Busway runs with nominal voltage levels exceeding 600V, having sections located both inside and outside of buildings, must have
      a _____ at the building wall to prevent interchange of air between indoor and outdoor sections.

      (a) waterproof rating   (b) vapor seal   (c) fire seal   (d) b and c

      Answer: _____   Section: _____._____

15.   Cablebus is not permitted for _____.

      (a) a service   (b) branch circuits
      (c) exposed work   (d) concealed work through walls and floors except as allowed by 370.6.

      Answer: _____   Section: _____._____

16.   Conductors, including splices and taps, must not fill the auxiliary gutter to more than _____ percent of its cross-sectional area.

      (a) 20   (b) 40   (c) 60   (d) 75

      Answer: _____   Section: _____._____

17. Each length of RMC must be clearly and durably identified every _____.

    (a) 3 ft   (b) 5 ft   (c) 10 ft   (d) none of these

    Answer: _____   Section: _____._____

18. ENT is permitted for direct earth burial when used with fittings listed for this purpose.

    (a) True   (b) False

    Answer: _____   Section: _____._____

19. Expansion fittings for rigid nonmetallic conduit must be provided to compensate for thermal expansion and contraction when the length change in a straight run between securely mounted boxes, cabinets, elbows, or other conduit terminations is expected to be _____ or greater.

    (a) 1/4 in.   (b) 1/2 in.   (c) 1 in.   (d) none of these

    Answer: _____   Section: _____._____

20. FMC can be installed exposed or concealed where not subject to physical damage.

    (a) True   (b) False

    Answer: _____   Section: _____._____

21. HDPE is not permitted to be installed _____.

    (a) where exposed
    (b) within a building
    (c) for conductors operating at a temperature above the rating of the raceway
    (d) all of these

    Answer: _____   Section: _____._____

22. Horizontal runs of EMT supported by openings through framing members at intervals not greater than _____, and securely fastened within 3 ft of termination points, are permitted.

    (a) 1.4 ft   (b) 12 in.   (c) 4 1/2 ft   (d) 10 ft

    Answer: _____   Section: _____._____

23. Horizontal runs of flexible metal conduit supported by openings through framing members at intervals not greater than _____ and securely fastened within 12 in. of termination points are permitted.

    (a) 1.4 ft   (b) 12 in.   (c) 4 1/2 ft   (d) 6 ft

    Answer: _____   Section: _____._____

24. In a building without a fire sprinkler system, ENT is permitted to be installed above a suspended ceiling if the suspended ceiling provides a thermal barrier having at least a _____-minute finish rating as identified in listings of fire-rated assemblies.

    (a) 5   (b) 10   (c) 15   (d) none of these

    Answer: _____   Section: _____._____

25. In electrical nonmetallic tubing, the maximum number of bends between pull points cannot exceed _____ degrees, including any offsets.

    (a) 320   (b) 270   (c) 360   (d) unlimited

    Answer: _____   Section: _____._____

26. Liquidtight flexible metal conduit is not required to be fastened when used for tap conductors to luminaires up to _____ in length.

    (a) 4 1/2 ft   (b) 18 in.   (c) 6 ft   (d) no limit on length

    Answer: _____   Section: _____._____

27. Nonmetallic extensions must be secured in place by approved means at intervals not exceeding _____

    (a) 6 in.   (b) 8 in.   (c) 10 in.   (d) 16 in.

    Answer: _____   Section: _____._____

28. NUCC must be capable of being supplied on reels without damage or _____, and must be of sufficient strength to withstand abuse, such as impact or crushing in handling and during installation, without damage to conduit or conductors.

    (a) distortion   (b) breakage   (c) shattering   (d) all of these

    Answer: _____   Section: _____._____

29. Power distribution blocks installed in metal wireways must _____.

    (a) allow for sufficient wire-bending space at terminals   (b) not have exposed live parts after installation
    (c) either a or b   (d) both a and b

    Answer: _____   Section: _____._____

30. Rigid nonmetallic conduit and fittings must be composed of suitable nonmetallic material that is resistant to moisture and chemical atmospheres. For use above ground it must have additional characteristics including _____.

    (a) flame retardance   (b) resistance to low temperatures and sunlight effects
    (c) resistance to distortion from heat   (d) all of these

    Answer: _____   Section: _____._____

31. Rigid nonmetallic conduit can be used to support nonmetallic conduit bodies not larger than the largest raceway, but the conduit bodies must not contain devices, luminaires, or other equipment.

    (a) True   (b) False

    Answer: _____   Section: _____._____

32. Strut-type channel raceway enclosures must have a means for connecting an equipment grounding conductor. The raceway is permitted as an equipment grounding conductor in accordance with 250.118(14).

    (a) True   (b) False

    Answer: _____   Section: _____._____

33. The adjustment factors of 310.15(B)(2)(a), (Notes to Ampacity Tables of 0 through 2,000V), do not apply to conductors installed in surface metal raceways where _____.

    (a) the cross-sectional area exceeds 4 sq in.
    (b) the current-carrying conductors do not exceed 30 in number
    (c) the total cross-sectional area of all conductors does not exceed 20 percent of the interior cross-sectional area of the raceway
    (d) all of these

    Answer: _____   Section: _____._____

34. The derating factors in 310.15(B)(2)(a) must be applied to a metal wireway only where the number of current-carrying conductors in the wireway exceeds _____.

    (a) 30   (b) 20   (c) 80   (d) 3

    Answer: _____   Section: _____._____

35. The header on a cellular concrete floor raceway must be installed _____ to the cells.

    (a) in a straight line   (b) at right angles   (c) a and b   (d) none of these

    Answer: _____   Section: _____._____

36. The minimum radius for a field bend of 1 in. rigid metal conduit is _____, when using a one-shot bender.

    (a) 10 1/2 in.   (b) 11 1/2 in.   (c) 5 3/4 in.   (d) 9 1/2 in.

    Answer: _____   Section: _____._____

37. The sum of the cross-sectional areas of all contained conductors at any cross section of a nonmetallic wireway must not exceed _____.

    (a) 50 percent   (b) 20 percent   (c) 25 percent   (d) 80 percent

    Answer: _____   Section: _____._____

38. The use of NUCC is permitted _____.

    (a) for direct-burial underground installations   (b) to be encased or embedded in concrete
    (c) in cinder fill   (d) all of these

    Answer: _____   Section: _____._____

39. Trade Size 2 RMC must typically be supported every _____.

    (a) 10 ft   (b) 12 ft   (c) 14 ft   (d) 15 ft

    Answer: _____   Section: _____._____

40. Vertical runs of metal wireways must be securely supported at intervals not exceeding _____ and must not have more than one joint between supports.

    (a) 5 ft   (b) 20 ft   (c) 10 ft   (d) 15 ft

    Answer: _____   Section: _____._____

41. When a vertical busway penetrates the floor (in other than industrial establishments), a minimum 4 in.-high curb must be installed around the busway floor opening to prevent liquids from entering the vertical busway. The curb must be installed within _____ of the floor opening for the busway and electrical equipment must be located so that liquids retained by the 4 in. curb will not damage equipment.

    (a) 12 in.   (b) 6 in.   (c) 12 ft   (d) 6 ft

    Answer: _____   Section: _____._____

42. When an auxiliary gutter is used to supplement wiring space at meter centers, distribution centers, switchboards, and similar points, it is not allowed to extend a distance greater than _____ beyond the equipment that it supplements.

    (a) 50 ft   (b) 30 ft   (c) 10 ft   (d) 25 ft

    Answer: _____   Section: _____._____

43. When an outlet is _____ from a cellular concrete floor raceway, the sections of circuit conductors supplying the outlet must be removed from the raceway.

    (a) discontinued   (b) abandoned   (c) removed   (d) any of these

    Answer: _____   Section: _____._____

44. When LFNC is used to connect equipment requiring flexibility, a separate _____ must be installed.

    (a) equipment grounding conductor   (b) expansion fitting
    (c) flexible nonmetallic connector   (d) none of these

    Answer: _____   Section: _____._____

45. When threadless couplings and connectors used in the installation of RMC are buried in masonry or concrete, they must be of the _____ type.

    (a) raintight   (b) wet and damp location   (c) nonabsorbent   (d) concrete-tight

    Answer: _____   Section: _____._____

46. Where trade size 3/8 FMT has a fixed bend for installation purposes and is not flexed for service, the minimum radius measured to the inside of the bend must not be less than _____

    (a) 8 in.   (b) 12 1/2 in.   (c) 3 1/2 in.   (d) 4 in.

    Answer: _____   Section: _____._____

47. Where equipment grounding is required for an installation of HDPE, a separate equipment grounding conductor must be _____.

    (a) an insulated copper conductor   (b) installed within the conduit
    (c) stranded bare copper wire   (d) a solid bare copper wire

    Answer: _____   Section: _____._____

48. Where flexibility _____ liquidtight flexible metal conduit is permitted to be used as an equipment grounding conductor when installed in accordance with 250.118(6).

    (a) is required   (b) is not required   (c) either a or d   (d) is optional

    Answer: _____   Section: _____._____

49. Where run vertically, nonmetallic wireways must be securely supported at intervals not exceeding _____, with no more than one joint between supports.

    (a) 5 ft   (b) 10 ft   (c) 4 ft   (d) 6 ft

    Answer: _____   Section: _____._____

50. Wireways are permitted for _____.

    (a) exposed work   (b) concealed work   (c) wet locations if listed for the purpose   (d) a and c

    Answer: _____   Section: _____._____

1. Metal conduit and metal piping within _____ of the inside walls of the pool that are not separated from the pool by a permanent barrier are required to be bonded.

   (a) 4 ft   (b) 5 ft   (c) 8 ft   (d) 10 ft

   Answer: _____   Section: _____._____

2. Metal enclosures and raceways for service conductors and equipment must be _____.

   (a) isolated   (b) insulated   (c) grounded   (d) gray

   Answer: _____   Section: _____._____

3. Metal equipment racks and enclosures for permanent audio system installations must be grounded.

   (a) True   (b) False

   Answer: _____   Section: _____._____

4. Metal multioutlet assemblies can pass through a dry partition, provided no receptacle is concealed in the partition and the cover of the exposed portion of the system can be removed.

   (a) True   (b) False

   Answer: _____   Section: _____._____

5. Metal poles used to support luminaires must be bonded to a(n) _____.

   (a) grounding electrode   (b) grounded conductor
   (c) equipment grounding conductor   (d) any of these

   Answer: _____   Section: _____._____

6. Metal surface type enclosures in damp or wet locations must be mounted so there is at least _____ airspace between the enclosure and the wall or supporting surface.

   (a) 1/16 in.   (b) 1 1/4 in.   (c) 1/4 in.   (d) 6 in.

   Answer: _____   Section: _____._____

7. Metal surfaces that are within 5 ft of the inside walls of an indoor spa or hot tub, and not separated from the indoor spa or hot tub area by a permanent barrier, are not required to be bonded.

   (a) True   (b) False

   Answer: _____   Section: _____._____

8. Metal wireways are sheet metal troughs with _____ for housing and protecting electric wires and cable.

    (a) removable covers   (b) hinged covers   (c) a or b   (d) none of these

    Answer: _____   Section: _____._____

9. Mobile home service equipment must be located adjacent to the mobile home and not mounted in or on the mobile home. The service equipment must be located in sight from but not more than _____ from the exterior wall of the mobile home it serves.

    (a) 15 ft   (b) 20 ft   (c) 30 ft   (d) none of these

    Answer: _____   Section: _____._____

10. Motor control circuits must be arranged so that they will be disconnected from all sources of supply when the disconnecting means is in the open position. Where separate devices are used for the motor and control circuit, they must be located immediately adjacent to each other.

    (a) True   (b) False

    Answer: _____   Section: _____._____

11. Motor overload protection is not required where _____.

    (a) conductors are oversized by 125 percent   (b) conductors are part of a limited-energy circuit
    (c) it might introduce additional or increased hazards   (d) short-circuit protection is provided

    Answer: _____   Section: _____._____

12. Multiwire branch circuits that supply power to the wired partitions of office furnishings for _____ must be provided with a means to simultaneously disconnect all ungrounded conductors where the branch circuit originates.

    (a) fixed-type partitions   (b) free-standing type partitions
    (c) both a and b   (d) none of these

    Answer: _____   Section: _____._____

13. NFPA 70E, Standard for Electrical Safety in the Workplace provides information to help determine the electrical safety training requirements expected of a "qualified person."

    (a) True   (b) False

    Answer: _____   Section: _____._____

14. No tap conductor can supply another tap conductor.

    (a) True   (b) False

    Answer: _____   Section: _____._____

15. No wiring of any type can be installed in ducts used to transport _____.

    (a) dust   (b) flammable vapors   (c) loose stock   (d) all of these

    Answer: _____   Section: _____._____

16. Nonferrous raceways, cable trays, cablebus, auxiliary gutters, cable armor, boxes, cable sheathing, cabinets, elbows, couplings, nipples, fittings, supports, and support hardware _____ must be provided with supplementary corrosion protection.

(a) embedded or encased in concrete   (b) in direct contact with the earth
(c) likely to become energized   (d) a or b

Answer: _____   Section: _____._____

17. Nonmetallic raceways of all types may be installed within the raised floor area of an information technology equipment room.

(a) True   (b) False

Answer: _____   Section: _____._____

18. Nonmetallic wireways are permitted for _____.

(a) exposed work   (b) concealed work   (c) wet locations if listed for the purpose   (d) a and c

Answer: _____   Section: _____._____

19. NUCC larger than _____ must not be used.

(a) 1 in.   (b) 2 in.   (c) 3 in.   (d) 4 in.

Answer: _____   Section: _____._____

20. On a 3-phase, 4-wire, delta-connected service where the midpoint of one phase winding is grounded, the service conductor having the higher-phase voltage-to-ground must be durably and permanently marked by an outer finish that is _____ in color, or by other effective means, at each termination or junction point.

(a) orange   (b) red   (c) blue   (d) any of these

Answer: _____   Section: _____._____

21. On the load side of the service disconnecting means, the _____ circuit conductor is permitted to ground meter enclosures if all meter enclosures are located near the service disconnecting means and no service ground-fault protection is installed.

(a) grounding   (b) bonding   (c) grounded   (d) phase

Answer: _____   Section: _____._____

22. One receptacle outlet must be installed at each island or peninsular countertop space with a long dimension of 2 ft or greater, and a short dimension of 12 in. or greater. When breaks occur in countertop spaces for appliances, sinks, etc., there is never a need for more than one receptacle outlet.

(a) True   (b) False

Answer: _____   Section: _____._____

23. Only wiring, raceways, and cables used directly in connection with the elevator must be inside the hoistway and the machine room.

(a) True   (b) False

Answer: _____   Section: _____._____

24. Openings in cabinets, cutout boxes, and meter socket enclosures through which conductors enter must be _____.

    (a) adequately closed
    (b) made using concentric knockouts only
    (c) centered in the cabinet wall
    (d) identified

    Answer: _____   Section: _____._____

25. Optical fiber cable not terminated at equipment and not identified for future use with a tag are considered abandoned.

    (a) True
    (b) False

    Answer: _____   Section: _____._____

26. Optical fiber cables are not required to be listed and marked where the length of the cable within the building, measured from its point of entrance, does not exceed _____ and the cable enters the building from the outside and is terminated in an enclosure.

    (a) 25 ft
    (b) 30 ft
    (c) 50 ft
    (d) 100 ft

    Answer: _____   Section: _____._____

27. Optical fiber cables installed _____ on the surface of ceilings and sidewalls must be supported by the building structure in such a manner that the cable will not be damaged by normal building use.

    (a) exposed
    (b) concealed
    (c) hidden
    (d) a and b

    Answer: _____   Section: _____._____

28. Optical fiber cables utilized for fire alarm circuits must be installed in accordance with Article 770.

    (a) True
    (b) False

    Answer: _____   Section: _____._____

29. Optical fibers are permitted in the same cable, and conductive and nonconductive optical fiber cables are permitted in the same cable tray, enclosure, or raceway with conductors of power-limited fire alarm circuits in compliance with Article 760.

    (a) True
    (b) False

    Answer: _____   Section: _____._____

30. Optional standby system wiring is permitted to occupy the same raceways, cables, boxes, and cabinets with other general wiring.

    (a) True
    (b) False

    Answer: _____   Section: _____._____

31. Outlet boxes can be secured to suspended-ceiling framing members by mechanical means such as _____, or other means identified for the suspended-ceiling framing member(s).

    (a) bolts
    (b) screws
    (c) rivets
    (d) all of these

    Answer: _____   Section: _____._____

32. Overcurrent protection devices for emergency power systems _____ all supply-side overcurrent protective devices.

    (a) must be selectively coordinated with
    (b) are allowed to be selectively coordinated with
    (c) must be the same amperage as
    (d) must be a larger amperage than

    Answer: _____   Section: _____._____

33. Overcurrent protection devices for legally required power systems _____ all supply-side overcurrent protective devices.

(a) must be selectively coordinated with   (b) are allowed to be selectively coordinated with
(c) must be the same amperage as   (d) must be a higher amperage than

Answer: _____   Section: _____._____

34. Overhead conductors must have a minimum of _____ vertical clearance from final grade over residential property and driveways, as well as those commercial areas not subject to truck traffic where the voltage is limited to 300 volts-to-ground.

(a) 10 ft   (b) 12 ft   (c) 15 ft   (d) 18 ft

Answer: _____   Section: _____._____

35. Overhead conductors over a swimming pool must meet the clearance requirements of Article 680. Where a minimum clearance from the water level is given, it is taken from the _____ water level of the specified body of water.

(a) average   (b) maximum   (c) minimum   (d) nominal

Answer: _____   Section: _____._____

36. Overhead service conductors can be supported to hardwood trees.

(a) True   (b) False

Answer: _____   Section: _____._____

37. Panelboards supplied by a 3-phase, 4-wire, delta-connected system must have that phase with the higher voltage-to-ground (high-leg) connected to the _____ phase.

(a) A   (b) B   (c) C   (d) any of these

Answer: _____   Section: _____._____

38. Pendant luminaires installed in Class I, Division 1 locations must be suspended by and supplied through threaded conduit stems, and threaded joints must be provided with set screws or other means to prevent loosening. Stems _____.

(a) must not be longer than 12 in.
(b) over 12 in. must be provided with lateral bracing
(c) must be provided with a fitting or flexible connector approved for the Class I, Division 1 location
(d) any of these

Answer: _____   Section: _____._____

39. Pendant luminaires installed in Class II, Division 1 locations must be suspended by threaded conduit stems, by chains with approved fittings, or by other approved means. Stems _____.

(a) must not be longer than 12 in.
(b) if over 12 in., must be provided with lateral bracing
(c) must be provided with a fitting or flexible connector listed for the location
(d) any of these

Answer: _____   Section: _____._____

40. Plug fuses of the Edison-base type must be used _____.

(a) where overfusing is necessary   (b) only as replacement in existing installations
(c) as a replacement for Type S fuses   (d) only for 50A and above

Answer: _____   Section: _____._____

41. Plug-in-type circuit breakers that are back-fed (to supply a panelboard) must be _____ by an additional fastener that requires more than a pull to release.

(a) grounded   (b) secured in place   (c) shunt tripped   (d) none of these

Answer: _____   Section: _____._____

42. Portable distribution or terminal boxes installed outdoors at carnivals, circuses, or fairs must be weatherproof and mounted so the bottom of the enclosure is not less than _____ above the ground.

(a) 6 in.   (b) 2 ft   (c) 6 ft 6 in.   (d) 5 ft 6 in.

Answer: _____   Section: _____._____

43. Power distribution blocks installed in metal wireways must be listed.

(a) True   (b) False

Answer: _____   Section: _____._____

44. Power for sensitive electronic equipment, called "Technical Power" is a separately derived 1-phase, 3-wire system with _____ volts to a grounded conductor on each of two ungrounded conductors. The line-to-line voltage is _____.

(a) 30, 60   (b) 60, 120   (c) 120, 120   (d) none of these

Answer: _____   Section: _____._____

45. Power-limited fire alarm (PLFA) cables can be supported by strapping, taping, or attaching to the exterior of a conduit or raceway.

(a) True   (b) False

Answer: _____   Section: _____._____

46. Raceways or cable trays containing electric conductors must not contain any pipe, tube, or equal for steam, water, air, gas, drainage, or any service other than _____.

(a) allowed by the authority having jurisdiction   (b) electrical
(c) pneumatic   (d) designed by the engineer

Answer: _____   Section: _____._____

47. Raceways, cable trays, cable bus, auxiliary gutters, cable armor, boxes, cable sheathing, cabinets, elbows, couplings, fittings, supports, and support hardware must be of materials suitable for _____.

(a) corrosive locations   (b) wet locations
(c) the environment in which they are to be installed (d) none of these

Answer: _____   Section: _____._____

48. Receptacle outlet(s) for a _____ must be GFCI protected.

    (a) self-contained spa or hot tub
    (b) packaged spa or hot tub equipment assembly
    (c) field-assembled spa or hot tub with a heater load of 50A or less
    (d) all of these

    Answer: _____   Section: _____._____

49. Receptacle outlets can be installed below the countertop surface in dwelling units when necessary for the physically impaired, or if there is no means available to mount a receptacle above an island or peninsular countertop.

    (a) True   (b) False

    Answer: _____   Section: _____._____

50. Receptacles and cord connectors having grounding terminals must have those terminals effectively _____.

    (a) grounded   (b) bonded   (c) labeled   (d) listed

    Answer: _____   Section: _____._____

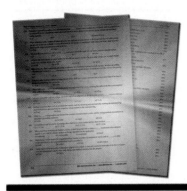

Unit 7
NEC Review Quiz
Articles 386 through 410

(• Indicates that 75% or fewer exam takers get the question correct)

Article 386 Surface Metal Raceways (continued)

1. The conductors, including splices and taps, in a metal surface raceway having a removable cover must not fill the raceway to more than _____ percent of its cross-sectional area at that point.

    (a) 75   (b) 40   (c) 38   (d) 53

    Answer: _____   Section: _____._____

2. Where combination surface metal raceways are used for both signaling and for lighting and power circuits, the different systems must be run in separate compartments identified by _____ of the interior finish.

    (a) stamping   (b) imprinting   (c) color-coding   (d) any of these

    Answer: _____   Section: _____._____

Article 388 Surface Nonmetallic Raceways

A surface nonmetallic raceway is intended to be surface mounted with associated accessories. Conductors are placed after the raceway has been installed as a complete system.

3. •The use of surface nonmetallic raceways is permitted _____.

    (a) in dry locations   (b) where concealed   (c) in hoistways   (d) all of these

    Answer: _____   Section: _____._____

4. The maximum number of conductors permitted in any surface raceway must be _____.

    (a) no more than 30 percent of the inside diameter   (b) no greater than the number for which it was designed
    (c) no more than 75 percent of the cross-sectional area   (d) that which is permitted in Table 312.6(A)

    Answer: _____   Section: _____._____

5. Where combination surface nonmetallic raceways are used for both signaling conductors and for lighting and power circuits, the different systems must be run in separate compartments identified by _____ of the interior finish.

    (a) stamping   (b) imprinting   (c) color-coding   (d) any of these

    Answer: _____   Section: _____._____

Article 390 Underfloor Raceways

This article covers the use and installation requirements for underfloor raceways.

6.   The combined area of all conductors installed at any point of an underfloor raceway must not exceed _____ percent of the internal cross-sectional area.

(a) 75   (b) 60   (c) 40   (d) 0

Answer: _____   Section: _____._____

7.   When an outlet from an underfloor raceway is discontinued, the circuit conductors supplying the outlet _____.

(a) may be spliced   (b) may be reinsulated   (c) may be cut and capped off   (d) must be removed from
the raceway

Answer: _____   Section: _____._____

8.   Inserts set in fiber underfloor raceways after the floor is laid must be _____ into the raceway.

(a) taped   (b) glued   (c) screwed   (d) mechanically secured

Answer: _____   Section: _____._____

Article 392 Cable Trays

A cable tray system is a unit or assembly of units or sections with associated fittings that form a structural system used to securely fasten or support cables and raceways. A cable tray isn't a raceway, but a support system for raceways, cables, and enclosures.

9.   Cable trays can be used as a support system for _____.

(a) services, feeders, and branch circuits   (b) communications circuits
(c) control and signaling circuits   (d) all of these

Answer: _____   Section: _____._____

10.   Where exposed to direct rays of the sun, insulated conductors and jacketed cables must be _____ as being sunlight resistant.

(a) listed   (b) approved   (c) identified   (d) none of these

Answer: _____   Section: _____._____

11.   Nonmetallic cable trays are permitted in corrosive areas and in areas requiring voltage isolation.

(a) True   (b) False

Answer: _____   Section: _____._____

12.   Cable trays must _____.

(a) include fittings for changes in direction and elevation
(b) have side rails or equivalent structural members
(c) be made of corrosion-resistant material or protected from corrosion as required by 300.6
(d) all of these

Answer: _____   Section: _____._____

13. Each run of cable tray must be _____ before the installation of cables.

(a) tested for 25 ohms resistance
(c) completed

(b) insulated
(d) all of these

Answer: _____ Section: _____._____

14. Cable trays can extend through partitions and walls or vertically through platforms and floors where the installation is made in accordance with the fire seal requirements of 300.21.

(a) True
(b) False

Answer: _____ Section: _____._____

15. In industrial facilities where conditions of maintenance and supervision ensure that only qualified persons will service the installation, cable tray systems can be used to support _____.

(a) raceways
(b) cables
(c) boxes and conduit bodies
(d) all of these

Answer: _____ Section: _____._____

16. Steel or aluminum cable tray systems can used as an equipment grounding conductor provided the cable tray sections and fittings are identified for _____ purposes, among other requirements.

(a) grounding
(b) special
(c) industrial
(d) all

Answer: _____ Section: _____._____

17. Steel cable trays must not be used as equipment grounding conductors for circuits with ground-fault protection above _____.

(a) 200A
(b) 300A
(c) 600A
(d) 800A

Answer: _____ Section: _____._____

18. Cable _____ made and insulated by approved methods can be located within a cable tray provided they are accessible, and do not project above the side rails.

(a) connections
(b) jumpers
(c) splices
(d) conductors

Answer: _____ Section: _____._____

19. Where single conductor cables comprising each phase or grounded conductor of a circuit are connected in parallel in a cable tray, the conductors must be installed _____ , to prevent current unbalance in the paralleled conductors due to inductive reactance.

(a) in groups consisting of not more than three conductors per phase or neutral
(b) in groups consisting of not more than one conductor per phase or neutral
(c) as individual conductors securely bound to the cable tray
(d) in separate groups

Answer: _____ Section: _____._____

Article 394 Concealed Knob-and-Tube Wiring

This article covers the use, installation, and construction specifications of concealed knob-and-tube wiring. Which is a wiring method using knobs, tubes, and flexible nonmetallic tubing for the protection and support of single insulated conductors.

20. Concealed knob-and-tube wiring can be used in commercial garages, theaters and similar locations, motion picture studios, hazardous (classified) locations or in the hollow spaces of walls, ceilings and attics where such spaces are insulated by loose, rolled or foamed-in-place insulating material that envelops the conductors.

    (a) True　　　　　　　　(b) False

    Answer: _____　　Section: _____._____

21. Supports for concealed knob-and-tube wiring must be installed within _____ in. of each side of each tap or splice and at intervals not exceeding _____ ft.

    (a) 3, 2 1/2　　　(b) 2, 3 1/2　　　(c) 6, 4 1/2　　　(d) 4, 6 1/2

    Answer: _____　　Section: _____._____

Article 396 Messenger-Supported Wiring

This article covers the use, installation, and construction specifications for messenger supported wiring.

22. An exposed wiring support system using a messenger wire to support insulated conductors is known as _____.

    (a) open wiring　　　　　(b) messenger-supported wiring
    (c) field wiring　　　　　(d) none of these

    Answer: _____　　Section: _____._____

23. The conductors supported by messenger is permitted to come into contact with the messenger supports or any structural members, walls, or pipes.

    (a) True　　　　　　　　(b) False

    Answer: _____　　Section: _____._____

Article 398 Open Wiring on Insulators

This article covers the use, installation, and construction specifications of open wiring on insulators. Which is an exposed wiring method using cleats, knobs, tubes, and flexible tubing for the protection and support of single insulated conductors run in or on buildings.

24. Open wiring on insulators is a(n) _____ wiring method using cleats, knobs, tubes, and flexible tubing for the protection and support of single insulated conductors run in or on buildings and not concealed by the building structure.

    (a) temporary　　　(b) acceptable　　　(c) enclosed　　　(d) exposed

    Answer: _____　　Section: _____._____

25. •Open wiring on insulators within _____ from the floor are considered exposed to physical damage.

    (a) 4 ft　　　(b) 2 ft　　　(c) 7 ft　　　(d) none of these

    Answer: _____　　Section: _____._____

26. A conductor used for open wiring that must penetrate a wall, floor, or other framing member must be carried through a _____.

    (a) separate sleeve or tube   (b) weatherproof tube   (c) tube of absorbent material   (d) grounded metallic tube

    Answer: _____   Section: _____._____

27. Conductors smaller than 8 AWG for open wiring on insulators must be supported within _____ of a tap or splice.

    (a) 6 in.   (b) 8 in.   (c) 10 in.   (d) 12 in.

    Answer: _____   Section: _____._____

28. When screws are used to mount knobs for the support of open wiring on insulators, they must be of a length sufficient to penetrate the wood to a depth equal to at least _____ the height of the knob and the full thickness of the cleat.

    (a) one-eighth   (b) one-quarter   (c) one-third   (d) 1/2

    Answer: _____   Section: _____._____

Chapter 4 Equipment for General Use

Article 400 Flexible Cords and Cables

This article covers the general requirements, applications, and construction specifications for flexible cords and flexible cables.

29. HPD cord is permitted for _____ usage.

    (a) normal   (b) hard   (c) extra-hard   (d) all of these

    Answer: _____   Section: _____._____

30. The allowable ampacity of flexible cords and cables is found in _____.

    (a) Table 310.16   (b) Table 400.5(A) and (B)   (c) Table 1, Chapter 9   (d) Table 430.52

    Answer: _____   Section: _____._____

31. Conductors within flexible cords and cables must not be associated together in such a way (with respect to the kind of circuit, the wiring method used, or the number of conductors) that the _____ temperature of the conductors is exceeded.

    (a) operating   (b) governing   (c) ambient   (d) limiting

    Answer: _____   Section: _____._____

32. Flexible cords and cables can be used for _____.

    (a) wiring of luminaires
    (b) connection of portable lamps or appliances
    (c) connection of utilization equipment to facilitate frequent interchange
    (d) all of these

    Answer: _____   Section: _____._____

33. Unless specifically permitted in 400.7, flexible cords and cables must not be used where _____.

(a) run through holes in walls, ceilings, or floors   (b) run through doorways, windows, or similar openings
(c) attached to building surfaces   (d) all of these

Answer: _____   Section: _____._____

34. Repair of hard-service cord having conductors _____ AWG and larger is permitted if conductors are spliced in accordance with 110.14(B) and the completed splice retains the insulation, outer sheath properties, and usage characteristics of the cord being spliced.

(a) 16   (b) 15   (c) 14   (d) 12

Answer: _____   Section: _____._____

35. Flexible cords and cables must be protected by _____ where passing through holes in covers, outlet boxes, or similar enclosures.

(a) bushings   (b) fittings   (c) a or b   (d) none of these

Answer: _____   Section: _____._____

36. One conductor of flexible cords intended to be used as a(n) _____ conductor must have a continuous marker readily distinguishing it from the other conductor or conductors.

(a) grounded neutral   (b) equipment grounding   (c) ungrounded   (d) all of these

Answer: _____   Section: _____._____

37. A flexible cord conductor intended to be used as a(n) _____ conductor must have a continuous identifying marker readily distinguishing it from the other conductor or conductors.

(a) ungrounded   (b) equipment grounding   (c) service   (d) high-leg

Answer: _____   Section: _____._____

Article 402 Fixture Wires

This article covers the general requirements and construction specifications for fixture wires.

38. The smallest size fixture wire permitted in the *NEC* is _____ AWG.

(a) 22   (b) 20   (c) 18   (d) 16

Answer: _____   Section: _____._____

39. Fixture wires are used to connect luminaires to the _____ conductors supplying the luminaires.

(a) service   (b) branch-circuit   (c) feeder   (d) none of these

Answer: _____   Section: _____._____

40. Fixture wires cannot be used for branch-circuit wiring.

(a) True   (b) False

Answer: _____   Section: _____._____

41. Three-way and four-way switches must be wired so that all switching is done only in the _____ circuit conductor.

    (a) ungrounded   (b) grounded   (c) equipment ground   (d) neutral

    Answer: _____   Section: _____._____

42. Switches or circuit breakers must not disconnect the grounded conductor of a circuit unless the switch or circuit breaker _____.

    (a) can be opened and closed by hand levers only
    (b) simultaneously disconnects all conductors of the circuit
    (c) opens the grounded conductor before it disconnects the ungrounded conductors
    (d) none of these

    Answer: _____   Section: _____._____

Article 404 Switches

The requirements of Article 404 apply to switches of all types. These include snap (toggle) switches, dimmers, fan switches, knife switches, circuit breakers used as switches, and automatic switches such as time clocks, timers, and switches and circuit breakers used for disconnecting means.

43. Switches or circuit breakers in a wet location or outside of a building must be enclosed in a _____ enclosure or cabinet that complies with 312.2(A).

    (a) weatherproof   (b) rainproof   (c) watertight   (d) raintight

    Answer: _____   Section: _____._____

44. Single-throw knife switches must be installed so that gravity will tend to close the switch.

    (a) True   (b) False

    Answer: _____   Section: _____._____

45. All switches and circuit breakers used as switches must be installed so that they may be operated from a readily accessible place. They must be installed so that the center of the grip of the operating handle of the switch or circuit breaker, when in its highest position, is not more than 6 ft 7 in. above the floor or working platform.

    (a) True   (b) False

    Answer: _____   Section: _____._____

46. Snap switches must not be grouped or ganged in enclosures with other _____ if the voltage between adjacent devices exceeds 300V, unless barriers are permanently installed between adjacent devices.

    (a) snap switches   (b) receptacles   (c) similar devices   (d) all of these

    Answer: _____   Section: _____._____

47. All snap switches, including dimmer and similar control switches, must be effectively grounded so that they can provide a means to ground metal faceplates, whether or not a metal faceplate is installed.

    (a) True   (b) False

    Answer: _____   Section: _____._____

48. A faceplate for a flush-mounted snap switch must not be less than _____ thick when made of a nonferrous metal.

(a) 0.03 in.   (b) 0.04 in.   (c) 0.003 in.   (d) 0.004 in.

Answer: _____   Section: _____._____

49. A hand-operable circuit breaker equipped with a _____, or a power operated circuit breaker capable of being opened by hand in the event of a power failure, is permitted to serve as a switch if it has the required number of poles.

(a) lever   (b) handle   (c) shunt trip   (d) a or b

Answer: _____   Section: _____._____

50. Nonmetallic enclosures for switches and circuit breakers must be installed with a wiring method that provides or includes _____.

(a) a grounded conductor   (b) an equipment ground   (c) an inductive balance   (d) none of these

Answer: _____   Section: _____._____

51. Alternating current general-use snap switches, suitable only for use on ac circuits, can control _____.

(a) resistive and inductive loads that do not exceed the ampere and voltage rating of the switch   (b) tungsten-filament lamp loads that do not exceed the ampere rating of the switch at 120V (c) motor loads that do not exceed 80 percent of the ampere and voltage rating of the switch (d) all of these

Answer: _____   Section: _____._____

52. Snap switches rated _____ or less directly connected to aluminum conductors must be listed and marked CO/ALR.

(a) 15A   (b) 20A   (c) 25A   (d) 30A

Answer: _____   Section: _____._____

53. Switches must be marked with _____.

(a) current   (b) voltage
(c) maximum horsepower, if horsepower rated   (d) all of these

Answer: _____   Section: _____._____

54. A fused switch must not have fuses _____ except as permitted in 240.8.

(a) in series   (b) in parallel   (c) less than 100A   (d) over 15A

Answer: _____   Section: _____._____

Article 406 Receptacles, Cord Connectors, and Attachment Plugs (Caps)

This article covers the rating, type, and installation of receptacles, cord connectors, and attachment plugs (cord caps).

55. Receptacles rated 20A or less and designed for the direct connection of aluminum conductors must be marked _____.

(a) aluminum rated   (b) alum 20a   (c) CO/ALR   (d) al wire

Answer: _____   Section: _____._____

56. Isolated ground receptacles installed in nonmetallic boxes must be covered with a nonmetallic faceplate because a metal faceplate cannot be connected to the circuit equipment grounding conductor.

    (a) True   (b) False

    Answer: _____   Section: _____._____

57. When replacing a receptacle, and the grounding means exists in the receptacle enclosure, or a grounding conductor is installed in accordance with 250.130(C), _____-type receptacles must be used.

    (a) isolated ground   (b) grounding   (c) GFCI   (d) two-wire

    Answer: _____   Section: _____._____

58. •When replacing a nongrounding type receptacle in a bedroom of a dwelling unit where no grounding means exists in the receptacle enclosure, you must use a _____.

    (a) nongrounding receptacle   (b) grounding receptacle   (c) GFCI-type receptacle   (d) a or c

    Answer: _____   Section: _____._____

59. Receptacles mounted in boxes set back of the wall surface must be installed so that the mounting _____ of the receptacle is/are held rigidly at the surface of the wall.

    (a) screws or nails   (b) yoke or strap   (c) face plate   (d) none of these

    Answer: _____   Section: _____._____

60. Receptacles mounted to and supported by a cover must be secured by more than one screw unless listed and identified for securing by a single screw.

    (a) True   (b) False

    Answer: _____   Section: _____._____

61. Metal faceplates for receptacles must be grounded.

    (a) True   (b) False

    Answer: _____   Section: _____._____

62. Attachment plugs and cord connectors must be listed for the purpose and marked with the _____.

    (a) manufacturer's name or identification   (b) voltage rating
    (c) amperage rating   (d) all of these

    Answer: _____   Section: _____._____

63. Attachment plugs must be installed so that their prongs, blades, or pins are not energized unless inserted into an energized receptacle. No receptacle can be installed so as to require an energized attachment plug as its _____.

    (a) load   (b) source of supply   (c) protective device   (d) none of these

    Answer: _____   Section: _____._____

64. A receptacle is considered to be in a location protected from the weather when located under roofed open porches, canopies, marquees, and the like, where it will not be subjected to _____.

    (a) spray from a hose   (b) a direct lightning hit
    (c) beating rain or water runoff   (d) falling or wind-blown debris

    Answer: _____   Section: _____._____

65. An outdoor receptacle in a location protected from the weather, or another damp location, must be installed in an enclosure that is weatherproof when the receptacle is _____.

    (a) covered   (b) enclosed   (c) protected   (d) none of these

    Answer: _____   Section: _____._____

66. _____, 125 and 250V receptacles installed in a wet location must have an enclosure that is weatherproof whether or not the attachment plug cap is inserted.

    (a) 15A   (b) 20A   (c) a and b   (d) none of these

    Answer: _____   Section: _____._____

67. An enclosure that is weatherproof, only when no attachment plug is connected, can be used for receptacles in a wet location other than outdoors when the receptacle is used for _____ while attended.

    (a) portable equipment (b) portable tools   (c) fixed equipment   (d) a and b

    Answer: _____   Section: _____._____

68. A receptacle installed in an outlet box flush-mounted on a finished surface in a damp or wet location must be made weatherproof by means of a weatherproof faceplate assembly that provides a _____ connection between the plate and the finished surface.

    (a) sealed   (b) weathertight   (c) sealed and protected (d) watertight

    Answer: _____   Section: _____._____

Article 408 Switchboards and Panelboards

This article covers specific requirements for switchboards, panelboards, and distribution boards that control light and power circuits.

69. Conductors and busbars on a switchboard, panelboard, or control board must be located so as to be free from _____ and must be held firmly in place.

    (a) obstructions   (b) physical damage   (c) a and b   (d) none of these

    Answer: _____   Section: _____._____

70. Each switchboard or panelboard used as service equipment must be provided with a main bonding jumper within the panelboard, or one of the sections of the switchboard, for connecting the grounded service conductor on its _____ side to the switchboard or panelboard frame.

    (a) load   (b) supply   (c) phase   (d) high-leg

    Answer: _____   Section: _____._____

71. The purpose or use of panelboard circuits and circuit _____ must be legibly identified on a circuit directory located on the face or inside of the doors of a panelboard, and at each switch on a switchboard.

    (a) manufacturers   (b) conductors   (c) feeders   (d) modifications

    Answer: _____   Section: _____._____

72. Noninsulated busbars must have a minimum space of _____ between the bottom of enclosure and busbar or other obstructions.

    (a) 6 in.   (b) 8 in.   (c) 10 in.   (d) 12 in.

    Answer: _____   Section: _____._____

73. Switchboards must be placed so as to reduce to a minimum the probability of communicating _____ to adjacent combustible materials.

    (a) sparks   (b) backfeed   (c) fire   (d) all of these

    Answer: _____   Section: _____._____

74. An insulated conductor used within a switchboard must be _____.

    (a) listed   (b) flame-retardant
    (c) rated for the highest voltage it may contact   (d) all of these

    Answer: _____   Section: _____._____

75. To qualify as a lighting and appliance branch-circuit panelboard, the number of circuits rated at 30A or less and having a neutral conductor must be _____ of the total.

    (a) more than 10 percent   (b) 10 percent   (c) 20 percent   (d) 40 percent

    Answer: _____   Section: _____._____

76. A lighting and appliance branch-circuit panelboard must be provided with physical means to prevent the installation of more _____ devices than that number for which the panelboard was designed, rated, and approved.

    (a) overcurrent   (b) equipment   (c) circuit breaker   (d) all of these

    Answer: _____   Section: _____._____

77. A lighting and appliance branch-circuit panelboard is not required to be individually protected if the panelboard _____ conductor has protection not greater than the panelboard rating.

    (a) grounded neutral   (b) feeder   (c) branch circuit   (d) none of these

    Answer: _____   Section: _____._____

78. When a lighting and appliance branch-circuit panelboard is supplied from a transformer, the overcurrent protection must be located _____.

    (a) on the secondary side of the transformer   (b) on the primary side of the transformer
    (c) none is required   (d) either a or b

    Answer: _____   Section: _____._____

79. When equipment grounding conductors are installed in panelboards, a _____ is required for the proper termination of the equipment grounding conductors.

(a) grounded conductor   (b) terminator strip   (c) grounding terminal bar   (d) none of these

Answer: _____   Section: _____._____

80. Pilot lights, instruments, potential transformers, current transformers, and other switchboard devices with potential coils must be supplied by a circuit that is protected by overcurrent devices rated _____.

(a) 15A or more   (b) 15A or less   (c) 20A or less   (d) 10A or less

Answer: _____   Section: _____._____

Article 410 Luminaires, Lampholders, and Lamps

Article 410 contains the requirements for luminaires, lampholders, and lamps. Because of the many types and applications of luminaires, manufacturer's instructions are very important and helpful for proper installation. UL produces a pamphlet called the Luminaire Marking Guide, which provides information for properly installing common types of incandescent, fluorescent, and high-intensity discharge (HID) luminaires.

81. Article 410 covers luminaires, lampholders, pendants, and _____, and the wiring and equipment forming part of such products and lighting installations.

(a) decorative lighting products
(b) lighting accessories for temporary seasonal and holiday use
(c) portable flexible lighting products
(d) all of these

Answer: _____   Section: _____._____

82. A luminaire marked "Suitable for Damp Locations" _____ be used in a wet location.

(a) can   (b) cannot

Answer: _____   Section: _____._____

83. No part of cord-connected luminaires, hanging luminaires, track lighting, pendants, or paddle fans may be located within a zone measured 3 ft horizontally and _____ vertically from the top of the bathtub rim or shower stall threshold.

(a) 4 ft   (b) 6 ft   (c) 8 ft   (d) none of these

Answer: _____   Section: _____._____

84. Luminaires using a _____ lamp, that are subject to physical damage and installed in playing and spectator seating areas of indoor sports, mixed-use, or all-purpose facilities, must be of the type that protects the lamp with a glass or plastic lens. Such luminaires are permitted to have an additional guard.

(a) mercury vapor   (b) metal halide   (c) fluorescent   (d) a or b

Answer: _____   Section: _____._____

85. Unless an individual switch is provided for each luminaire located over combustible material, lampholders must be located at least _____ above the floor, or must be located or guarded so that the lamps cannot be readily removed or damaged.

(a) 3 ft   (b) 6 ft   (c) 8 ft   (d) 10 ft

Answer: _____   Section: _____._____

86. Incandescent luminaires that have open lamps, and pendant-type luminaires, can be installed in clothes closets where proper clearance is maintained from combustible products.

    (a) True   (b) False

    Answer: _____   Section: _____._____

87. In clothes closets, recessed incandescent luminaires with a completely enclosed lamp are permitted to be installed in the wall or on the ceiling, provided there is a minimum clearance of _____ between the luminaire and the nearest point of a storage space.

    (a) 3 in.   (b) 6 in.   (c) 9 in.   (d) 12 in.

    Answer: _____   Section: _____._____

88. Electric-discharge luminaires supported independently of the outlet box must be connected to the branch circuit through _____.

    (a) raceways   (b) Type MC, AC, MI, NM, or NMC cable
    (c) flexible cords   (d) a, b, or c

    Answer: _____   Section: _____._____

89. The maximum weight of a luminaire that can be supported by the screw-shell of a lampholder is _____

    (a) 2 lbs   (b) 6 lbs   (c) 3 lbs   (d) 50 lbs

    Answer: _____   Section: _____._____

90. Metal or nonmetallic poles over 20 ft in height above grade that support luminaires must meet which of the following requirements? _____.

    (a) They must have an accessible handhole (sized 2 x 4 in.) with a raintight cover
    (b) The grounding terminal must be accessible from the handhole
    (c) a and b
    (d) none of these

    Answer: _____   Section: _____._____

91. Luminaires attached to the framing of a suspended-ceiling must be secured to the framing member(s) by mechanical means such as bolts, screws, or rivets. Clips _____ and identified for use with the type of ceiling framing member(s) and luminaires are also permitted.

    (a) marked   (b) labeled   (c) identified   (d) listed

    Answer: _____   Section: _____._____

92. Exposed conductive parts of luminaires must be _____.

    (a) grounded   (b) painted   (c) removed   (d) a and b

    Answer: _____   Section: _____._____

93. Luminaires must be wired with conductors having insulation suitable for the environmental conditions and _____ to which the conductors will be subjected.

    (a) temperature   (b) voltage   (c) current   (d) all of these

    Answer: _____   Section: _____._____

94. Splices and taps must not be located within luminaire (fixture) _____.

(a) arms or stems   (b) bases or screw-shells   (c) a and b   (d) a or b

Answer: _____   Section: _____._____

95. _____ conductors must be used for wiring on luminaire (fixture) chains and on other movable or flexible parts.

(a) Solid   (b) Covered   (c) Insulated   (d) Stranded

Answer: _____   Section: _____._____

96. Luminaires that require adjustment or aiming after installation can be cord-connected without an attachment plug.

(a) True   (b) False

Answer: _____   Section: _____._____

97. The flexible cord used to connect a luminaire may be terminated _____.

(a) in a grounding-type attachment plug cap
(b) as a part of a listed assembly incorporating a manufactured wiring system connector
(c) as a part of a listed luminaire assembly with a strain relief and canopy
(d) all of these

Answer: _____   Section: _____._____

98. Branch-circuit conductors within _____ of a ballast must have an insulation temperature rating not lower than 90°C (194°F) unless supplying a luminaire that is listed and marked as suitable for a different insulation temperature.

(a) 1 in.   (b) 3 in.   (c) 6 in.   (d) none of these

Answer: _____   Section: _____._____

99. Tubing used as arms or stems on luminaires and provided with cut threads must have a wall thickness not less than _____

(a) 0.020 in.   (b) 0.025 in.   (c) 0.040 in.   (d) 0.015 in.

Answer: _____   Section: _____._____

100. Edison-base screw-shell lampholders are designed to hold lamps and to hold screw-in receptacle adapters.

(a) True   (b) False

Answer: _____   Section: _____._____

(• Indicates that 75% or fewer exam takers get the question correct)

1. Surface metal raceway enclosures providing a transition from other wiring methods must have a means for connecting a(n) _____.

    (a) grounded conductor   (b) ungrounded conductor
    (c) equipment grounding conductor   (d) all of these

    Answer: _____   Section: _____._____

2. •The intent of Article 392 is to limit the use of cable trays to industrial establishments only.

    (a) True   (b) False

    Answer: _____   Section: _____._____

3. 18 AWG TFFN has an ampacity of _____.

    (a) 14A   (b) 10A   (c) 8A   (d) 6A

    Answer: _____   Section: _____._____

4. A 3-conductor 16 AWG, SJE cable (one conductor is used for grounding) has a maximum ampacity of _____ for each conductor.

    (a) 13A   (b) 12A   (c) 15A   (d) 8A

    Answer: _____   Section: _____._____

5. A receptacle is considered to be in a location protected from the weather (damp location) where _____.

    (a) located under a roofed open porch   (b) not subjected to beating rain or water runoff
    (c) a or b   (d) a and b

    Answer: _____   Section: _____._____

6. A receptacle must not be installed within, or directly over, a bathtub or shower space.

    (a) True   (b) False

    Answer: _____   Section: _____._____

7. A snap switch without a grounding connection is allowed for replacement purposes only where the wiring method does not include an equipment ground and must be _____.

    (a) provided with a faceplate of nonconducting, noncombustible material
    (b) protected by a ground-fault circuit interrupter
    (c) a or b
    (d) none of these

    Answer: _____   Section: _____._____

8.   A space of _____ or more must be provided between the top of any switchboard and any combustible ceiling.

      (a) 12 in.   (b) 18 in.   (c) 2 ft   (d) 3 ft

      Answer: _____   Section: _____._____

9.   A switching device with a marked "OFF" position must completely disconnect all _____ conductors of the load it controls.

      (a) grounded   (b) ungrounded   (c) grounding   (d) all of these

      Answer: _____   Section: _____._____

10.   AC or DC general-use snap switches, suitable for use on either ac or dc circuits, may be used for control of inductive loads not exceeding _____ percent of the ampere rating of the switch at the applied voltage.

      (a) 75   (b) 90   (c) 100   (d) 50

      Answer: _____   Section: _____._____

11.   Barriers must be placed in all service switchboards such that no uninsulated, ungrounded service _____ or service terminal is exposed to inadvertent contact by persons or maintenance equipment while servicing load terminations.

      (a) busbar   (b) conductors   (c) cables   (d) none of these

      Answer: _____   Section: _____._____

12.   Cable tray systems must not be used _____.

      (a) in hoistways   (b) where subject to severe physical damage
      (c) in hazardous locations   (d) a and b

      Answer: _____   Section: _____._____

13.   Conduits and raceways, including end fittings, must not rise more than _____ above the bottom of a switchboard enclosure.

      (a) 3 in.   (b) 4 in.   (c) 5 in.   (d) 6 in.

      Answer: _____   Section: _____._____

14.   Coves for luminaires must have adequate space and must be located so that the lamps and equipment can be properly installed and _____.

      (a) maintained   (b) protected from physical damage
      (c) tested   (d) inspected

      Answer: _____   Section: _____._____

15.   Each _____ conductor must terminate within the panelboard at an individual terminal that is not also used for another conductor.

      (a) grounded   (b) ungrounded   (c) grounding   (d) all of these

      Answer: _____   Section: _____._____

16.   Fixture wires are permitted for installation in luminaires and in similar equipment where enclosed or protected and not subject to _____ in use, or for connecting luminaires to the branch-circuit conductors supplying the luminaires.

      (a) bending or twisting   (b) knotting   (c) stretching or straining (d) none of these

      Answer: _____   Section: _____._____

17. Fixture wires used as pendant conductors for incandescent luminaires with intermediate or candelabra-base lampholders must not be smaller than _____ AWG.

    (a) 22   (b) 18   (c) 16   (d) 14

    Answer: _____   Section: _____._____

18. Flat-top underfloor raceways over 4 in. but not over 8 in. wide with a minimum of 1 in. spacing between raceways must be covered with concrete to a depth of not less than 1 in. Raceways spaced less than 1 in. apart must be covered with concrete to a depth of _____

    (a) 1 in.   (b) 4 in.   (c) 1 1/2 in.   (d) 2 in.

    Answer: _____   Section: _____._____

19. Flexible cords and cables must not be concealed behind building _____, or run through doorways, windows, or similar openings.

    (a) structural ceilings   (b) suspended or dropped ceilings
    (c) floors or walls   (d) all of these

    Answer: _____   Section: _____._____

20. For raceways terminating at the tray, a(n) _____ cable tray clamp or adapter must be used to securely fasten the raceway to the cable tray system.

    (a) listed   (b) approved   (c) identified   (d) none of these

    Answer: _____   Section: _____._____

21. Handholes in metal or nonmetallic poles supporting luminaires are not required for poles _____ or less in height above finished grade, if the pole is provided with a hinged base and the grounding terminal is accessible within the hinged base.

    (a) 8 ft   (b) 18 ft   (c) 20 ft   (d) none of these

    Answer: _____   Section: _____._____

22. In industrial establishments where conditions of maintenance and supervision ensure that only qualified persons service the installation, flexible cords and cables are permitted to be installed in aboveground raceways that are no longer than _____, to protect the flexible cord or cable from physical damage.

    (a) 25 ft   (b) 50 ft   (c) 100 ft   (d) no limit

    Answer: _____   Section: _____._____

23. It is permissible to run unbroken lengths of surface nonmetallic raceways through dry _____.

    (a) walls   (b) partitions   (c) floors   (d) all of these

    Answer: _____   Section: _____._____

24. Luminaires designed for end-to-end connection to form a continuous assembly, or luminaires connected together by recognized wiring methods, are permitted to contain the conductors of a 2-wire branch circuit, or one _____ branch circuit, supplying the connected luminaires and need not be listed as a raceway.

    (a) small-appliance   (b) appliance   (c) multiwire   (d) industrial

    Answer: _____   Section: _____._____

25. Luminaires located in bathtub and shower zones must be listed for damp locations, or listed for wet locations where _____.

(a) below 7 ft in. height   (b) below 6 ft 7 in. in height   (c) subject to shower spray   (d) not GFCI protected

Answer: _____   Section: _____._____

26. Luminaires, lampholders, and receptacles must have no live parts normally exposed to contact. But cleat-type lampholders located at least _____ above the floor are permitted to have exposed terminals.

(a) 3 ft   (b) 6 ft   (c) 8 ft   (d) none of these

Answer: _____   Section: _____._____

27. Metal enclosures for switches or circuit breakers must be _____ as specified in Article 250.

(a) ventilated   (b) dust proof   (c) grounded   (d) sealed

Answer: _____   Section: _____._____

28. Not counting the main breaker, the maximum number of overcurrent devices that can be installed in any one cabinet of a lighting and appliance branch-circuit panelboard is _____.

(a) 12   (b) 42   (c) 6   (d) none of these

Answer: _____   Section: _____._____

29. One of the requirements that must be met to use steel or aluminum cable tray systems as equipment grounding conductors, is that the cable tray sections and fittings have been _____ marked to show the cross-sectional area of metal in channel cable trays, or cable trays of one-piece construction and total cross sectional area of both side rails for ladder or trough cable trays.

(a) legibly   (b) durably   (c) a or b   (d) a and b

Answer: _____   Section: _____._____

30. Panelboards equipped with snap switches rated at 30A or less must have overcurrent protection not exceeding _____.

(a) 30A   (b) 50A   (c) 100A   (d) 200A

Answer: _____   Section: _____._____

31. Portable lamps must be wired with _____ recognized by 400.4, and have an attachment plug of the polarized or grounding type.

(a) flexible cable   (b) flexible cord
(c) nonmetallic flexible cable   (d) nonmetallic flexible cord

Answer: _____   Section: _____._____

32. Receptacle faceplate covers made of insulating material must be noncombustible and not less than _____ in thickness.

(a) 0.10 in.   (b) 0.04 in.   (c) 0.01 in.   (d) 0.22 in.

Answer: _____   Section: _____._____

33. Receptacles incorporating an isolated grounding connection intended for the reduction of electrical noise must be identified by _____ on the face of the receptacle.

(a) an orange triangle   (b) a green triangle
(c) a completely orange device   (d) the engraved word "ISOLATED"

Answer: _____   Section: _____._____

34. Receptacles mounted in boxes flush with the wall surface or projecting beyond it must be installed so that the mounting yoke or strap of the receptacle is _____.

    (a) held rigidly against the box or box cover   (b) mounted behind the wall surface
    (c) held rigidly at the finished surface   (d) none of these

    Answer: _____   Section: _____._____

35. Receptacles, cord connectors, and attachment plugs must be constructed so that the receptacles or cord connectors do not accept an attachment plug with a different _____ or current rating than that for which the device is intended.

    (a) voltage rating   (b) amperage interrupting capacity
    (c) temperature rating   (d) all of these

    Answer: _____   Section: _____._____

36. Supports for cable trays must be provided in accordance with _____.

    (a) installation instructions   (b) the *NEC*   (c) a or b   (d) none of these

    Answer: _____   Section: _____._____

37. Switches and circuit breakers used as switches can be mounted _____ if they are installed adjacent to motors, appliances, or other equipment that they supply and are accessible by portable means.

    (a) never more than 6 ft 7 in.   (b) higher than the standard maximum of 6 ft 7 in.
    (c) only in the mechanical equipment room   (d) up to 8 ft high

    Answer: _____   Section: _____._____

38. Switches must not be installed within wet locations in tub or shower spaces unless installed as part of a listed tub or shower assembly.

    (a) True   (b) False

    Answer: _____   Section: _____._____

39. The messenger must be supported at dead ends and at intermediate locations so as to eliminate _____ on the conductors.

    (a) static   (b) magnetism   (c) tension   (d) induction

    Answer: _____   Section: _____._____

40. The *NEC* requires a lighting outlet in clothes closets.

    (a) True   (b) False

    Answer: _____   Section: _____._____

41. TPT and TST cords are permitted in lengths not exceeding _____ when attached directly, or by means of a special type of plug, to a portable appliance rated 50W or less.

    (a) 8 ft   (b) 10 ft   (c) 15 ft   (d) none of these

    Answer: _____   Section: _____._____

42. Trees can to be used to support outdoor luminaires.

    (a) True   (b) False

    Answer: _____   Section: _____._____

43. Underfloor raceways must be laid so that a straight line from the center of one _____ to the center of the next _____ will coincide with the centerline of the raceway system.

    (a) termination point   (b) junction box   (c) receptacle   (d) panelboard

    Answer: _____   Section: _____._____

44. When grouping conductors of three-way and four-way switch loops in the same raceway to avoid inductive heating according to 300.20(A), it is not necessary to include a grounded conductor in every switch loop.

    (a) True   (b) False

    Answer: _____   Section: _____._____

45. When nails are used to mount knobs for the support of open wiring on insulators, they must not be smaller than _____-penny.

    (a) six   (b) eight   (c) ten   (d) none of these

    Answer: _____   Section: _____._____

46. When replacing receptacles in locations that would require GFCI protection under the current *Code*,_____ receptacles must be installed.

    (a) two wire   (b) isolated ground   (c) GFCI-protected   (d) grounding

    Answer: _____   Section: _____._____

47. Where a solid-bottom cable tray having a usable inside depth of 6 in. or less contains multiconductor control and/or signal cables only, the sum of the cross-sectional areas of all cables at any cross-section must not exceed _____ percent of the interior cross-sectional area of the cable tray.

    (a) 25   (b) 30   (c) 35   (d) 40

    Answer: _____   Section: _____._____

48. Where open conductors cross ceiling joists and wall studs, and are exposed to physical damage, they must be protected by a substantial running board. Running boards must extend at least _____ in. outside the conductors, but not more than _____ in., and the protecting sides must be at least 2 in. high and at least 1 in., nominal, in thickness.

    (a) 1/2, 1   (b) 1/2, 2   (c) 1, 2 1/2   (d) 1, 2

    Answer: _____   Section: _____._____

49. Where solid knobs are used, conductors must be securely tied to them by _____ equivalent to that of the conductor.

    (a) tie wires having insulation   (b) wires having an AWG   (c) nonconductive material   (d) none of these

    Answer: _____   Section: _____._____

50. Wiring on fixture chains and other movable parts must be _____.

    (a) rated for 110°C   (b) stranded   (c) hard usage rated   (d) none of these

    Answer: _____   Section: _____._____

1. Receptacles and cord connectors must be rated not less than _____ at 125V, or at 250V and must be of a type not suitable for use as lampholders.

   (a) 30A   (b) 20A   (c) 15A   (d) 10A

   Answer: _____   Section: _____._____

2. Receptacles connected to circuits having different voltages, frequencies, or types of current (ac or dc) on the _____ must be of such design that the attachment plugs used on these circuits are not interchangeable.

   (a) building   (b) interior   (c) same premises   (d) exterior

   Answer: _____   Section: _____._____

3. Receptacles in countertops and similar work surfaces in dwelling units must not be installed _____.

   (a) in the sides of cabinets   (b) in a face-up position   (c) on GFCI circuits   (d) on the kitchen small-appliance circuit

   Answer: _____   Section: _____._____

4. Receptacles installed behind a bed in the guest rooms in hotels and motels must be located so as to prevent the bed from contacting an attachment plug, or the receptacle must be provided with a suitable guard.

   (a) True   (b) False

   Answer: _____   Section: _____._____

5. Receptacles installed outdoors, in a location protected from the weather or other damp locations, must be in an enclosure that is _____ when the receptacle is covered.

   (a) raintight   (b) weatherproof   (c) rainproof   (d) weathertight

   Answer: _____   Section: _____._____

6. Recessed incandescent luminaires must have _____ protection and must be identified as thermally protected.

   (a) physical   (b) corrosion   (c) thermal   (d) all of these

   Answer: _____   Section: _____._____

7. Rigid metal conduit that is directly buried outdoors must have at least _____ of cover.

   (a) 6 in.   (b) 12 in.   (c) 18 in.   (d) 24 in.

   Answer: _____   Section: _____._____

8. Rigid nonmetallic conduit and fittings can be used in areas of dairies, laundries, canneries, or other wet locations and in locations where walls are frequently washed. However, the entire conduit system including boxes and _____ must be installed and equipped to prevent water from entering the conduit.

    (a) luminaires   (b) fittings   (c) supports   (d) all of these

    Answer: _____   Section: _____._____

9. Rigid nonmetallic conduit must be securely fastened within _____ of each box.

    (a) 6 in.   (b) 24 in.   (c) 12 in.   (d) 36 in.

    Answer: _____   Section: _____._____

10. Running threads must not be used on rigid metal conduit for connection at _____.

    (a) boxes   (b) cabinets   (c) couplings   (d) meter sockets

    Answer: _____   Section: _____._____

11. Running threads of IMC must not be used on conduit for connection at couplings.

    (a) True   (b) False

    Answer: _____   Section: _____._____

12. Seals in a Class II hazardous (classified) location are required to be explosionproof.

    (a) True   (b) False

    Answer: _____   Section: _____._____

13. Separately-installed pressure connectors must be used with conductors at the _____ not exceeding the ampacity at the listed and identified temperature rating of the connector.

    (a) voltages   (b) temperatures   (c) listings   (d) ampacities

    Answer: _____   Section: _____._____

14. Service conductors only originate from the service point and terminate at the service equipment (disconnect).

    (a) True   (b) False

    Answer: _____   Section: _____._____

15. Service conductors that are not encased in concrete and that are buried 18 in. or more below grade must have their location identified by a warning ribbon placed in the trench at least _____ above the underground installation.

    (a) 6 in.   (b) 12 in.   (c) 18 in.   (d) none of these

    Answer: _____   Section: _____._____

16. Service raceways threaded into metal service equipment such as bosses (hubs) are considered to be effectively _____ to the service metal enclosure.

    (a) attached   (b) bonded   (c) grounded   (d) none of these

    Answer: _____   Section: _____._____

17. Short sections of metal enclosures or raceways used to provide support or protection of _____ from physical damage are not required to be grounded.

    (a) conduit   (b) 600V feeders   (c) cable assemblies   (d) none of these

    Answer: _____   Section: _____._____

18. Short sections of raceways used for _____ are not required to be installed complete between outlet, junction, or splicing points.

    (a) meter to service enclosure connection   (b) protection of cables from physical damage
    (c) nipples   (d) separately derived systems

    Answer: _____   Section: _____._____

19. Signaling, alarm, remote-control, and local loudspeaker communications systems are not required to comply with Article 503 when installed in Class III, Division 1 and 2 locations.

    (a) True   (b) False

    Answer: _____   Section: _____._____

20. Signs and outline lighting systems must be installed so that adjacent combustible materials are not subjected to temperatures in excess of _____.

    (a) 90°C   (b) 60°C   (c) 75°C   (d) 40°C

    Answer: _____   Section: _____._____

21. Signs or outline lighting systems operated by electronic or electromechanical controllers located external to the sign or outline lighting system are permitted to have a disconnecting means that disconnects all ungrounded supply conductors located _____when capable of being locked in the open position.

    (a) within sight of the controller   (b) in the same enclosure with the controller
    (c) a or b   (d) none of these

    Answer: _____   Section: _____._____

22. Since Class 3 control circuits permit higher allowable levels of voltage and current than do Class 2 control circuits, additional _____ are specified to provide protection against the electric shock hazard that could be encountered.

    (a) circuits   (b) safeguards   (c) conditions   (d) requirements

    Answer: _____   Section: _____._____

23. Single conductors as specified in Table 310.13 are only permitted when installed as part of a recognized wiring method of Chapter _____ of the *NEC*.

    (a) 4   (b) 3   (c) 2   (d) 9

    Answer: _____   Section: _____._____

24. Single-pole breakers utilizing approved handle ties cannot be used for the required disconnecting means for gasoline dispensing equipment.

    (a) True   (b) False

    Answer: _____   Section: _____._____

25. Snap switches installed in recessed boxes must have the _____ seated against the finished wall surface.

(a) mounting yoke   (b) body   (c) toggle   (d) all of these

Answer: _____   Section: _____._____

26. Snap switches must not be grouped or ganged in enclosures unless they can be arranged so that the voltage between adjacent devices does not exceed _____, or unless they are installed in enclosures equipped with permanently installed barriers between adjacent devices.

(a) 100V   (b) 200V   (c) 300V   (d) 400V

Answer: _____   Section: _____._____

27. Splices and taps are permitted within a nonmetallic wireway provided they are accessible. The conductors, including splices and taps, must not fill the wireway to more than _____ percent of its area at that point.

(a) 25   (b) 80   (c) 125   (d) 75

Answer: _____   Section: _____._____

28. Supplementary overcurrent devices used in luminaires or appliances are not required to be readily accessible.

(a) True   (b) False

Answer: _____   Section: _____._____

29. Surface metal raceways and their fittings must be so designed that the sections can be _____.

(a) electrically coupled together   (b) mechanically coupled together
(c) installed without subjecting the wires to abrasion   (d) all of these

Answer: _____   Section: _____._____

30. Surface metal raceways must be secured and supported at intervals _____.

(a) in accordance with the manufacturer's installation instructions
(b) appropriate for the building design
(c) not exceeding 8 ft
(d) not exceeding 4 ft

Answer: _____   Section: _____._____

31. Surface metal raceways must not be used _____.

(a) where subject to severe physical damage   (b) where subject to corrosive vapors
(c) in hoistways   (d) all of these

Answer: _____   Section: _____._____

32. Surface mounted enclosures (boxes) must be _____ the building surface.

(a) rigidly and securely fastened to
(b) supported by cables that protrude from
(c) supported by cable entries from the top and allowed to rest against
(d) none of these

Answer: _____   Section: _____._____

33. Surface-mounted fluorescent luminaires in clothes closets can be installed on the wall above the door, or on the ceiling, provided there is a minimum clearance of _____ between the luminaire and the nearest point of a storage space.

    (a) 3 in.   (b) 6 in.   (c) 9 in.   (d) 12 in.

    Answer: _____   Section: _____._____

34. Switch or circuit-breaker enclosures can be used as a junction box or raceway for conductors feeding through splices or taps, when installed in accordance with 312.8.

    (a) True   (b) False

    Answer: _____   Section: _____._____

35. Switchboards, panelboards, industrial control panels, meter socket enclosures, and motor control centers that are in other than dwelling occupancies and are likely to require examination, adjustment, servicing, or maintenance while _____ must be field marked to warn qualified persons of potential electric arc flash hazards.

    (a) being installed   (b) energized   (c) de-energized   (d) in fault condition

    Answer: _____   Section: _____._____

36. Switches must be located at least _____, measured horizontally, from the inside walls of an indoor spa or hot tub.

    (a) 4.7 ft   (b) 5 ft   (c) 7 ft 6 in.   (d) 12 ft

    Answer: _____   Section: _____._____

37. Switching devices must be at least 5 ft horizontally from the inside walls of a pool unless the switch is listed as being acceptable for use within 5 ft. An example of a switch that meets this requirement would be a pneumatic switch listed for this purpose.

    (a) True   (b) False

    Answer: _____   Section: _____._____

38. Table 430.91 provides the basis for selecting enclosures for use in specific locations other than _____ .

    (a) agricultural buildings   (b) hazardous locations   (c) recreational vehicle parks   (d) assembly occupancies

    Answer: _____   Section: _____._____

39. Temporary electrical power and lighting installations are permitted for a period not to exceed 90 days for _____ decorative lighting and similar purposes.

    (a) Christmas   (b) New Year's   (c) July 4th   (d) holiday

    Answer: _____   Section: _____._____

40. The _____ of a circuit must be so selected and coordinated as to permit the circuit protective devices to clear a fault without extensive damage to the electrical components of the circuit.

    (a) overcurrent protective devices   (b) total circuit impedance
    (c) component short-circuit current ratings (d) all of these

    Answer: _____   Section: _____._____

41. The _____ of alcohol-based windshield washer fluid does not cause the areas used for service and repair operations in connection with self-propelled vehicles to be classified as hazardous.

    (a) storage

    (b) handling

    (c) dispensing into motor vehicles

    (d) any of these

    Answer: _____ Section: _____._____

42. The _____ pool bonding conductor must be connected to the equipotential bonding grid either by exothermic welding or by pressure connectors that are labeled as being suitable for the purpose.

    (a) 8 AWG   (b) insulated or bare   (c) copper   (d) all of these

    Answer: _____ Section: _____._____

43. The alternate power source (generator, UPS, etc.) of an emergency system can supply emergency, legally required standby, and optional standby system loads where automatic selective load pickup and load shedding is provided as needed to ensure adequate power for all of these purposes equally.

    (a) True   (b) False

    Answer: _____ Section: _____._____

44. The ampacity adjustment factors of Table 310.15(B)(2)(a) do not apply to AC or MC cable without an overall outer jacket, if which of the following conditions are met?

    (a) Each cable has not more than three current-carrying conductors.
    (b) The conductors are 12 AWG copper.
    (c) No more than 20 current-carrying conductors are bundled or stacked.
    (d) all of these

    Answer: _____ Section: _____._____

45. The ampacity for the supply conductors for a resistance welder with a duty cycle of 15 percent and a primary current of 21A is _____.

    (a) 9.45A   (b) 8.19A   (c) 6.72A   (d) 5.67A

    Answer: _____ Section: _____._____

46. The ampacity of a conductor can be different along the length of the conductor. The higher ampacity is permitted to be used beyond the point of transition for a distance no more than _____ ft or no more than _____ percent of the circuit length figured at the higher ampacity, whichever is less.

    (a) 10, 20   (b) 20, 10   (c) 10, 10   (d) 15, 15

    Answer: _____ Section: _____._____

47. The ampacity of the supply conductors to an individual electric welder must not be less than the effective current value on the rating plate.

    (a) True   (b) False.

    Answer: _____ Section: _____._____

48. The antenna mast and antenna discharge unit grounding conductor must be guarded from physical damage.

    (a) True   (b) False

    Answer: _____   Section: _____._____

49. The bonding jumper used to bond the metal water piping system to the service must be sized in accordance with _____.

    (a) Table 250.66   (b) Table 250.122   (c) Table 310.16   (d) Table 310.15(B)(6)

    Answer: _____   Section: _____._____

50. The *Code* covers underground installations in mines and self-propelled mobile surface mining machinery and its attendant electrical trailing cable.

    (a) True   (b) False

    Answer: _____   Section: _____._____

(• Indicates that 75% or fewer exam takers get the question correct)

Article 410 Luminaires, Lampholders, and Lamps (continue)

1. Switched lampholders must be of such construction that the switching mechanism interrupts the electrical connection to the _____.

    (a) lampholder   (b) center contact   (c) branch circuit   (d) screw shell only

    Answer: _____   Section: _____._____

2. A recessed incandescent luminaire (fixture) must be installed so that adjacent combustible material will not be subjected to temperatures in excess of _____°C.

    (a) 75   (b) 90   (c) 125   (d) 150

    Answer: _____   Section: _____._____

3. A recessed luminaire (fixture) that is not identified for contact with insulation must have all recessed parts spaced not less than _____ from combustible materials, except for points of support and the trim finishing off the opening in the ceiling or wall.

    (a) 1/4 in.   (b) 1/2 in.   (c) 1 1/4 in.   (d) 6 in.

    Answer: _____   Section: _____._____

4. Thermal insulation must not be installed above a recessed luminaire or within _____ of the recessed luminaire's enclosure, wiring compartment, or ballast unless it is a Type IC luminaire.

    (a) 6 in.   (b) 12 in.   (c) 3 in.   (d) 1/2 in.

    Answer: _____   Section: _____._____

5. The raceway or cable for tap conductors to recessed luminaires must have a minimum length of _____

    (a) 6 in.   (b) 12 in.   (c) 18 in.   (d) 24 in.

    Answer: _____   Section: _____._____

6. Ballasts for fluorescent or electric-discharge lighting installed indoors must have _____ protection.

    (a) AFCI   (b) supplementary   (c) integral thermal   (d) none of these

    Answer: _____   Section: _____._____

7. In indoor locations, other than dwellings and associated accessory structures, fluorescent luminaires that utilize double-ended lamps and contain ballast(s) that can be serviced or re-ballasted in place must have a disconnecting means, to disconnect simultaneously all conductors of the ballast, including the _____ conductor if any. The disconnecting means must be accessible to qualified persons. This requirement will become effective January 1, 2008

   (a) high leg   (b) grounded neutral   (c) equipment ground   (d) b and c

   Answer: _____   Section: _____._____

8. Auxiliary equipment not installed as part of a luminaire (lighting fixture) assembly must be enclosed in accessible, permanently installed _____.

   (a) nonmetallic cabinets   (b) enclosures   (c) metal cabinets   (d) all of these

   Answer: _____   Section: _____._____

9. Electric-discharge luminaires having an open-circuit voltage exceeding _____ must not be installed in or on dwelling occupancies.

   (a) 120V   (b) 250V   (c) 600V   (d) 1,000V

   Answer: _____   Section: _____._____

10. Lighting track is a manufactured assembly designed to support and _____ luminaires that are capable of being readily repositioned on the track.

    (a) connect   (b) protect   (c) energize   (d) all of these

    Answer: _____   Section: _____._____

11. Track lighting must not be installed _____.

    (a) where subject to physical damage   (b) in wet or damp locations
    (c) a and b   (d) none of these

    Answer: _____   Section: _____._____

12. Lighting track must not be installed within the zone measured 3 ft horizontally and _____ vertically from the top of the bathtub rim.

    (a) 2 ft   (b) 3 ft   (c) 4 ft   (d) 8 ft

    Answer: _____   Section: _____._____

13. Lighting track must be securely mounted so each fastening will be suitable to support the maximum weight of _____.

    (a) 35 lbs   (b) 50 lbs
    (c) luminaires that can be installed   (d) none of these

    Answer: _____   Section: _____._____

14. Decorative lighting and similar accessories used for holiday lighting and similar purposes in accordance with 590.3(B) must be _____.

    (a) approved   (b) listed   (c) arc-fault protected   (d) all of these

    Answer: _____   Section: _____._____

Article 411 Lighting Systems Operating at 30V or Less

This article covers lighting systems and their associated components operating at 30V or less.

15. Lighting systems operating at 30V or less are allowed to be concealed or extended through a building wall without regard to the wiring method used.

    (a) True   (b) False

    Answer: _____   Section: _____._____

16. Lighting systems operating at 30V or less must not be installed within 10 ft of pools, spas, fountains, or similar locations except as permitted by Article 680.

    (a) True   (b) False

    Answer: _____   Section: _____._____

Article 422 Appliances

Article 422 covers electric appliances used in any occupancy.

17. Individual circuits for nonmotor-operated appliances that are continuously loaded must have the branch-circuit rating sized no less than _____ percent of the appliance marked ampere rating.

    (a) 150   (b) 100   (c) 125   (d) 80

    Answer: _____   Section: _____._____

18. Infrared lamps for industrial heating appliances must have overcurrent protection not exceeding _____.

    (a) 30A   (b) 40A   (c) 50A   (d) 60A

    Answer: _____   Section: _____._____

19. Central heating equipment, other than fixed electric space-heating equipment, must be supplied by a(n) _____ branch circuit.

    (a) multiwire   (b) individual
    (c) multipurpose   (d) small-appliance branch circuit

    Answer: _____   Section: _____._____

20. A waste disposal can be cord-and-plug connected, but the cord must not be less than 18 in. or more than _____ in length and must be protected from physical damage.

    (a) 30 in.   (b) 36 in.   (c) 42 in.   (d) 48 in.

    Answer: _____   Section: _____._____

21. Range hoods are permitted to be cord-and-plug connected with a flexible cord identified as suitable for use on range hoods in the manufacturer's instructions when necessary conditions are met, including: _____.

    (a) The cord must not be less than 18 in. in length
    (b) The cord must be no longer than 36 in. in length
    (c) The receptacle must be supplied by an individual branch circuit
    (d) all of these

    Answer: _____   Section: _____._____

22. The maximum allowable hp rating of a permanently connected appliance, when the branch-circuit overcurrent protection device is used as the appliance disconnecting means, is _____ or 300 VA.

    (a) 1/8 hp   (b) 1/4 hp   (c) 1/2 hp   (d) 3/4 hp

    Answer: _____   Section: _____._____

23. For cord-and-plug connected appliances, an accessible separable connector or _____ plug and receptacle is permitted to serve as the disconnecting means.

    (a) a labeled   (b) an accessible   (c) a metal enclosed   (d) none of these

    Answer: _____   Section: _____._____

24. Appliances that have a unit switch with a marked _____ setting that disconnects all the ungrounded conductors is permitted to serve as the disconnecting means for the appliance, where other means of disconnection are also provided in accordance with 422.34.

    (a) "on"   (b) "off"   (c) "on/off"   (d) all of these

    Answer: _____   Section: _____._____

25. Electrically heated smoothing irons must be equipped with an identified _____ means.

    (a) disconnecting   (b) temperature-limiting   (c) current-limiting   (d) none of these

    Answer: _____   Section: _____._____

26. Cord-and-plug connected vending machines manufactured or remanufactured on or after January 1, 2005 must include a ground-fault circuit interrupter as an integral part of the attachment plug or in the power-supply cord within 12 in. of the attachment plug. Cord-and-plug connected vending machines not incorporating integral GFCI protection must _____.

    (a) be re-manufactured   (b) be disabled
    (c) be connected to a GFCI-protected outlet   (d) be connected to an AFCI-protected circuit

    Answer: _____   Section: _____._____

Article 424 Fixed Electric Space-Heating Equipment

This article covers fixed electrical equipment used for space heating. For the purpose of this article, heating equipment includes heating cable, unit heaters, boilers, central systems, and other fixed electric space-heating equipment. This article does not apply to process heating and room air conditioning.

27. Fixed electric space-heating equipment is considered a(n) _____ load.

    (a) noncontinuous   (b) intermittent   (c) continuous   (d) none of these

    Answer: _____   Section: _____._____

28. Fixed electric space-heating equipment requiring supply conductors with insulation rated over _____ must be clearly and permanently marked.

    (a) 75°C   (b) 60°C   (c) 90°C   (d) all of these

    Answer: _____   Section: _____._____

29. Means must be provided to disconnect the _____ of all fixed electric space-heating equipment from all ungrounded conductors.

    (a) heater
    (b) motor controller(s)
    (c) supplementary overcurrent protective device(s)
    (d) all of these

    Answer: _____   Section: _____._____

30. A unit switch with a marked "off" position that is part of a fixed space heater, and disconnects all ungrounded conductors, is permitted as the disconnecting means required by Article 424 for one-family dwellings.

    (a) True
    (b) False

    Answer: _____   Section: _____._____

31. •Electric space-heating appliances employing resistance-type heating elements rated more than _____ must have the heating elements subdivided.

    (a) 60A
    (b) 50A
    (c) 48A
    (d) 35A

    Answer: _____   Section: _____._____

32. On space-heating cables, blue leads indicate a cable rated for use on a circuit voltage of _____, nominal.

    (a) 120V
    (b) 240V
    (c) 208V
    (d) 277V

    Answer: _____   Section: _____._____

33. Electric space-heating cables must not extend beyond the room or area in which they _____.

    (a) provide heat
    (b) originate
    (c) terminate
    (d) are connected

    Answer: _____   Section: _____._____

34. The minimum clearance between an electric space-heating cable and an outlet box used for surface luminaires must not be less than _____

    (a) 8 in.
    (b) 14 in.
    (c) 18 in.
    (d) 6 in.

    Answer: _____   Section: _____._____

35. Duct heater controller equipment must have a disconnecting means installed within _____ the controller.

    (a) 25 ft of
    (b) sight from
    (c) the side of
    (d) none of these

    Answer: _____   Section: _____._____

36. A boiler employing resistance-type immersion heating elements contained in an ASME-rated and stamped vessel, and rated at more than 120A, must have the heating elements subdivided into loads not exceeding _____.

    (a) 70A
    (b) 100A
    (c) 120A
    (d) 150A

    Answer: _____   Section: _____._____

37. Electrode-type boilers, which are designed so that in normal operation there is no change in state of the heat transfer medium, must be equipped with a temperature-sensitive _____.

    (a) protective device
    (b) limiting means
    (c) shut-off device
    (d) all of these

    Answer: _____   Section: _____._____

Article 426 Fixed Outdoor Electric Deicing and Snow-Melting Equipment

The requirements of this article shall apply to electrically energized heating systems and the installation of these systems.

38. Examples of snow-melting resistance heaters include _____.

(a) tubular heaters and strip heaters
(b) heating panels
(c) heating cables or heating tape
(d) all of these

Answer: _____   Section: _____._____

39. Embedded deicing and snow-melting cables, units, and panels must not be installed where they bridge _____, unless provision is made for expansion and contraction.

(a) roads   (b) water spans   (c) runways   (d) expansion joints

Answer: _____   Section: _____._____

40. An impedance heating system that is operating at a(n) _____ greater than 30, but not more than 80, must be grounded at a designated point(s).

(a) voltage   (b) amperage   (c) wattage   (d) temperature

Answer: _____   Section: _____._____

Article 427 Fixed Electric Heating Equipment for Pipelines and Vessels

The requirements of this article shall apply to electrically energized heating systems and the installation of these systems used with pipelines or vessels or both.

41. Pipeline resistance heating elements include heating _____.

(a) blankets   (b) tape   (c) cables   (d) all of these

Answer: _____   Section: _____._____

42. External surfaces of pipeline and vessel heating equipment that operates at temperatures exceeding _____ must be physically guarded, isolated, or thermally insulated to protect against contact by personnel in the area.

(a) 110°F   (b) 120°F   (c) 130°F   (d) 140°F

Answer: _____   Section: _____._____

43. For a skin-effect heating installation complying with Article 427, the provisions of 300.20 must apply to the installation of a single conductor in a ferromagnetic envelope (metal enclosure).

(a) True   (b) False

Answer: _____   Section: _____._____

Article 430 Motors, Motor Circuits, and Controllers

This article contains the specific requirements for conductor sizing, overcurrent protection, control circuit conductors, motor controllers, and disconnecting means. The installation requirements for motor control centers are covered in Article 430, Part VIII.

44.   The motor _____ current as listed in Tables 430.247 through 430.250 must be used for sizing motor circuit conductors and short-circuit, ground-fault protection devices.

   (a) nameplate   (b) full-load   (c) power factor   (d) service factor

   Answer: _____   Section: _____._____

45.   Motor controllers and terminals of control circuit devices are required to be connected with copper conductors unless identified for use with a different type of conductor.

   (a) True   (b) False

   Answer: _____   Section: _____._____

46.   Where motors are provided with terminal housings, the housings must be of _____ and of substantial construction.

   (a) steel   (b) iron   (c) metal   (d) copper

   Answer: _____   Section: _____._____

47.   Motors must be located so that adequate _____ is provided and so that maintenance, such as lubrication of bearings and replacing of brushes, can be readily accomplished.

   (a) space   (b) ventilation   (c) protection   (d) all of these

   Answer: _____   Section: _____._____

48.   In determining the highest-rated motor for purposes of 430.24, the highest-rated motor must be based on the rated full-load current as selected _____.

   (a) from the motor nameplate   (b) from tables 430.247, 430.248, 430.249, and 430.250
   (c) from taking the horsepower times 746 watts   (d) using the largest horsepower motor

   Answer: _____   Section: _____._____

49.   Conductors supplying several motors must not be sized smaller than _____ of the full-load current rating of the highest rated motor plus the sum of the full-load current ratings of all other motors in the group as determined by 430.6(A), plus the ampacity for any other loads.

   (a) 80 percent   (b) 100 percent   (c) 125 percent   (d) 150 percent

   Answer: _____   Section: _____._____

50.   Overload devices are intended to protect motors, motor control apparatus, and motor branch-circuit conductors against _____.

   (a) excessive heating due to motor overloads   (b) excessive heating due to failure to start
   (c) short circuits and ground faults   (d) a and b

   Answer: _____   Section: _____._____

51. An overload device used to protect continuous-duty motors (rated more than 1 hp) must be selected to trip, or be rated, at no more than _____ percent of the motor nameplate full-load current rating for motors with a marked service factor of 1.15 or greater.

    (a) 110   (b) 115   (c) 120   (d) 125

    Answer: _____ Section: _____._____

52. When an overload relay, selected in accordance with 430.32(A)(1) and (B)(1), is not sufficient to start the motor or carry the load, higher-size sensing elements or incremental settings are permitted to be used as long as the trip current does not exceed _____ percent of the motor full-load current rating when the motor is marked with a service factor of 1.12.

    (a) 100   (b) 110   (c) 120   (d) 130

    Answer: _____ Section: _____._____

53. Motor overload protection must not be shunted or cut out during the starting period if the motor is _____.

    (a) not automatically started   (b) automatically started   (c) manually started   (d) none of these

    Answer: _____ Section: _____._____

54. The minimum number of overload unit(s) required for a 3-phase ac motor is/are _____.

    (a) one   (b) two   (c) three   (d) any of these

    Answer: _____ Section: _____._____

55. A motor _____ device that can restart a motor automatically after overload tripping must not be installed if automatic restarting of the motor can result in injury to persons.

    (a) short-circuit   (b) ground-fault   (c) overcurrent   (d) overload

    Answer: _____ Section: _____._____

56. The motor branch-circuit short-circuit and ground-fault protective device must be capable of carrying the _____ current of the motor.

    (a) varying   (b) starting   (c) running   (d) continuous

    Answer: _____ Section: _____._____

57. Where the motor short-circuit and ground-fault protection devices determined by Table 430.52 do not correspond to the standard sizes or ratings, a higher size may be used that does not exceed the next higher standard ampere rating.

    (a) True   (b) False

    Answer: _____ Section: _____._____

58. •A feeder must have a protective device with a rating or setting _____ branch-circuit short-circuit and ground-fault protective device for any motor in the group, plus the sum of the full-load currents of the other motors of the group.

    (a) not greater than the largest rating or setting of the   (b) 125 percent of the largest rating of any
    (c) equal to the largest rating of any   (d) none of these

    Answer: _____ Section: _____._____

59. Overcurrent protection for motor control circuits must not exceed 400 percent if the conductor does not extend beyond the motor control equipment enclosure.

(a) True   (b) False

Answer: _____   Section: _____._____

60. Motor control circuit transformers, with a primary current rating of less than 2A, can have the primary protection device set at no more than _____ percent of the rated primary current rating.

(a) 150   (b) 200   (c) 400   (d) 500

Answer: _____   Section: _____._____

61. If the control circuit transformer is located in the controller enclosure, the transformer must be connected to the _____ side of the control circuit disconnect.

(a) line   (b) load   (c) adjacent   (d) none of these

Answer: _____   Section: _____._____

62. The motor controller must have horsepower ratings at the application voltage not _____ the horsepower rating of the motor.

(a) lower than   (b) higher than   (c) equal to   (d) none of these

Answer: _____   Section: _____._____

63. For stationary motors of 2 horsepower or less and 300V or less on ac circuits, the controller is permitted to be an ac-rated general use snap switch where the motor full-load current rating is not more than _____ percent of the rating of the switch.

(a) 80   (b) 50   (c) 75   (d) 125

Answer: _____   Section: _____._____

64. Each motor must be provided with an individual controller.

(a) True   (b) False

Answer: _____   Section: _____._____

65. A disconnecting means is required to disconnect the _____ from all ungrounded supply conductors.

(a) motor   (b) motor or controller   (c) controller   (d) motor and controller

Answer: _____   Section: _____._____

66. The motor disconnecting means is not required to be in sight from the motor and the driven machinery location, provided _____.

(a) the controller disconnecting means is capable of being individually locked in the open position
(b) the provisions for locking are permanently installed on, or at, the switch or circuit breaker used as the controller disconnecting means
(c) locating the motor disconnecting means within sight of the motor is impractical or introduces additional or increased hazards to people or property
(d) all of these

Answer: _____   Section: _____._____

67. The motor disconnecting means must _____ whether it is in the open (off) or closed (on) position.

(a) plainly indicate   (b) provide current   (c) be in the upper position   (d) none of these

Answer: _____   Section: _____._____

68. The motor disconnecting means can be a _____.

(a) circuit breaker   (b) motor-circuit switch rated in horsepower
(c) molded-case switch   (d) any of these

Answer: _____   Section: _____._____

69. A branch-circuit overcurrent protection device such as a plug fuse may serve as the disconnecting means for a stationary motor of 1/8 hp or less.

(a) True   (b) False

Answer: _____   Section: _____._____

70. The disconnecting means for a 50 hp, 460V, 3-phase induction motor (FLC 65A) must have an ampere rating of not less than _____.

(a) 126   (b) 75   (c) 91   (d) 63

Answer: _____   Section: _____._____

71. An oil switch is permitted to be used as both the controller and disconnecting means on a circuit whose rating _____ or 100A.

(a) does not exceed 300V   (b) exceeds 600V   (c) does not exceed 600V   (d) none of these

Answer: _____   Section: _____._____

Article 440 Air-Conditioning and Refrigerating Equipment

This article applies to electrically driven air-conditioning and refrigeration equipment with a motorized hermetic refrigerant compressor. The requirements in this article are in addition to, or amend, the requirements in Article 430 and other articles.

72. Article 440 applies to electric motor-driven air-conditioning and refrigerating equipment that has a hermetic refrigerant motor-compressor.

(a) True   (b) False

Answer: _____   Section: _____._____

73. Equipment such as _____ are considered appliances, and the provisions of Article 422 are applicable in addition to Article 440.

(a) room air conditioners   (b) household refrigerators and freezers
(c) drinking water coolers and beverage dispensers (d) all of these

Answer: _____   Section: _____._____

74. For cord-connected equipment such as _____, a separable connector or an attachment plug and receptacle is permitted to serve as the disconnecting means.

(a) room air conditioners   (b) household refrigerators and freezers
(c) drinking water coolers and beverage dispensers (d) all of these

Answer: _____   Section: _____._____

75. Disconnecting means must be located within sight from and readily accessible from the air-conditioning or refrigerating equipment. The disconnecting means is permitted to be installed _____ the air-conditioning or refrigerating equipment, but not on panels that are designed to allow access to the air-conditioning or refrigeration equipment.

    (a) on   (b) within   (c) a or b   (d) none of these

    Answer: _____   Section: _____._____

76. The rating of the branch-circuit short-circuit and ground-fault protection device for an individual motor-compressor must not exceed _____ percent of the rated-load current or branch-circuit selection current, whichever is greater, if the protection device will carry the starting current of the motor.

    (a) 100   (b) 125   (c) 175   (d) none of these

    Answer: _____   Section: _____._____

77. Conductors supplying more than one motor-compressor must have an ampacity not less than the sum of the rated load or branch-circuit current ratings, whichever is larger, of all the motor- compressors plus the full-load currents of any other motors, plus _____ percent of the highest motor or motor compressor rating in the group.

    (a) 80   (b) 50   (c) 25   (d) 100

    Answer: _____   Section: _____._____

78. The rating of the attachment plug and receptacle must not exceed _____ at 250V for a cord-and-plug connected air conditioner.

    (a) 15A   (b) 20A   (c) 30A   (d) 40A

    Answer: _____   Section: _____._____

79. An attachment plug and receptacle is permitted to serve as the disconnecting means for a 1-phase room air conditioner rated 250V or less if _____.

    (a) manual controls on the air conditioner are readily accessible within 6 ft of the floor
    (b) an approved operable switch is installed in a readily-accessible location within sight of the air conditioner
    (c) a pushbutton kill switch is installed at the entrance to the room
    (d) a or c

    Answer: _____   Section: _____._____

Article 445 Generators

This article contains the electrical installation requirements for generators, such as where they can be installed, nameplate markings, conductor ampacity, and disconnecting means.

80. Each generator must be provided with a _____ listing the manufacturer's name, the rated frequency, power factor, number of phases (if of alternating current), and the rating in kilowatts or kilovolt-amperes.

    (a) list   (b) faceplate   (c) nameplate   (d) sticker

    Answer: _____   Section: _____._____

81. The ampacity of ungrounded (phase) conductors from the generator terminals to the first overcurrent protection devices must not be less than _____ percent of the nameplate rating of the generator.

    (a) 75   (b) 115   (c) 125   (d) 140

    Answer: _____   Section: _____._____

Article 450 Transformers and Transformer Vaults

This article covers the installation of all transformers.

82. According to Article 450, a transformer rated 600V, nominal, or less, and whose primary current rating is 9A or more, is protected against overcurrent only when _____.

    (a) an individual overcurrent device on the primary side is set at not more than 125 percent of the rated primary current of the transformer.
    (b) a secondary overcurrent device is set at not more than 125 percent of the rated secondary current of the transformer, and a primary overcurrent device is set at not more than 250 percent of the rated primary current of the transformer.
    (c) a or b
    (d) none of these

    Answer: _____   Section: _____._____

83. What size "primary only" overcurrent protection is required for a 600 volt, 45 kVA transformer that has a primary current rating of 54A?

    (a) 70   (b) 80   (c) 90   (d) 100

    Answer: _____   Section: _____._____

84. A secondary tie of a transformer is a circuit operating at _____ nominal, or less, between phases that connects two power sources or power-supply points.

    (a) 600V   (b) 1,000V   (c) 12,000V   (d) 35,000V

    Answer: _____   Section: _____._____

85. Each transformer must be provided with a nameplate listing the name of the manufacturer, rated kilovolt-amperes, frequency, primary and secondary voltage, impedance of transformers _____ and larger, required clearances for transformers with ventilating openings, and the amount and kind of insulating liquid where used.

    (a) 112 kVA   (b) 25 kVA   (c) 33 kVA   (d) 50 kVA

    Answer: _____   Section: _____._____

86. Indoor transformers of greater than _____ rating must be installed in a transformer room of fire-resistant construction.

    (a) 35,000 kVA   (b) 87 1/2 kVA   (c) 112 1/2 kVA   (d) 75 kVA

    Answer: _____   Section: _____._____

87. Indoor transformers rated over 35,000V, and insulated with nonflammable dielectric fluid, must be installed in a vault furnished with a _____.

    (a) liquid confinement area
    (b) pressure-relief vent
    (c) means for absorbing or venting any gases generated by arcing
    (d) all of these

    Answer: _____   Section: _____._____

88. The walls and roofs of transformer vaults must be constructed of materials that have adequate structural strength for the conditions with a minimum fire resistance of _____ hour(s).

    (a) 1   (b) 2   (c) 3   (d) 4

    Answer: _____   Section: _____._____

89. Personnel doors for transformer vaults must _____ and be equipped with panic bars, pressure plates, or other devices that are normally latched but open under simple pressure.

    (a) be clearly identified   (b) swing out   (c) a and b   (d) a or b

    Answer: _____   Section: _____._____

90. For phase converters serving variable loads, the ampacity of the 1-phase supply conductors must not be less than _____ percent of the 1-phase input full-load amperes listed on the phase converter nameplate.

    (a) 75   (b) 100   (c) 125   (d) 150

    Answer: _____   Section: _____._____

91. The phase converter disconnecting means must be _____ and located in sight from the phase converter.

    (a) protected from physical damage   (b) readily accessible
    (c) easily visible   (d) clearly identified

    Answer: _____   Section: _____._____

Article 460 Capacitors

This article covers the installation of capacitors, including those in hazardous (classified) locations as modified by Articles 501 through 503.

92. Capacitors must be _____ so that persons cannot come into accidental contact or bring conducting materials into accidental contact with exposed energized parts, terminals, or buses associated with them.

    (a) enclosed   (b) located   (c) guarded   (d) any of these

    Answer: _____   Section: _____._____

93. The ampacity of capacitor circuit conductors must not be less than _____ percent of the rated current of the capacitor.

    (a) 100   (b) 115   (c) 125   (d) 135

    Answer: _____   Section: _____._____

94. A separate overcurrent device is not required for a capacitor connected on the load side of a motor overload protective device.

    (a) True   (b) False

    Answer: _____   Section: _____._____

95. A separate disconnecting means is required where a capacitor is connected on the load side of a motor controller

    (a) True   (b) False

    Answer: _____   Section: _____._____

96. Where a motor installation includes a capacitor connected on the load side of the motor overload device, the effect of a capacitor must be disregarded in determining the motor circuit conductor size in accordance with 430.22.

(a) True   (b) False

Answer: _____   Section: _____._____

Article 470 Resistors and Reactors

This article covers the installation of separate resistors and reactors on electric circuits.

97. For installations of resistors and reactors, a thermal barrier is required if the space between them and any combustible material is less than _____

(a) 2 in.   (b) 3 in.   (c) 6 in.   (d) 12 in.

Answer: _____   Section: _____._____

Article 480 Storage Batteries

The provisions of this article shall apply to all stationary installations of storage batteries.

98. Nominal Battery Voltage: The voltage computed on the basis of _____ per cell for the lead-acid type and _____ per cell for the alkali type.

(a) 6V, 12V   (b) 12V, 24V   (c) 2V, 1.2V   (d) 1.2V, 2V

Answer: _____   Section: _____._____

99. Provisions must be made for sufficient diffusion and ventilation of the gases from the storage battery to prevent the accumulation of a(n) _____ mixture.

(a) corrosive   (b) explosive   (c) toxic   (d) all of these

Answer: _____   Section: _____._____

Chapter 5 Special Occupancies

Article 500 Hazardous (Classified) Locations

A hazardous (classified) location is an area where the possibility of fire or explosion exists because of the presence of flammable gases or vapors, combustible dusts, or ignitible fibers or flyings. The three components necessary to create a fire or explosion are fuel, oxygen, and a source of ignition.

100. Portable battery-operated devices such as cordless drills, cell phones, etc., must be listed for use in a hazardous (classified) location and the equipment must comply with the requirements of Chapter 5. This is because battery-operated devices can produce enough energy in a hazardous (classified) location to ignite a fire or cause an explosion.

(a) True   (b) False

Answer: _____   Section: _____._____

(• Indicates that 75% or fewer exam takers get the question correct)

1. A 1,000W incandescent lamp requires a _____ base.

   (a) mogul   (b) standard   (c) medium   (d) copper

   Answer: _____   Section: _____._____

2. •A _____ must be located in sight from the motor location and the driven machinery location.

   (a) controller   (b) protection device   (c) disconnecting means   (d) all of these

   Answer: _____   Section: _____._____

3. •Exposed live parts of motors and controllers operating at _____ or more between terminals must be guarded against accidental contact by enclosure or by location.

   (a) 24V   (b) 50V   (c) 150V   (d) 60V

   Answer: _____   Section: _____._____

4. A disconnecting means that serves a hermetic refrigerant motor-compressor must be selected on the basis of the nameplate rated-load current or branch-circuit selection current, whichever is greater. It must have an ampere rating of at least _____ percent of the nameplate rated-load current or branch-circuit selection current, whichever is greater.

   (a) 125   (b) 80   (c) 100   (d) 115

   Answer: _____   Section: _____._____

5. A heating panel is a complete assembly provided with a junction box or length of flexible conduit for connection to a(n) _____.

   (a) wiring system   (b) service   (c) branch circuit   (d) approved conductor

   Answer: _____   Section: _____._____

6. A hermetic motor-compressor controller must have a _____ current rating not less than the respective nameplate rating(s) on the compressor.

   (a) continuous-duty full-load   (b) locked-rotor   (c) a or b   (d) (a) and (b)?

   Answer: _____   Section: _____._____

7. A motor can be provided with combined overcurrent protection using a single protective device to provide branch-circuit _____ where the rating of the device provides the necessary overload protection specified in 430.32.

   (a) short-circuit protection   (b) ground-fault protection   (c) motor-overload protection   (d) all of these

   Answer: _____   Section: _____._____

8. A storage-type water heater having a capacity of _____ gallons or less is considered a continuous load.

   (a) 60   (b) 75   (c) 90   (d) 120

   Answer: _____   Section: _____._____

9. A Type IC recessed luminaire, which is identified for contact with insulation, is permitted to be in contact with _____.

   (a) combustible material at recessed parts
   (b) points of support
   (c) portions passing through or finishing off the opening in the building structure
   (d) all of these

   Answer: _____   Section: _____._____

10. All transformers and transformer vaults must be readily accessible to qualified personnel for inspection and maintenance, except that _____.

    (a) dry-type transformers 600V, nominal, or less, located in the open on walls, columns, or structures, are not required to be readily accessible
    (b) dry-type transformers rated not more than 50 kVA and not over 600V are permitted to be installed in hollow spaces of buildings not permanently closed in by structure as long as requirements are met concerning ventilation and separation from combustible materials
    (c) a or b
    (d) none of these

    Answer: _____   Section: _____._____

11. An infrared heating lamp used in a medium-base lampholder must be rated _____ or less.

    (a) 150W   (b) 300W   (c) 600W   (d) 750W

    Answer: _____   Section: _____._____

12. An overcurrent device must be provided in each ungrounded conductor for each capacitor bank. The rating or setting of the overcurrent device must be _____.

    (a) 20A   (b) as low as practicable
    (c) 400% of conductor ampacity   (d) 100A

    Answer: _____   Section: _____._____

13. Capacitors containing more than _____ of flammable liquid must be enclosed in vaults or outdoor fenced enclosures.

    (a) 10 gallons   (b) 5 gallons   (c) 3 gallons   (d) 11 gallons

    Answer: _____   Section: _____._____

14. Ceiling-suspended (paddle) fans must be supported independently of an outlet box or by outlet boxes or outlet box systems _____ for the application and installed in accordance with 314.27(D).

    (a) satisfactory   (b) approved   (c) strong enough   (d) identified

    Answer: _____   Section: _____._____

15. Each vented cell of a battery must be equipped with _____ that is/are designed to prevent destruction of the cell due to ignition of gases within the cell by an external spark or flame under normal operating conditions.

   (a) pressure relief   (b) a flame arrester   (c) fluid level indicators   (d) none of these

   Answer: _____   Section: _____._____

16. Electric space-heating cables must be furnished complete with factory-assembled nonheating leads that are at least _____ in length.

   (a) 6 in.   (b) 18 in.   (c) 3 ft   (d) 7 ft

   Answer: _____   Section: _____._____

17. Electric space-heating cables must not be installed over cabinets whose clearance from the ceiling is less than the minimum _____ dimension of the cabinet to the nearest cabinet edge that is open to the room or area.

   (a) horizontal   (b) vertical   (c) overall   (d) depth

   Answer: _____   Section: _____._____

18. Exposed elements of impedance heating systems must be physically guarded, isolated, or thermally insulated with a _____ jacket to protect against contact by personnel in the area.

   (a) corrosion-resistant   (b) waterproof   (c) weatherproof   (d) flame-retardant

   Answer: _____   Section: _____._____

19. Feeder tap conductors supplying motor circuits, with an ampacity of at least one-third that of the feeder, must not exceed _____ in length.

   (a) 10 ft   (b) 15 ft   (c) 20 ft   (d) 25 ft

   Answer: _____   Section: _____._____

20. Fixed electric heating equipment for pipelines and vessels is considered to be a(n) _____ load.

   (a) noncontinuous   (b) insignificant   (c) continuous   (d) proprietary

   Answer: _____   Section: _____._____

21. For cord-and-plug connected household electric ranges, an attachment plug and receptacle connection at the rear base of the range, if it is _____ is allowed to serve as the disconnecting means.

   (a) less than 40A   (b) a flush-mounted receptacle
   (c) GFCI-protected   (d) accessible by removal of a drawer

   Answer: _____   Section: _____._____

22. For general motor applications, the motor branch-circuit short-circuit and ground-fault protection device must be sized based on the _____ amperes.

   (a) motor nameplate   (b) NEMA standard   (c) NEC Table   (d) Factory Mutual

   Answer: _____   Section: _____._____

23. If a protective device rating is marked on an appliance, the branch-circuit overcurrent protection device rating must not be greater than _____ percent of the protective device rating marked on the appliance.

(a) 100   (b) 50   (c) 80   (d) 115

Answer: _____   Section: _____._____

24. If a(n) _____ shutdown is necessary to reduce hazards to persons, the overload sensing devices are permitted to be connected to a supervised alarm instead of causing immediate interruption of the motor circuit.

(a) emergency   (b) normal   (c) orderly   (d) none of these

Answer: _____   Section: _____._____

25. If the disconnect is not within sight of the fixed electric space heater which includes a motor rated over 1/8 hp (without supplementary overcurrent protection devices), it must be capable of being _____.

(a) locked   (b) locked in the closed position
(c) locked in the open position   (d) within sight

Answer: _____   Section: _____._____

26. Incandescent luminaires must be marked to indicate the maximum allowable _____ of lamps.

(a) voltage   (b) amperage   (c) rating   (d) wattage

Answer: _____   Section: _____._____

27. Lighting systems operating at 30V or less are allowed to be concealed or extended through a building wall using _____.

(a) any of the wiring methods specified in Chapter 3
(b) wiring supplied by a listed class 2 power source installed in accordance with 725.52
(c) both a and b
(d) metal raceways only

Answer: _____   Section: _____._____

28. Lighting track is a manufactured assembly and its length may not be altered by the addition or subtraction of sections of track.

(a) True   (b) False

Answer: _____   Section: _____._____

29. Lighting track must have 2 supports for a single section of _____ or shorter in length and each individual section of not more than 4 ft attached to it must have one additional support.

(a) 4 ft   (b) 6 ft   (c) 10 ft   (d) 2 ft

Answer: _____   Section: _____._____

30. Lighting track must not be installed less than _____ above the finished floor except where protected from physical damage or track operating at less than 30V RMS, open-circuit voltage.

(a) 4 ft   (b) 5 ft   (c) 5 1/2 ft   (d) 6 ft

Answer: _____   Section: _____._____

31. Motor control circuit conductors that extend beyond the motor control equipment enclosure are required to have short-circuit and ground-fault protection sized not greater than _____ percent of the conductor ampacity as listed in Table 430.72(B) for 60°C conductors.

    (a) 100   (b) 150   (c) 300   (d) 500

    Answer: _____   Section: _____._____

32. Open motors having commutators or collector rings must be located or protected so that sparks cannot reach adjacent combustible material. This must not prohibit the installation of these motors _____.

    (a) on wooden floors   (b) over combustible fiber
    (c) under combustible material   (d) none of these

    Answer: _____   Section: _____._____

33. Permanently-installed electric baseboard heaters equipped with factory-installed receptacle outlets are permitted to be used as the outlets required by 210.50(B).

    (a) True   (b) False

    Answer: _____   Section: _____._____

34. Resistors and reactors rated over 600V must be isolated by _____ to protect personnel from accidental contact with energized parts.

    (a) an enclosure   (b) elevation   (c) a or b   (d) a and b

    Answer: _____   Section: _____._____

35. Short-circuit and ground-fault protection for an individual motor compressor must not exceed _____ percent of the motor-compressor rated-load current or branch-circuit protection current, whichever is greater.

    (a) 80   (b) 125   (c) 175   (d) 250

    Answer: _____   Section: _____._____

36. Surface-mounted luminaires with a ballast must have a minimum clearance of _____ from combustible low-density cellulose fiberboard, unless the fixture is marked "Suitable for Surface Mounting on Combustible Low-Density Cellulose Fiberboard."

    (a) 1/2 in.   (b) 1 in.   (c) 1 1/2 in.   (d) 2 in.

    Answer: _____   Section: _____._____

37. The _____ current for a hermetic refrigerant motor-compressor is the current resulting when the motor-compressor is operated at the rated load, rated voltage, and rated frequency of the equipment it serves.

    (a) full-load current   (b) nameplate rating   (c) selection current   (d) rated-load current

    Answer: _____   Section: _____._____

38. The branch-circuit protective device is permitted to serve as the controller for a stationary motor rated at _____ or less that is normally left running and cannot be damaged by overload or failure to start.

    (a) 1/8 hp   (b) 1/4 hp   (c) 3/8 hp   (d) 1/2 hp

    Answer: _____   Section: _____._____

39. The controller is required to open all conductors to the motor.

    (a) True   (b) False

    Answer: _____   Section: _____._____

40. The disconnecting means for a torque motor must have an ampere rating of at least _____ percent of the motor nameplate current.

    (a) 100   (b) 115   (c) 125   (d) 175

    Answer: _____   Section: _____._____

41. The ultimate trip current of a thermally-protected motor with a full-load current not exceeding 9A must not exceed _____ percent of the motor full-load current as listed in Tables 430.248, 430.249, and 430.250.

    (a) 140   (b) 156   (c) 170   (d) none of these

    Answer: _____   Section: _____._____

42. Torque requirements for motor control circuit device terminals must be a minimum of _____ lbs-inch (unless otherwise identified) for screw-type pressure terminals used for 14 AWG and smaller copper conductors.

    (a) 7   (b) 9   (c) 10   (d) 15

    Answer: _____   Section: _____._____

43. Transformer vaults must be located where they can be ventilated to the outside air without using flues or ducts, wherever such an arrangement is _____.

    (a) permitted   (b) practicable   (c) required   (d) all of these

    Answer: _____   Section: _____._____

44. Unless two restrictive conditions exist, a generator must be equipped with one or more disconnecting means to disconnect the generator, its protective devices, and all control apparatus entirely from the circuits supplied by the generator.

    (a) True   (b) False

    Answer: _____   Section: _____._____

45. When fuses are used for motor overload protection, a fuse must be inserted in each ungrounded conductor and also in the grounded conductor if the supply system is _____ with one conductor grounded.

    (a) 2-wire, 3-phase dc   (b) 2-wire, 3-phase ac   (c) 3-wire, 3-phase dc   (d) 3-wire, 3-phase ac

    Answer: _____   Section: _____._____

46. When installing duct heaters, sufficient clearance must be maintained to permit replacement and adjustment of controls and heating elements.

    (a) True   (b) False

    Answer: _____   Section: _____._____

47. When supplying a room air conditioner rated 120V, the length of the flexible supply cord must not exceed _____

    (a) 4 ft   (b) 6 ft   (c) 8 ft   (d) 10 ft

    Answer: _____   Section: _____._____

48. Where a motor installation includes a capacitor connected on the load side of the motor overload device, the rating or setting of the motor overload device must be based on the improved power factor of the motor circuit.

    (a) True   (b) False

    Answer: _____   Section: _____._____

49. Where more than one motor disconnecting means is provided in the same motor branch circuit, only one of the disconnecting means is required to be readily accessible.

    (a) True   (b) False

    Answer: _____   Section: _____._____

50. Where practicable, transformer vaults containing more than _____ total kVA transformer capacity must be provided with a drain or other means that will carry off any accumulation of oil or water in the vault, unless local conditions make this impracticable.

    (a) 100   (b) 150   (c) 200   (d) 250

    Answer: _____   Section: _____._____

1. The *Code* prohibits damage to the internal parts of electrical equipment by foreign material such as paint, plaster, cleaners, etc. Precautions must be taken to provide protection from the detrimental effects of paint, plaster, cleaners, etc. on internal parts such as _____.

   (a) busbars   (b) wiring terminals   (c) insulators   (d) all of these

   Answer: _____   Section: _____._____

2. The conductors for the TVSS cannot be any longer than _____, and unnecessary bends should be avoided.

   (a) 6 in.   (b) 12 in.   (c) 18 in.   (d) none of these

   Answer: _____   Section: _____._____

3. The conductors, including splices and taps, in a nonmetallic surface raceway having a removable cover, must not fill the raceway to more than _____ percent of its cross-sectional area at that point.

   (a) 75   (b) 40   (c) 38   (d) 53

   Answer: _____   Section: _____._____

4. The connection between the grounded circuit conductor and the equipment grounding conductor at a separately derived system is the _____.

   (a) main bonding jumper   (b) system bonding jumper   (c) circuit bonding jumper   (d) equipment bonding jumper

   Answer: _____   Section: _____._____

5. The continuity of the grounding conductor system used to reduce electrical shock hazards at carnivals, fairs, and similar locations must be verified each time the portable electrical equipment is connected.

   (a) True   (b) False

   Answer: _____   Section: _____._____

6. The cord for a dishwasher and trash compactor must not be longer than _____ measured from the back of the appliance.

   (a) 2 ft   (b) 4 ft   (c) 6 ft   (d) 8 ft

   Answer: _____   Section: _____._____

7. The cross-sectional area of 1 in. IMC is approximately _____

   (a) 1.22 sq in.   (b) 0.62 sq in.   (c) 0.96 sq in.   (d) 2.13 sq in.

   Answer: _____   Section: _____._____

8.   The cross-sectional area of the conductors permitted in a sealing fitting must not exceed _____ percent of the cross-sectional area of rigid metal conduit of the same trade size unless the seal is specifically listed for a higher percentage of conductor fill.

      (a) 25   (b) 50   (c) 100   (d) 125

      Answer: _____   Section: _____._____

9.   The dedicated space above a panelboard extends to a dropped or suspended ceiling, which is considered a structural ceiling.

      (a) True   (b) False

      Answer: _____   Section: _____._____

10.   The demand factors of Table 220.56 apply to space heating, ventilating, or air-conditioning equipment.

      (a) True   (b) False

      Answer: _____   Section: _____._____

11.   The dimension of working clearance for access to live parts operating at 300V, nominal-to-ground, where there are exposed live parts on both sides of the workspace is _____ according to Table 110.26(A)(1).

      (a) 3 ft   (b) 3 1/2 ft   (c) 4 ft   (d) 4 1/2 ft

      Answer: _____   Section: _____._____

12.   The disconnecting means for air-conditioning and refrigerating equipment must be _____ from the air-conditioning or refrigerating equipment.

      (a) readily accessible   (b) within sight   (c) a or b   (d) a and b

      Answer: _____   Section: _____._____

13.   The disconnecting means for the controller and motor must open all ungrounded supply conductors and must be designed so that no pole can be operated independently.

      (a) True   (b) False

      Answer: _____   Section: _____._____

14.   The disconnecting means is not required to be located at the building or structure where documented safe switching procedures are established and maintained, and where the installation is monitored by _____ persons.

      (a) maintenance   (b) management   (c) service   (d) qualified

      Answer: _____   Section: _____._____

15.   The electrical datum plane (in land areas subject to tidal fluctuation) is a horizontal plane _____ above the highest high tide under normal circumstances.

      (a) 1 ft   (b) 2 ft   (c) 3 ft   (d) none of these

      Answer: _____   Section: _____._____

16.   The environment of a wiring method under the eaves of a house having a roofed open porch would be considered a _____ location.

      (a) dry   (b) damp   (c) wet   (d) moist

      Answer: _____   Section: _____._____

17. The feeder and service conductors for motors must be computed in accordance with Article _____.

(a) 450   (b) 240   (c) 430   (d) 100

Answer: _____   Section: _____._____

18. The feeder demand load for nine 12 kW ranges is _____.

(a) 13,000W   (b) 14,700W   (c) 24,000W   (d) 16,000W

Answer: _____   Section: _____._____

19. The grounding conductor for a CATV system must be connected to the nearest accessible location included on the list in 820.100(B)(2) when the building _____.

(a) has a grounding means   (b) is without a grounding means
(c) has an emergency transfer switch   (d) is wired using a metallic cable or raceway system

Answer: _____   Section: _____._____

20. The highest current at rated voltage that a device is intended to interrupt under standard test conditions is the _____.

(a) interrupting rating   (b) manufacturer's rating   (c) interrupting capacity   (d) GFCI rating

Answer: _____   Section: _____._____

21. The insulation rating of ungrounded conductors in Type NM cable must be _____.

(a) 60°C   (b) 75°C   (c) 90°C   (d) any of these

Answer: _____   Section: _____._____

22. The intentional electrical connection of one system terminal to ground without the insertion of any resistor or impedance device is _____.

(a) grounded   (b) solidly grounded   (c) effectively grounded   (d) grounding conductor

Answer: _____   Section: _____._____

23. The localization of an overcurrent condition to restrict outages to the circuit or equipment affected, accomplished by the choice of overcurrent-protective devices is called _____.

(a) overcurrent protection   (b) interrupting capacity   (c) selective coordination   (d) overload protection

Answer: _____   Section: _____._____

24. The location of the disconnecting means for an elevator must be _____ to qualified persons.

(a) accessible   (b) readily accessible   (c) disclosed only   (d) accessible only with a key

Answer: _____   Section: _____._____

25. The maximum length of an unprotected feeder tap conductor in a high-bay manufacturing building over 35 ft high is _____.

(a) 15 ft   (b) 20 ft   (c) 50 ft   (d) 100 ft

Answer: _____   Section: _____._____

26. The maximum rating or setting of an inverse-time breaker used as the motor branch-circuit short-circuit and ground-fault protective device for a 1-phase motor is _____ percent of the full load current given in Table 430.248.

(a) 125   (b) 175   (c) 250   (d) 300

Answer: _____   Section: _____._____

27. The metal water-pipe system of a building or structure is not required to be bonded to the separately derived system neutral terminal where the metal frame of the building or structure is used as the grounding electrode for the separately derived system and is bonded to the metal water piping in the area served by the separately derived system.

(a) True   (b) False

Answer: _____   Section: _____._____

28. The minimum distance that an outlet box containing tap supply conductors can be placed from a recessed luminaire (fixture) is _____.

(a) 1 ft   (b) 2 ft   (c) 3 ft   (d) 4 ft

Answer: _____   Section: _____._____

29. The minimum headroom of working spaces about motor control centers must be _____.

(a) 3 ft   (b) 5 ft   (c) 6 ft   (d) 6 1/2 ft

Answer: _____   Section: _____._____

30. The *NEC* requires that electrical work be installed _____.

(a) in a neat and workmanlike manner   (b) under the supervision of a qualified person
(c) completed before being inspected   (d) all of these

Answer: _____   Section: _____._____

31. The number of conductors allowed in rigid nonmetallic conduit must not exceed that permitted by the percentage fill specified in _____.

(a) Table 1, Chapter 9   (b) Table 250.66   (c) Table 310.16   (d) 240.6

Answer: _____   Section: _____._____

32. The number of fixture wires in a single conduit or tubing must not exceed that permitted by the percentage fill specified in _____.

(a) Table 1, Chapter 9   (b) Table 250.66   (c) Table 310.16   (d) 240.6

Answer: _____   Section: _____._____

33. The number of nonpower-limited fire alarm (NPLFA) conductors in a raceway is not required to be in accordance with the fill requirements contained in 300.17.

(a) True   (b) False

Answer: _____   Section: _____._____

34. The parallel conductors in each phase or grounded conductor must _____.

(a) be the same length and conductor material   (b) have the same circular mil area and insulation type
(c) be terminated in the same manner   (d) all of these

Answer: _____   Section: _____._____

35. The patient care area is any portion of a health care facility where patients are intended to be _____.

    (a) examined   (b) treated   (c) registered   (d) a or b

    Answer: _____   Section: _____._____

36. The power source for a Class 2 circuit must be _____.

    (a) a listed Class 2 or 3 transformer
    (b) a listed Class 2 or 3 power supply
    (c) other listed equipment marked to identify the Class 2 or Class 3 power source
    (d) any of these

    Answer: _____   Section: _____._____

37. The power source for a nonpower-limited fire alarm (NPLFA) circuit must not operate at more than _____.

    (a) 600V   (b) 300V   (c) 20A   (d) 120V

    Answer: _____   Section: _____._____

38. The power source for a power-limited fire alarm (PLFA) circuit is allowed to be supplied through a ground-fault circuit interrupter or an arc-fault circuit interrupter.

    (a) True   (b) False

    Answer: _____   Section: _____._____

39. The rating or setting of an overcurrent protection device for a 16.3A single nonmotor-operated- appliance must not exceed _____.

    (a) 15A   (b) 35A   (c) 25A   (d) 45A

    Answer: _____   Section: _____._____

40. The requirement for maintaining a 3 ft vertical clearance from the edge of the roof does not apply to the final conductor span where the conductors are attached to _____.

    (a) a building pole   (b) the side of a building   (c) an antenna   (d) the base of a building

    Answer: _____   Section: _____._____

41. The rules of _____, as applicable, apply to air-conditioning and refrigerating equipment that do not incorporate a hermetic refrigerant motor-compressor.

    (a) Article 422   (b) Article 424   (c) Article 430   (d) all of these

    Answer: _____   Section: _____._____

42. The scope of Article 285 applies to devices such as cord-and-plug connected TVSS units or receptacles or appliances that have integral TVSS protection.

    (a) True   (b) False

    Answer: _____   Section: _____._____

43. The screw shell of a luminaire or lampholder must be connected to the _____

    (a) grounded conductor   (b) ungrounded conductor
    (c) equipment grounding conductor   (d) forming shell terminal

    Answer: _____   Section: _____._____

44. The size of the grounded conductor for a feeder must not be smaller than specified in _____.

     (a) Table 250.122   (b) Table 250.66   (c) Table 310.16   (d) Table 430.52

     Answer: _____   Section: _____._____

45. The size of the grounding electrode conductor for a building or structure supplied by a feeder cannot be smaller than that identi-
     fied in _____ based on the largest ungrounded supply conductor.

     (a) 250.66   (b) 250.122   (c) Table 310.16   (d) not specified

     Answer: _____   Section: _____._____

46. The small-appliance branch circuits can supply the _____ as well as the kitchen.

     (a) dining room   (b) refrigerator   (c) breakfast room   (d) all of these

     Answer: _____   Section: _____._____

47. The total rating of a cord-and-plug connected room air conditioner, connected to the same branch circuit which supplies lighting
     units, other appliances, or general use receptacles, must not exceed _____ percent of the branch circuit rating.

     (a) 80   (b) 70   (c) 50   (d) 40

     Answer: _____   Section: _____._____

48. The upper end of the rod electrode must be _____ ground level unless the aboveground end and the grounding electrode con-
     ductor attachment are protected against physical damage.

     (a) above   (b) flush with   (c) below   (d) b or c

     Answer: _____   Section: _____._____

49. The use of listed and marked LFNC is permitted for _____.

     (a) direct burial where listed and marked for the purpose   (b) exposed work
     (c) concealed work   (d) all of these

     Answer: _____   Section: _____._____

50. The voltage at the line terminals of a fire-pump motor controller must not drop more than _____ percent below the controller's
     normal rated voltage under motor-starting conditions.

     (a) 5   (b) 10   (c) 15   (d) any of these

     Answer: _____   Section: _____._____

Unit 9
NEC Review Quiz
Articles 500 through 517

(• Indicates that 75% or fewer exam takers get the question correct)

Article 500 Hazardous (Classified) Locations (continue)

1. Hazardous (classified) locations are classified based on the properties of the _____ that may be present, and the likelihood that a flammable or combustible concentration or quantity is present.

    (a) flammable vapors   (b) flammable gases or liquids
    (c) combustible dusts or fibers   (d) all of these

    Answer: _____   Section: _____._____

2. Class I, Division 1 locations are those in which ignitible concentrations of _____ can exist under normal operating conditions.

    (a) combustible dust   (b) easily ignitible fibers or flyings
    (c) flammable gases or vapors   (d) flammable liquids or gases

    Answer: _____   Section: _____._____

3. Class I, Division 2 usually includes locations where volatile flammable liquids or flammable gases or vapors are used but that, in the judgment of the authority having jurisdiction, would become hazardous only in case of an accident or of some unusual operating condition.

    (a) True   (b) False

    Answer: _____   Section: _____._____

4. Class II locations are those that are hazardous because of the presence of _____.

    (a) combustible dust   (b) easily ignitible fibers or flyings
    (c) flammable gases or vapors   (d) flammable liquids or gases

    Answer: _____   Section: _____._____

5. Class III locations are those that are hazardous because of the presence of _____.

    (a) combustible dust   (b) easily ignitible fibers or flyings
    (c) flammable gases or vapors   (d) flammable liquids or gases

    Answer: _____   Section: _____._____

6. Locations in which easily ignitible combustible fibers are stored or handled other than in the process of manufacturing are designated as _____.

    (a) Class II, Division 2   (b) Class III, Division 1   (c) Class III, Division 2   (d) nonhazardous

    Answer: _____   Section: _____._____

7.   In Class _____ locations for Groups A, B, C, and D, the classification involves determinations of maximum explosion pressure and maximum safe clearance between parts of a clamped joint in an enclosure .

(a) I   (b) II   (c) III   (d) all of these

Answer: _____   Section: _____._____

8.   Electrical equipment installed in hazardous (classified) locations must be constructed for the class, division, and group. An atmosphere containing _____ is classified as Group C.

(a) hydrogen   (b) ethylene   (c) propylene oxide   (d) all of these

Answer: _____   Section: _____._____

9.   An atmosphere containing carbon black, charcoal, coal, or coke dusts that have been sensitized by other materials so they present an explosive hazard is classified as Group F.

(a) True   (b) False

Answer: _____   Section: _____._____

10.   For Class _____ locations, the classification of Groups E, F, and G involves the tightness of the joints of assembly and shaft openings to prevent entrance of dust in the dust-ignition proof enclosure, the blanketing effect of layers of dust on the equipment that may cause overheating, and the ignition temperature of the dust.

(a) I   (b) II   (c) III   (d) all of these

Answer: _____   Section: _____._____

11.   Suitability of equipment for a specific purpose, environment, or application may be determined by:
(a) Equipment listing or labeling.
(b) Evidence of equipment evaluation from a qualified testing laboratory or inspection agency concerned with product evaluation
(c) Evidence acceptable to the authority having jurisdiction, such as a manufacturer's self evaluation or an owner's engineering judgment.
(d) any of these

Answer: _____   Section: _____._____

12.   All threaded conduits or fittings referred to in hazardous locations must be threaded with a _____ taper per foot.

(a) 1/2 in.   (b) 3/4 in.   (c) 1 in.   (d) all of these

Answer: _____   Section: _____._____

13.   or listed explosionproof equipment, factory threaded entries must be made up with at least _____ threads fully engaged.

(a) 5   (b) 4 1/2   (c) 6   (d) no minimum

Answer: _____   Section: _____._____

Article 501 Class I Hazardous (Classified) Locations

A Class I hazardous (classified) location is an area where flammable gases or vapors may be present in quantities sufficient to produce an explosive or ignitible mixture.

14. Article 501 covers the requirements for electrical and electronic equipment and wiring for all voltages in Class I, Divisions 1 and 2 locations where fire or explosion hazards may exist due to _____.

    (a) flammable gases   (b) vapors   (c) flammable liquids   (d) any of these

    Answer: _____   Section: _____._____

15. Wiring methods permitted in Class I, Division 1 locations include _____.

    (a) threaded rigid metal or threaded intermediate metal conduit   (b) flexible fittings listed for Class I, Division 1 locations
    (c) boxes approved for Class I, Division 1 locations   (d) all of these

    Answer: _____   Section: _____._____

16. When provisions for limited flexibility are required in a Class I, Division 2 location, such as motor terminations, flexible metal conduit with listed fittings may be used.

    (a) True   (b) False

    Answer: _____   Section: _____._____

17. Sealing compound is employed with MI cable terminal fittings in Class I locations for the purpose of _____.

    (a) preventing the passage of gas or vapor
    (b) excluding moisture and other fluids from the cable insulation
    (c) limiting a possible explosion
    (d) preventing the escape of powder

    Answer: _____   Section: _____._____

18. Each conduit leaving a Class I, Division 1 location requires a seal to be located on either side of the hazardous (classified) location boundary. Unions, couplings, boxes, or fittings are permitted between the seal and the point where the conduit leaves the Division 1 location.

    (a) True   (b) False

    Answer: _____   Section: _____._____

19. Where the Class I, Division 1 boundary is beneath the ground, the sealing fitting must be installed _____. Except for listed explosionproof reducers at the conduit seal, there must be no union, coupling, box or fitting between the conduit seal and the point at which the conduit leaves the ground.

    (a) after the conduit leaves the ground   (b) before the conduit leaves the ground
    (c) within 10 ft of where the conduit leaves the ground   (d) none of these

    Answer: _____   Section: _____._____

20. A sealing fitting is required for each conduit run passing from a Class I, Division 2 location into an unclassified location for the purpose of minimizing the passage of gases. It must be located no more than _____ from the boundary.

    (a) 3 ft   (b) 6 ft   (c) 10 ft   (d) 20 ft

    Answer: _____   Section: _____._____

21. No seal is required if a conduit (with no unions, couplings, boxes, or fittings) passes completely through a Class I, Division 2 location if the termination points of the unbroken conduit are in unclassified locations and it has no fittings less than _____ beyond each boundary of the classified location.

    (a) 6 in.   (b) 12 in.   (c) 18 in.   (d) 24 in.

    Answer: _____   Section: _____._____

22. The minimum thickness of sealing compound in Class I, Division 1 and 2 locations must not be less than the trade size of the conduit or sealing fitting and, in no case, less than _____

    (a) 1/8 in.   (b) 1/4 in.   (c) 3/8 in.   (d) 5/8 in.

    Answer: _____   Section: _____._____

23. When MC-HL cable containing shielded cables and/or twisted-pair cables is installed in a Class I, Division 1 location, the removal of the shielding material or the separation of the twisted pairs is not required, provided the termination is accomplished by a(n) _____ means to minimize the entrance of gases or vapors and to prevent propagation of flame into the cable core.

    (a) approved   (b) listed   (c) acceptable   (d) none of these

    Answer: _____   Section: _____._____

24. In Class I, Division 1 and 2 locations where condensed vapors or liquids may collect on or come in contact with the insulation on conductors, the insulation must be of a type _____.

    (a) identified for such use   (b) with integral drying agents
    (c) listed for contact with water   (d) enclosed only in liquidtight flexible metal conduit

    Answer: _____   Section: _____._____

25. When flexible metal conduit or LFMC is used as permitted in Class I, Division 2 locations, it must be installed with an _____ bonding jumper installed in parallel with the raceway conduit in compliance with 250.102.

    (a) internal   (b) external   (c) a or b   (d) a and b

    Answer: _____   Section: _____._____

26. Transformers and capacitors installed in Class I, Division 1 locations containing flammable liquids must be installed in vaults.

    (a) True   (b) False

    Answer: _____   Section: _____._____

27. Meters, instruments and relays including kilowatt-hour meters, instrument transformers, resistors, rectifiers, and thermionic tubes in Class I, Division 1 locations must be installed in explosionproof enclosures or purged and pressurized enclosures.

    (a) True   (b) False

    Answer: _____   Section: _____._____

28. Switches, circuit breakers, motor controllers, and fuses including pushbuttons, relays, and similar devices in Class I, Division 1 locations must be installed in enclosures, and the enclosure(s) together with the enclosed apparatus must be identified as a complete assembly for use in Class I locations.

    (a) True   (b) False

    Answer: _____   Section: _____._____

29. In Class I, Division 2 locations, fused or unfused disconnect and isolating switches for transformers or capacitor banks that are not intended to interrupt current in normal performance are permitted to be installed in general-purpose enclosures.

(a) True   (b) False

Answer: _____   Section: _____._____

30. Motors, generators, or other rotating electric machinery that are identified for Class I, Division 2 locations are allowed to be used in a Class 1, Division 1 location.

(a) True   (b) False

Answer: _____   Section: _____._____

31. Totally-enclosed motors of the type specified in 501.125(A)(2) or (A)(3) must have a device to de-energize the motor or sound an alarm if there is an increase in temperature of the motor beyond designed limits when operating in Class I, Division 1 locations.

(a) True   (b) False

Answer: _____   Section: _____._____

32. Luminaires installed in Class I, Division 1 locations must be protected from physical damage by a suitable _____.

(a) warning label   (b) pendant   (c) guard or by location   (d) all of these

Answer: _____   Section: _____._____

33. Boxes, box assemblies, or fittings used to support luminaires in Class I, Division 1 locations must be identified for Class 1 locations.

(a) True   (b) False

Answer: _____   Section: _____._____

34. In Class I, Division 1 and 2 locations, flexible cords are never permitted.

(a) True   (b) False

Answer: _____   Section: _____._____

35. In Class I, Division 1 locations, all apparatus and equipment of signaling, alarm, remote-control, and communications systems, _____, must be identified for Class I, Division 1 locations.

(a) above 50V   (b) above 100V-to-ground   (c) regardless of voltage   (d) except under 24V

Answer: _____   Section: _____._____

Article 502 Class II Hazardous (Classified) Locations

A Class II hazardous (classified) location is an area where combustible dust may be suspended in the air in quantities sufficient to ignite or explode.

36. Raceways permitted as a wiring method in a Class II, Division 1 hazardous (classified) location include _____.

(a) threaded rigid metal conduit and intermediate metal conduit
(b) rigid nonmetallic conduit
(c) electrical metallic tubing
(d) any of these

Answer: _____   Section: _____._____

37. In Class II locations where combustible, electrically conductive dust is present, flexible connections can be made with _____.

    (a) flexible metal conduit   (b) AC armored cable
    (c) hard-usage cord   (d) liquidtight flexible metal conduit with listed fittings

    Answer: _____   Section: _____._____

38. Rigid metal conduit and intermediate metal conduit are not required to be threaded when used in a Class II, Division 2 location.

    (a) True   (b) False

    Answer: _____   Section: _____._____

39. In Class II, Division 1 and 2 locations, an approved method of bonding is the use of _____.

    (a) bonding jumpers with approved fittings   (b) double locknut types of contacts
    (c) locknut-bushing types of contacts   (d) any of the above are approved methods of bonding

    Answer: _____   Section: _____._____

40. In a Class II, Division 1 location, a multiwire branch circuit is allowed when using a disconnect on the circuit which opens all of the circuits simultaneously.

    (a) True   (b) False

    Answer: _____   Section: _____._____

41. In a Class II, Division 1 location where dust from magnesium, aluminum, aluminum bronze powders, or other metals of similarly hazardous characteristics may be present, fuses, switches, motor controllers, and circuit breakers must have enclosures specifically approved for such locations.

    (a) True   (b) False

    Answer: _____   Section: _____._____

42. In Class II, Division 1 locations, control transformers, solenoids, impedance coils and resistors, and any overcurrent devices or switching mechanism associated with them, must have dust-ignitionproof enclosures identified for _____.

    (a) Class I, Division 1 locations   (b) control transformer duty
    (c) general duty   (d) Class II locations

    Answer: _____   Section: _____._____

43. In Class II, Division 2 locations, motors, generators, or other rotating electric machinery must be _____.

    (a) totally enclosed non-ventilated or pipe ventilated   (b) totally enclosed water-air-cooled or fan cooled
    (c) dust-ignition proof   (d) any of these

    Answer: _____   Section: _____._____

44. Luminaires installed in Class II, Division 1 locations must be protected from physical damage by a suitable _____.

    (a) warning label   (b) pendant   (c) guard or by location   (d) all of these

    Answer: _____   Section: _____._____

45. Luminaires installed in Class II, Division 2 locations must be protected from physical damage by a suitable _____.

    (a) warning label   (b) pendant   (c) guard or by location   (d) all of these

    Answer: _____   Section: _____._____

46. Flexible cords used in a Class II, Division 1 or 2 location _____.

(a) must be listed for hard usage
(c) are not permitted

(b) must be listed for extra-hard usage
(d) none of these

Answer: _____   Section: _____._____

47. In Class II, Division 2 locations, receptacles and attachment plugs must be of the type providing for connection to the grounding conductor of the flexible cord and must be designed so that connection to the supply circuit cannot be made or broken _____.

(a) while live parts are exposed
(c) unless the disconnect is open

(b) except by qualified persons
(d) unless proper ventilation equipment is functional

Answer: _____   Section: _____._____

Article 503 Class III Hazardous (Classified) Locations

Class III locations are hazardous due to the presence of easily ignitible fibers or flyings, but these materials aren't likely to be suspended in the air in quantities sufficient to produce ignitible mixtures. This would include materials such as cotton and rayon, which are found in textile mills and clothing manufacturing plants. It can also include establishments and industries such as woodworking plants. There are no "Group" classifications for Class III locations as there are for Class I and Class II locations.

48. Raceways permitted as a wiring method in a Class III hazardous (classified) location include _____.

(a) rigid metal conduit and intermediate metal conduit
(c) electrical metallic tubing

(b) rigid nonmetallic conduit
(d) any of these

Answer: _____   Section: _____._____

49. In Class III, Division 1 and 2 locations, locknut-bushing and double-locknut types of fittings are depended on for bonding purposes.

(a) True   (b) False

Answer: _____   Section: _____._____

50. In Class III, Division 1 and 2 locations, switches, circuit breakers, motor controllers, and fuses, including pushbuttons, relays, and similar devices, must be provided with _____.

(a) Class I enclosures   (b) general duty enclosures
(c) dusttight enclosures   (d) seal offs at each enclosure

Answer: _____   Section: _____._____

51. In Class III, Divisions 1 and 2, motors, generators, and other rotating machinery must be _____.

(a) totally enclosed nonventilated
(c) totally enclosed fan cooled

(b) totally enclosed pipe ventilated
(d) any of these

Answer: _____   Section: _____._____

52. Luminaires in a Class III location that may be exposed to physical damage must be protected by a(n) _____ guard.

(a) plastic   (b) metal   (c) suitable   (d) explosionproof

Answer: _____   Section: _____._____

53. In Class III, Division 1 and 2 locations, portable lighting equipment must be equipped with handles and protected with substantial guards. Lampholders must be of the unswitched type with no provisions for _____.

    (a) receiving attachment plugs   (b) grounding connections
    (c) lamp installation   (d) hooks or hangers

    Answer: _____   Section: _____._____

54. In Class III, Division 1 and 2 locations, receptacles and attachment plugs must be of the grounding type, must be designed so as to minimize the accumulation or the entry of _____, and must prevent the escape of sparks or molten particles.

    (a) gases or vapors   (b) particles of combustion   (c) fibers or flyings   (d) none of these

    Answer: _____   Section: _____._____

55. The power supply to contact conductors of a crane in a Class III location must be _____.

    (a) isolated from all other systems   (b) equipped with an acceptable ground detector
    (c) have an alarm in the case of a ground fault   (d) all of these

    Answer: _____   Section: _____._____

Article 504 Intrinsically Safe Systems

This article covers the installation of intrinsically safe apparatus, wiring and systems for Class I, II, and III locations. An intrinsically safe circuit doesn't develop sufficient electrical energy to cause ignition of a specified gas or vapor under normal or abnormal operating conditions. An intrinsically safe system reduces the risk of ignition by electrical equipment or circuits and offers an optional wiring method in hazardous (classified) locations.

56. An assembly of interconnected intrinsically safe apparatus, associated apparatus, and interconnecting cables designed so that those parts of the system that may be used in hazardous (classified) locations are intrinsically safe circuits is a(n) _____.

    (a) intrinsically safe system   (b) safe location   (c) reclassified location   (d) associated system

    Answer: _____   Section: _____._____

57. Intrinsically safe and associated apparatus aare permitted to be installed in _____.

    (a) any hazardous (classified) location for which they have been identified
    (b) Class I locations only
    (c) Class II locations only
    (d) any location that is less than 30V

    Answer: _____   Section: _____._____

58. Conductors of intrinsically safe circuits must be separated at least _____ from conductors of any nonintrinsically safe circuits within enclosures.

    (a) 6 in.   (b) 2 in.   (c) 18 in.   (d) 12 in.

    Answer: _____   Section: _____._____

59. Intrinsically safe apparatus, associated apparatus, cable shields, enclosures, and raceways (if of metal), must be grounded.

    (a) True   (b) False

    Answer: _____   Section: _____._____

60. Intrinsically safe conduit or cable runs that leave a Class I or II location must be sealed. The seal must be _____.

(a) explosionproof or flameproof
(b) flameproof
(c) a and b
(d) none of these

Answer: _____   Section: _____._____

61. Color coding of _____ is permitted to be used to identify cables, conduits, cable trays, and junction boxes that contain intrinsically safe wiring.

(a) red   (b) light blue   (c) yellow   (d) any of these

Answer: _____   Section: _____._____

Article 505 Class I, Zone 0, 1, and 2 Locations

This article covers the requirements for the zone classification system as an alternative to the division classification system covered in Article 500 for electrical and electronic equipment and wiring for all voltages in Class I, Zone 0, Zone 1, and Zone 2 hazardous (classified) locations where fire or explosion hazards may exist due to flammable gases, vapors, or liquids.

62. Multiwire branch circuits can be used in a Class I, Zone 1, location if the ungrounded conductors are opened simultaneously.

(a) True   (b) False

Answer: _____   Section: _____._____

Article 511 Commercial Garages, Repair, and Storage

These occupancies include locations used for service and repair operations in connection with self-propelled vehicles (including, but not limited to, passenger automobiles, buses, trucks, and tractors) in which petroleum-based chemicals (volatile organic compounds) are used for fuel or power.

63. Article _____ contains the requirements for the wiring of occupancy locations used for service and repair operations in connection with self-propelled vehicles (including passenger automobiles, buses, trucks, tractors, etc.) in which volatile flammable liquids or gases are used for fuel or power.

(a) 500   (b) 501   (c) 511   (d) 514

Answer: _____   Section: _____._____

64. Parking garages used for parking or storage and where no repair work is done except for exchange of parts and routine maintenance requiring no use of electrical equipment, open flame, welding, or the use of volatile flammable liquids, are not classified as hazardous (classified) locations.

(a) True   (b) False

Answer: _____   Section: _____._____

65. Areas adjacent to classified locations in commercial garages where flammable vapors are not likely to be released are not classified where mechanically ventilated at a rate of _____ or more air changes per hour, designed with positive air pressure, or where effectively cut off by walls or partitions.

(a) two   (b) four   (c) six   (d) none of these

Answer: _____   Section: _____._____

66. Where flammable liquids having a flash point below 100°F (such as gasoline, or gaseous fuels such as natural gas or LPG) will not be transferred, such location is considered to be a(n) _____ location.

   (a) Class I, Division 1   (b) Class I, Division 2   (c) Class II, Division 1   (d) unclassified

   Answer: _____   Section: _____._____

67. For each floor area inside a commercial garage where Class I liquids are transferred, the entire area up to a level of _____ above the floor is considered to be a Class I, Division 2 location.

   (a) 6 in.   (b) 12 in.   (c) 18 in.   (d) 24 in.

   Answer: _____   Section: _____._____

68. •Any ventilated pit or depression in a commercial garage lubrication or service room where Class I liquids or gaseous fuels are transferred is classified as a _____ location.

   (a) Class I, Division 2.   (b) Class II, Division 2   (c) Class II, Division 1   (d) Class I, Division 1

   Answer: _____   Section: _____._____

69. Wiring installed in a Class 1 Location of commercial garages must conform to the applicable provisions of Article 501.

   (a) True   (b) False

   Answer: _____   Section: _____._____

70. For portable lighting equipment used in commercial garages, unless the lamp and its cord are supported and arranged in such a manner that they cannot be used in the locations classified in 511.3, they must be of a type identified for _____.

   (a) hard usage   (b) Class I, Division 2 locations
   (c) Class I, Division 1 locations   (d) general duty

   Answer: _____   Section: _____._____

71. For pendants installed above Class I locations in a commercial garage, flexible cord _____.

   (a) must be suitable for the type of service   (b) must be listed for hard usage
   (c) a and b   (d) must not be used

   Answer: _____   Section: _____._____

72. In a commercial garage, over a Class I location, equipment less than _____ above the floor level that may produce arcs, sparks, or particles of hot metal, must be of the totally enclosed type or constructed so as to prevent the escape of sparks or hot metal particles.

   (a) 6 ft   (b) 10 ft   (c) 12 ft   (d) 18 ft

   Answer: _____   Section: _____._____

73. For commercial garages, seals conforming to the requirements of 501.5 and 501.5(B)(2) must be provided and apply to _____ boundaries of the defined Class I location.

   (a) vertical   (b) horizontal   (c) conduit only within the   (d) (a) and (b)

   Answer: _____   Section: _____._____

74. In commercial garages, GFCI protection for personnel must be provided on all 125-volt, single-phase, 15 and 20 ampere receptacles installed where _____ is (are) to be used.

(a) electrical diagnostic equipment
(b) electrical hand tools
(c) portable lighting equipment
(d) any of these

Answer: _____   Section: _____._____

Article 513 Aircraft Hangars

This article applies to buildings or structures in any part of which aircraft are housed or stored containing Class I (flammable) liquids or Class II (combustible) liquids whose temperatures are above their flash points, and in which aircraft might undergo service, repairs, or alterations. It isn't necessary to classify areas where only Class II combustible liquids are used or stored below the flash point. Article 513 doesn't apply to areas used exclusively for aircraft that have never contained fuel or for unfueled aircraft.

75. The entire area of an aircraft hangar, including any adjacent and communicating areas not suitably cut off from the hangar, are classified as a Class I, Division 2 or Zone 2 location up to a level of _____ above the floor.

(a) 6 in.   (b) 5 ft 6 in.   (c) 18 in.   (d) 12 in.

Answer: _____   Section: _____._____

76. Stock rooms and similar areas adjacent to classified locations of aircraft hangars, but effectively isolated and adequately ventilated, are designated as _____ locations.

(a) Class I, Division 2   (b) Class II, Division 1   (c) Class II, Division 2   (d) nonhazardous

Answer: _____   Section: _____._____

77. Attachment plugs and receptacles in Class I locations of aircraft hangars must be _____.

(a) identified for use in Class I locations
(b) designed so that they can not be energized while the connections are being made or broken
(c) a or b
(d) none of these

Answer: _____   Section: _____._____

78. For pendants in an aircraft hanger, not installed in Class I locations, flexible cords suitable for the type of service and identified for _____ must be used.

(a) hard usage   (b) extra-hard usage   (c) general duty   (d) a or b

Answer: _____   Section: _____._____

79. In aircraft hangers, equipment that is less than _____ above wings and engine enclosures of aircraft and that may produce arcs, sparks, or particles of hot metal must be of the totally enclosed type or constructed so as to prevent the escape of sparks or hot metal particles.

(a) 18 in.   (b) 5 ft 6 in.   (c) 10 ft   (d) 6 ft 6 in.

Answer: _____   Section: _____._____

80. All wiring installed in or under the aircraft hangar floor must comply with the requirements for _____ locations.

(a) Class I, Division 1   (b) Class I, Division 2   (c) Class II   (d) none of these

Answer: _____   Section: _____._____

81. Where a circuit in a Class I location of an aircraft hangar supplies portable equipment and includes a grounded conductor as provided in Article 200, _____, and similar devices must be of the grounding type, and the grounded conductor of the flexible cord must be connected to the grounded terminal of any utilization equipment supplied.

   (a) receptacles   (b) attachment plugs   (c) connectors   (d) all of these

   Answer: _____   Section: _____._____

Article 514 Motor Fuel Dispensing Facilities

This article applies to gasoline dispensing and service stations where gasoline or other volatile flammable liquids or liquefied flammable gases are transferred to fuel tanks of self-propelled vehicles. Wiring and equipment in the area of service and repair rooms of service stations must comply with the installation requirements in Article 511.

82. Article 514 contains requirements for the classification of areas where _____ is stored, handled, or dispensed from motor fuel dispensing facilities.

   (a) compressed natural gas   (b) liquefied natural gas   (c) liquefied petroleum gas   (d) any of these

   Answer: _____   Section: _____._____

83. A listed sealing fitting must be _____.

   (a) provided in each conduit run entering a dispenser
   (b) provided in each conduit run leaving a dispenser
   (c) the first fitting after the conduit emerges from the earth or concrete
   (d) all of these

   Answer: _____   Section: _____._____

84. Each circuit leading to or through a dispensing pump must be provided with a switch or other acceptable means to disconnect simultaneously from the source of supply all conductors of the circuit, including the _____ conductor, if any.

   (a) grounding   (b) grounded   (c) bonding   (d) all of these

   Answer: _____   Section: _____._____

85. Each circuit leading to gasoline dispensing equipment must be provided with a clearly identified and readily accessible switch or other acceptable means to disconnect all conductors of the circuit.

   (a) True   (b) False

   Answer: _____   Section: _____._____

86. The emergency controls for unattended self-service stations must be located not less than _____ or more than _____ from the gasoline dispensers.

   (a) 10 ft, 25 ft   (b) 20 ft, 50 ft   (c) 20 ft, 100 ft   (d) 50 ft, 100 ft

   Answer: _____   Section: _____._____

87. In motor fuel dispensing facilities, all metal raceways, the metal armor or metallic sheath on cables, and all noncurrent-carrying metal parts of fixed portable electrical equipment _____ must be grounded as provided in Article 250.

   (a) operating at under 600V   (b) regardless of voltage   (c) over 300V   (d) under 50V

   Answer: _____   Section: _____._____

Article 515 Bulk Storage Plants

This article covers a property or portion of a property where flammable liquids are received by tank vessel, pipelines, tank car, or tank vehicle and are stored or blended in bulk for the purpose of distributing such liquids by tank vessel, pipeline, tank car, tank vehicle, portable tank, or container.

88. Aboveground bulk storage tanks are classified as _____ for the space between 5 ft and 10 ft from the open end of a vent, extending in all directions.

(a) Class I, Division 1   (b) Class I, Division 2   (c) Class II, Division 1   (d) Class II, Division 2

Answer: _____   Section: _____._____

Article 516 Spray Application, Dipping, and Coating Processes

This article covers the regular or frequent application of flammable liquids, combustible liquids, and combustible powders by spray operations and the application of flammable liquids, or combustible liquids at temperatures above their flashpoint, by dipping, coating, or other means.

89. Locations where flammable paints are dried, with the ventilating equipment interlocked with the electrical equipment, may be designated as a(n) _____ location by the authority having jurisdiction.

(a) Class I, Division 2   (b) unclassified   (c) Class II, Division 2   (d) Class II, Division 1

Answer: _____   Section: _____._____

Article 517 Health Care Facilities

This article applies to electrical wiring in health care facilities such as hospitals, nursing homes, limited-care facilities, clinics, medical and dental offices, and ambulatory care, whether permanent or movable. This article isn't intended to apply to animal veterinary facilities.

90. A hospital is a building or part thereof used for the medical, psychiatric, obstetrical, or surgical care, on a 24-hour basis, of _____ or more inpatients.

(a) 10   (b) 100   (c) 4   (d) 2

Answer: _____   Section: _____._____

91. A nursing home is an area used for the lodging, boarding, and nursing care, on a 24-hour basis of _____ or more persons who, because of mental or physical incapacity may be unable to provide for their own needs and safety without assistance.

(a) 4   (b) 100   (c) 10   (d) 2

Answer: _____   Section: _____._____

92. The patient bed location would include an inpatient sleeping bed; or the bed or procedure table used in a critical patient care area.

(a) True   (b) False

Answer: _____   Section: _____._____

93. Patient vicinity is the space with surfaces likely to be contacted by the patient or an attendant who can touch the patient. This encloses a space not less than 6 ft beyond the perimeter of the patient bed in its normal location and extending vertically not less than _____ above the floor.

    (a) 7 1/2 ft   (b) 5 ft 6 in.   (c) 18 in.   (d) 6 ft

    Answer: _____ Section: _____._____

94. The outer metal sheath of interlocked Type MC cable is not listed as an acceptable grounding return path. However, if it contains an insulated equipment grounding conductor 12 AWG or larger, it can be used to supply branch circuits in patient care areas of health care facilities.

    (a) True   (b) False

    Answer: _____ Section: _____._____

95. Metal faceplates for switches and receptacles are permitted to be grounded by means of the metal mounting screws securing the faceplate to a grounded outlet box or grounded wiring device in patient care areas.

    (a) True   (b) False

    Answer: _____ Section: _____._____

96. In health care facilities, receptacles with insulated grounding terminals must be identified. Such identification must be visible _____.

    (a) on rough-in inspection   (b) by removal of faceplates
    (c) after installation   (d) on the blueprints only

    Answer: _____ Section: _____._____

97. Each general care area patient bed location must be provided with a minimum of _____ receptacle(s), which can be single, duplex, or a combination with each duplex counting as 2 receptacles.

    (a) 1   (b) 6   (c) 2   (d) 4

    Answer: _____ Section: _____._____

98. In critical care areas of health care centers, each patient bed location must be provided with a minimum of _____ receptacles.

    (a) 10   (b) 6   (c) 3   (d) 4

    Answer: _____ Section: _____._____

99. The wiring for the emergency system in hospitals may be installed in flexible metal raceways and listed metal sheathed cable assemblies for specific situations, including _____.

    (a) enclosing conductors smaller than 12 AWG only
    (b) within 50 feet of a disconnect for the branch circuit
    (c) where necessary for flexible connection to equipment
    (d) only where installed so the wiring method is exposed and accessible

    Answer: _____ Section: _____._____

100. Which one of the following functions must not be connected to the life safety branch in a hospital?

    (a) Exit signs   (b) Elevators
    (c) Administrative office lighting   (d) Communications systems

    Answer: _____ Section: _____._____

1. By using ingenuity in the layout of electrical installations for hazardous (classified) locations, it is frequently possible to locate much of the equipment in less hazardous or nonhazardous locations and thus reduce the amount of special equipment required.

   (a) True   (b) False

   Answer: _____   Section: _____._____

2. A fiber optic cable assembly that contains current-carrying conductors must be installed according to the applicable requirements of Articles 500, 501, 502, and 503.

   (a) True   (b) False

   Answer: _____   Section: _____._____

3. All branch circuits serving patient care areas must be installed in a metal raceway or cable that is listed in 250.118 as an acceptable grounding return path, such as EMT or Type AC cable.

   (a) True   (b) False

   Answer: _____   Section: _____._____

4. All fixed wiring in an aircraft hanger not installed in a Class I location must be installed in _____.

   (a) metal raceways   (b) Types MI, TC, or MC cable
   (c) nonmetallic raceways   (d) a or b

   Answer: _____   Section: _____._____

5. An aboveground tank in a bulk storage plant is a Class I, Division 1 location within _____ from the open end of a vent, extending in all directions.

   (a) 12 ft   (b) 10 ft   (c) 6 ft   (d) 5 ft

   Answer: _____   Section: _____._____

6. An atmosphere classified as Group G contains combustible dusts such as flour, grain, wood, plastic, and chemicals.

   (a) True   (b) False

   Answer: _____   Section: _____._____

7. An intrinsically safe circuit is a circuit in which any spark or thermal effect is incapable of causing ignition of a mixture of flammable or combustible material in air under _____.

   (a) water   (b) prescribed test conditions   (c) supervision   (d) duress

   Answer: _____   Section: _____._____

8.   Any pit or depression below a garage floor level of a lubrication or service room where Class I liquids are transferred is considered to be a Class I, Division _____ location up to floor level.

(a) 1   (b) 2   (c) 3   (d) not classified

Answer: _____   Section: _____._____

9.   Article 514 applies to _____ and fleet vehicle motor fuel dispensing facilities.

(a) motor fuel dispensing facilities located inside or outside   (b) marine fuel dispensing facilities
(c) commercial gas stations for motor vehicles only   (d) both a and b

Answer: _____   Section: _____._____

10. Battery chargers and their control equipment, and batteries being charged, are allowed to be located within any area of a commercial garage.

(a) True   (b) False

Answer: _____   Section: _____._____

11. Class III, Division _____ location(s) include areas where easily ignitible fibers or materials producing combustible flyings are handled, manufactured, or used.

(a) 1   (b) 2   (c) 3   (d) all of these

Answer: _____   Section: _____._____

12. Conductors of intrinsically safe circuits must not be placed in any _____ with conductors of any nonintrinsically safe system.

(a) raceway   (b) cable tray   (c) cable   (d) any of these

Answer: _____   Section: _____._____

13. Conduits 1 1/2 in. or smaller entering an explosionproof enclosure that houses switches intended to interrupt current in the normal performance of the function are not required to be sealed, if the current-interrupting contacts are within a chamber hermetically sealed against the entrance of gases and vapors.

(a) True   (b) False

Answer: _____   Section: _____._____

14. Each circuit leading to or through dispensing equipment, including equipment for remote pumping systems, must be provided with a switch or other acceptable means to disconnect _____ from the source of supply all conductors of the circuit, including the grounded conductor, if any.

(a) automatically   (b) simultaneously   (c) manually   (d) individually

Answer: _____   Section: _____._____

15. Equipment in an area containing acetylene gas must be rated as a Class I, Group A location.

(a) True   (b) False

Answer: _____   Section: _____._____

16. Equipment installed in hazardous locations must be approved and must be marked to show the _____.

(a) class
(b) group
(c) temperature class (T *Code*) or operating temperature at a 40°C ambient temperature
(d) all of these

Answer: _____   Section: _____._____

17. Fixed electrical equipment installed above a Class I location in a commercial garage must be _____.

(a) well ventilated   (b) located above the level of any defined Class I location
(c) identified for the location   (d) b or c

Answer: _____   Section: _____._____

18. For connections to enclosures that are required to be explosionproof in Class I, Division 2 locations, _____ must be located in accordance with 501.15(A)(1) and (A)4.

(a) mounting brackets   (b) conduit seals   (c) warning signs   (d) none of these

Answer: _____   Section: _____._____

19. Fuel dispensing units for liquid petroleum gas are allowed to be located within a commercial garage building if the requirements of Article 514 are applied.

(a) True   (b) False

Answer: _____   Section: _____._____

20. In a Class I, Division 1 location, a multiwire branch circuit is allowed to be protected using single-pole breakers.

(a) True   (b) False

Answer: _____   Section: _____._____

21. In a Class II, Division 2 location, enclosures for fuses, switches, circuit breakers, and motor controllers, including pushbuttons, relays, and similar devices, must be _____.

(a) dusttight   (b) raintight
(c) rated as Class I, Division 1 explosionproof   (d) general duty

Answer: _____   Section: _____._____

22. In aircraft hangers, metal-shell, fiber-lined lampholders must not be used for fixed incandescent lighting.

(a) True   (b) False

Answer: _____   Section: _____._____

23. In Class I, Division 1 locations, control transformers, impedance coils, and resistors, along with any switching mechanism associated with them, must be provided with enclosures identified for _____.

(a) Class I, Division 1 locations   (b) control transformer duty
(c) general duty   (d) NEMA 3

Answer: _____   Section: _____._____

24. In Class I, Division 2 locations for alarm and communications systems, enclosures that contain switches, circuit breakers, and make-and-break contacts of pushbuttons, relays, alarm bells, and horns must be identified for Class I, Division 1 locations.

    (a) True   (b) False

    Answer: _____   Section: _____._____

25. In Class II, Division 1 locations for alarm and communications systems, _____ for bells, howlers, sirens, and other devices in which sparks or arcs may be produced must be provided with enclosures identified for a Class II location.

    (a) switches   (b) circuit breakers   (c) current breaking contacts   (d) all of these

    Answer: _____   Section: _____._____

26. In Class II, Division 2 locations, flexible cord is allowed to serve as the supporting means for a fixture.

    (a) True   (b) False

    Answer: _____   Section: _____._____

27. In Class III, Division 1 and 2 locations, flexible cords must _____.

    (a) be listed as extra-hard usage   (b) contain a grounding conductor
    (c) terminate in an approved manner   (d) all of these

    Answer: _____   Section: _____._____

28. In hazardous (classified) locations, intrinsically safe apparatus must _____ in the hazardous (classified) location in accordance with 250.100.

    (a) be secured   (b) be bonded   (c) be painted   (d) not be used

    Answer: _____   Section: _____._____

29. ITC-HL cables, listed for use in Class I, Division 1 locations, with a gas/vaportight, continuous-corrugated, metallic sheath, an overall jacket of suitable polymeric material, and provided with termination fittings listed for the application can be installed in Class I, Division 1 _____ establishments with restricted public access.

    (a) commercial   (b) industrial   (c) institutional   (d) all of these

    Answer: _____   Section: _____._____

30. Luminaires for fixed lighting in Class III, Division 1 and 2 locations must have enclosures for lamps and lampholders that are designed to prevent the escape of _____. Each luminaire must be clearly marked to show the maximum wattage of the lamps that are permitted.

    (a) sparks   (b) burning material   (c) hot metal   (d) all of these

    Answer: _____   Section: _____._____

31. Luminaires installed in Class I, Division 1 locations must be identified as a complete assembly for the Class I, Division 1 location and must be clearly marked to indicate _____.

    (a) the maximum wattage of lamps intended   (b) the minimum conductor size
    (c) the maximum overcurrent protection allowed (d) all of these

    Answer: _____   Section: _____._____

32. Luminaires installed in Class II, Division 1 locations must be identified for Class II locations and must be clearly marked to indicate the _____.

(a) maximum wattage of lamps for which designed   (b) minimum conductor size
(c) maximum overcurrent protection allowed   (d) all of these

Answer: _____   Section: _____._____

33. Luminaires more than _____ above the floor and switches located outside the patient vicinity are not required to be grounded by an insulated equipment grounding conductor in patient care areas.

(a) 7 1/2 ft   (b) 8 ft   (c) 10 ft   (d) 18 in.

Answer: _____   Section: _____._____

34. Meters, instruments and relays installed in Class I, Division 2 locations can have switches, circuit breakers, and make-and-break contacts of push buttons, relays, alarm bells, and horns installed in general purpose enclosures if current-interrupting contacts are _____.

(a) immersed in oil   (b) enclosed within a hermetically-sealed chamber
(c) a or b   (d) a and b

Answer: _____   Section: _____._____

35. Raceways permitted as a wiring method in a Class II, Division 2 hazardous (classified) location include _____.

(a) rigid metal conduit and intermediate metal conduit   (b) electrical metallic tubing
(c) rigid nonmetallic conduit   (d) a or b

Answer: _____   Section: _____._____

36. Receptacles located within the rooms, bathrooms, playrooms, activity rooms, and patient care areas of pediatric wards, rooms, or areas must be listed as _____.

(a) tamper resistant   (b) isolated   (c) GFCI protected   (d) specification grade

Answer: _____   Section: _____._____

37. The cover plates for receptacles, or the receptacles themselves, supplied from the emergency system of essential electrical systems in hospitals must have a distinctive color or marking so as to be readily identifiable.

(a) True   (b) False

Answer: _____   Section: _____._____

38. The emergency controls for attended self-service stations must be located no more than _____ from the gasoline dispensers.

(a) 20 ft   (b) 50 ft   (c) 75 ft   (d) 100 ft

Answer: _____   Section: _____._____

39. The floor area where Class 1 liquids are transferred is not classified if the enforcing agency determines that there is mechanical ventilation that provides a minimum of four air changes per hour or _____ cu ft per minute of exchanged air for each square foot of floor area (cfm/sq. ft).

(a) 1   (b) 2   (c) 3   (d) 4

Answer: _____   Section: _____._____

40. The *NEC* contains a section covering the sealing and drainage requirements for conduits and cables in Zone classified systems.

    (a) True   (b) False

    Answer: _____   Section: _____._____

41. The patient care area is any portion of a health care facility, including business offices, corridors, lounges, day rooms, dining rooms, or similar areas.

    (a) True   (b) False

    Answer: _____   Section: _____._____

42. The requirements of Article 511 apply to locations used for service and repair operations in connection with self-propelled vehicles such as _____, in which volatile flammable liquids or flammable gases are used for fuel or power.

    (a) buses   (b) trucks   (c) tractors   (d) all of these

    Answer: _____   Section: _____._____

43. The requirements of Article 517 (Health Care Facilities) apply to buildings or portions of buildings in which medical, _____, or surgical care is provided.

    (a) psychiatric   (b) nursing   (c) obstetrical   (d) any of these

    Answer: _____   Section: _____._____

44. When determining a Class I, Division 2 location, _____ is a factor that must be considered in determining the classification and extent of the location.

    (a) the quantity of flammable material that might escape in case of an accident
    (b) the adequacy of ventilating equipment
    (c) the record of the industry or business with respect to explosions or fires
    (d) all of these

    Answer: _____   Section: _____._____

45. When luminaires are installed in Class I, Division 2 locations where the surface temperature may, under normal operating conditions, reach surface temperatures exceeding 80 percent of the ignition temperature of the gas or vapor involved, _____ fixtures must be used.

    (a) Class I, Division 1   (b) Class I, Division 3   (c) Class II, Division 1   (d) Class II, Division 2

    Answer: _____   Section: _____._____

46. When seals are required for Class I locations, they must comply with the following rule(s):

    (a) They must be listed for Class I locations and must be accessible.
    (b) The minimum thickness of the sealing compound must not be less than the trade size of the sealing fitting and, in no case, less than 5/8 in.
    (c) Splices and taps must not be made in the conduit seal.
    (d) all of these

    Answer: _____   Section: _____._____

47. When shielded cables and twisted-pair cables are installed in Class I, Division 2 locations, the removal of the shielding material or separation of the twisted pairs is not required, provided the termination is by an approved means to minimize the entrance of _____ and prevent propagation of flame into the cable core.

(a) gases   (b) vapors   (c) dust   (d) a or b

Answer: _____   Section: _____._____

48. Where liquidtight flexible metal conduit (LFMC) or liquidtight flexible nonmetallic conduit (LFNC) is used in a Class II location, as permitted in 502.10, it must be installed with _____.

(a) an internal bonding jumper   (b) an external bonding jumper no more than 6 ft long
(c) a or b   (d) none of these

Answer: _____   Section: _____._____

49. Where liquidtight flexible metal conduit (LFMC) or liquidtight flexible nonmetallic conduit (LFNC) is used in a Class III location, as permitted in 504.10, it must be installed with _____.

(a) an internal bonding jumper   (b) an external bonding jumper no more than 6 ft long
(c) a or b   (d) none of these

Answer: _____   Section: _____._____

50. Within the vicinity of aircraft in an aircraft hanger, the area within 5 ft horizontally from aircraft power plants or aircraft fuel tanks is classified as a Class I, Division 2 or Zone 2 location that extends upward from the floor to a level of _____ above the upper surface of wings and of engine enclosures.

(a) 18 in.   (b) 3 ft   (c) 5 ft   (d) 20 ft

Answer: _____   Section: _____._____

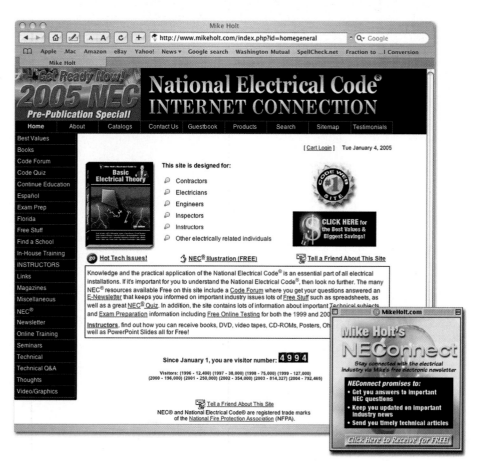

Get Ready Now!
2005 NEC

Order Mike's Code Change Library and SAVE OVER $450

1. The white conductor within a cable can be used for the ungrounded (hot) conductor, but the white conductor must be permanently reidentified to indicate its use as an ungrounded (hot) conductor at each location where the conductor is visible and accessible. Identification must _____.

    (a) be by painting or other effective means   (b) be a color other than white, gray, or green
    (c) both a and b   (d) none of these

    Answer: _____   Section: _____._____

2. The wiring contained inside which of the following are required to be accessible?

    (a) Outlet boxes   (b) Junction boxes   (c) Pull boxes   (d) all of these

    Answer: _____   Section: _____._____

3. The wiring for community television antenna systems must comply with Article 810 and the distribution coaxial wiring must comply with Article 820.

    (a) True   (b) False

    Answer: _____   Section: _____._____

4. The wiring for spas and hot tubs installed outdoors, such as receptacles, switches, lighting locations, grounding and bonding, and all topics covered in Parts I and II of Article 680, must comply with the same requirements as permanently installed pools except as permitted in 680.42(A) and (B).

    (a) True   (b) False

    Answer: _____   Section: _____._____

5. The wiring method used to supply signs and outline lighting systems must terminate within _____.

    (a) a sign   (b) an outline lighting system enclosure
    (c) a suitable box, or conduit body   (d) any of these

    Answer: _____   Section: _____._____

6. Totally-enclosed motors of the type specified in 501.125(A)(2) or (A)(3) must have no external surface with an operating temperature that exceeds _____ when operating in Class I, Division 1 locations.

    (a) absolute zero   (b) 80 percent of the ignition temperature of the gas or liquid involved
    (c) 100°C   (d) 40°C

    Answer: _____   Section: _____._____

7. Track lighting fittings are permitted to be equipped with general-purpose receptacles.

    (a) True   (b) False

    Answer: _____   Section: _____._____

8. Transformers and capacitors installed in Class I, Division 1 locations that do not contain flammable liquids are not required to be installed in vaults if they are approved for Class I locations.

   (a) True   (b) False

   Answer: _____   Section: _____._____

9. Transformers with ventilating openings must be installed so that the ventilating openings _____.

   (a) are a minimum 18 in. above the floor   (b) are not blocked by walls or obstructions
   (c) are aesthetically located   (d) are vented to the exterior of the building

   Answer: _____   Section: _____._____

10. Two 20A small-appliance branch circuits can supply more than one kitchen in a dwelling.

    (a) True   (b) False

    Answer: _____   Section: _____._____

11. Two or more grounding electrodes that are effectively bonded together are considered as a single grounding electrode system in this sense.

    (a) True   (b) False

    Answer: _____   Section: _____._____

12. Type _____ is a type of multiconductor cable permitted for use as an underground service-entrance cable.

    (a) SE   (b) NMC   (c) UF   (d) USE

    Answer: _____   Section: _____._____

13. Type CMX communications cables that are less than 1/4 in. in diameter can be installed in _____.

    (a) one- or two-family dwellings   (b) multifamily dwellings in nonconcealed spaces
    (c) a or b   (d) none of these

    Answer: _____   Section: _____._____

14. Type ITC cable can only be installed in industrial establishments where the conditions of maintenance and supervision ensure that only _____ will service the installation.

    (a) the authority having jurisdiction   (b) authorized persons
    (c) the general public   (d) qualified persons

    Answer: _____   Section: _____._____

15. Type MC cable installed in accessible attics or roof spaces must comply with the same requirements as given for AC cable in 320.24. This includes the installation of _____ to protect the cable when run across the top of floor joists if the space is accessible by permanent stairs or ladders.

    (a) GFCI protection   (b) Arc-fault protection   (c) rigid metal conduit   (d) guard strips

    Answer: _____   Section: _____._____

16. Type MC cable must be supported and secured at intervals not exceeding _____.

    (a) 3 ft   (b) 6 ft   (c) 4 ft   (d) 2 ft

    Answer: _____   Section: _____._____

17. Type NM and Type NMC cables must not be used in one- and two-family dwellings exceeding three floors above grade.

    (a) True   (b) False

    Answer: _____   Section: _____._____

18. Type NM cable installed through, or parallel to, framing members must be protected against physical damage in accordance with 300.4. Grommets or bushings for the protection of Type NM cable as required in 300.4(B)(1) must be _____ for the purpose, and they must remain in place.

    (a) marked   (b) approved   (c) identified   (d) listed

    Answer: _____   Section: _____._____

19. Type NM cable is allowed for wiring above a Class I location in a commercial garage.

    (a) True   (b) False

    Answer: _____   Section: _____._____

20. Type NM cable must be secured in place within _____ of every cabinet, box, or fitting.

    (a) 6 in.   (b) 10 in.   (c) 12 in.   (d) 18 in.

    Answer: _____   Section: _____._____

21. Type NM cable must closely follow the surface of the building finish or running boards when run exposed.

    (a) True   (b) False

    Answer: _____   Section: _____._____

22. Type NM cable, installed within accessible ceilings for the connections to luminaires and equipment, does not need to be secured within 12 in. from the luminaire or equipment when the free length does not exceed _____.

    (a) 4 1/2 ft   (b) 2 1/2 ft   (c) 3 1/2 ft   (d) any of these

    Answer: _____   Section: _____._____

23. Type S fuses, fuseholders, and adapters are required to be designed so that _____ would be difficult.

    (a) installation   (b) tampering   (c) shunting   (d) b or c

    Answer: _____   Section: _____._____

24. Type SE cable is permitted to be formed in a _____ and taped with self-sealing weather-resistant thermoplastic.

    (a) loop   (b) circle   (c) gooseneck   (d) none of these

    Answer: _____   Section: _____._____

25. Type SE service entrance cable may be used for interior wiring as long as it complies with the installation requirements of Parts I and II of Article 334, excluding 334.80.

    (a) True   (b) False

    Answer: _____   Section: _____._____

26. Under the optional method for calculating a single-family dwelling, general loads beyond the initial 10 kW are assessed at a _____ percent demand factor.

(a) 40   (b) 50   (c) 60   (d) 75

Answer: _____   Section: _____._____

27. Underground Feeder and branch circuit (Type UF) cable is allowed to be used as service entrance cable.

(a) True   (b) False

Answer: _____   Section: _____._____

28. Underground raceways and cable assemblies entering a handhole enclosure must extend into the enclosure, but they are not required to be _____.

(a) bonded
(b) insulated
(c) mechanically connected to the handhole enclosure
(d) below minimum cover requirements after leaving the handhole

Answer: _____   Section: _____._____

29. Underground wiring to gasoline dispensers must be installed in _____.

(a) threaded rigid metal conduit
(b) threaded intermediate metal conduit
(c) rigid nonmetallic conduit when buried under not less than 2 ft of cover
(d) any of these

Answer: _____   Section: _____._____

30. Unit equipment (battery packs) must be on the same branch circuit that serves the normal lighting in the area and connected _____ any local switches.

(a) with   (b) ahead of   (c) after   (d) none of these

Answer: _____   Section: _____._____

31. Unless specifically permitted in 240.4(E) through 240.4(G), the overcurrent protection must not exceed _____ after any correction factors for ambient temperature and the number of conductors has been applied.

(a) 15A for 14 AWG copper   (b) 20A for 12 AWG copper   (c) 30A for 10 AWG copper   (d) all of these

Answer: _____   Section: _____._____

32. Unused openings for circuit breakers and switches in switchboards and panelboards must be closed using _____ or other approved means that provide protection substantially equivalent to the wall of the enclosure.

(a) duct seal and tape   (b) identified closures   (c) exothermic welding   (d) sheet metal

Answer: _____   Section: _____._____

33. Using standard load calculations, the feeder demand factor for five household clothes dryers is _____ percent.

(a) 70   (b) 85   (c) 50   (d) 100

Answer: _____   Section: _____._____

34. Utilities include entities that install, operate, and maintain _____.

(a) communications systems (telephone, CATV, Internet, satellite, or data services)
(b) electric supply systems (generation, transmission, or distribution systems)
(c) Local Area Network wiring on premises
(d) a or b

Answer: _____   Section: _____._____

35. Vegetation such as trees must not be used for support of _____.

(a) overhead conductor spans   (b) surface wiring methods   (c) luminaires   (d) electric equipment

Answer: _____   Section: _____._____

36. Wet-niche luminaires that are not supplied by a flexible cord or flexible cable must be connected to an equipment grounding conductor that is not smaller than _____ AWG.

(a) 10   (b) 6   (c) 8   (d) 12

Answer: _____   Section: _____._____

37. What is the minimum size copper equipment bonding jumper required for equipment connected to a 40A circuit?

(a) 12 AWG   (b) 14 AWG   (c) 8 AWG   (d) 10 AWG

Answer: _____   Section: _____._____

38. When an electric-discharge luminaire is mounted directly over a concealed outlet box, which is not its sole means of support, the luminaire must provide access to the conductor wiring within the outlet box by means of suitable openings in the back of the fixture.

(a) True   (b) False

Answer: _____   Section: _____._____

39. When counting the number of conductors in a box, a conductor running through the box with no loop in it is counted as _____ conductor(s).

(a) one   (b) two   (c) zero   (d) none of these

Answer: _____   Section: _____._____

40. When ENT is installed concealed in walls, floors, and ceilings of buildings exceeding three floors above grade, a thermal barrier must be provided having a minimum _____-minute finish rating as listed for fire-rated assemblies.

(a) 5   (b) 10   (c) 15   (d) 30

Answer: _____   Section: _____._____

41. When equipment or devices are installed in ducts or plenum chambers used to transport environmental air, and illumination is necessary to facilitate maintenance and repair, enclosed _____-type luminaires are permitted.

(a) screw   (b) plug   (c) gasketed   (d) neon

Answer: _____   Section: _____._____

42. When flexible metal conduit is used to install equipment where flexibility is required, _____ must be installed.

(a) an equipment grounding conductor   (b) an expansion fitting
(c) flexible nonmetallic connectors   (d) a grounded conductor one size larger

Answer: _____   Section: _____._____

43. When LFNC is installed as an exposed raceway without need of flexibility, it must be securely fastened within _____ on each side of the box and must be fastened at intervals not exceeding _____.

    (a) 12 in., 4 1/2 ft   (b) 18 in., 3 ft   (c) 12 in., 3 ft   (d) 18 in., 4 ft

    Answer: _____   Section: _____._____

44. When metal raceways and cables with metal sheaths are connected to enclosures at oversized, concentric, or eccentric knockouts for circuits over 250V to ground that do not contain service conductors, the electrical continuity of the raceway or metal cable sheath must be ensured by bonding similar to the requirements for service raceways.

    (a) True   (b) False

    Answer: _____   Section: _____._____

45. When rigid nonmetallic conduit extends from the pool light forming shell to a suitable junction box, an 8 AWG _____ conductor must be installed in the raceway.

    (a) solid bare   (b) solid insulated   (c) stranded insulated   (d) b or c

    Answer: _____   Section: _____._____

46. When the service disconnecting means consists of more than one switch or circuit breaker, the combined ratings of all the switches or circuit breakers used _____ than the rating required by 230.79.

    (a) must be less   (b) must not be less   (c) must be more   (d) none of these

    Answer: _____   Section: _____._____

47. When the service disconnecting means is a power-operated switch or circuit breaker, it must be able to be opened by hand in the event of a _____.

    (a) ground fault   (b) short circuit   (c) power surge   (d) power-supply failure

    Answer: _____   Section: _____._____

48. When Type AC cable is run across the top of a floor joist in an attic without permanent ladders or stairs, substantial guard strips within _____ of the scuttle hole, or attic entrance, must protect the cable.

    (a) 7 ft   (b) 6 ft   (c) 5 ft   (d) 3 ft

    Answer: _____   Section: _____._____

49. When unable to maintain the minimum required distance from the edge of a wood framing member to a bored hole for cable or nonmetallic raceway installation, the cable or raceway must be protected from penetration by screws or nails by a steel plate or bushing at least _____ and of appropriate length and width to cover the area of the wiring. A thinner plate that provides equal or better protection may be used if listed and marked.

    (a) 1/4 in. thick   (b) 1/8 in. thick   (c) 1/16 in. thick   (d) 24 gauge

    Answer: _____   Section: _____._____

50. Where a box is used as the sole support of a ceiling-suspended (paddle) fan, the box must be listed for the application and must be marked with the weight of the fan to be supported if over 35 lbs.

    (a) True   (b) False

    Answer: _____   Section: _____._____

(• Indicates that 75% or fewer exam takers get the question correct)

Article 517 Health Care Facilities (continue)

1. The receptacles or the cover plates for the receptacles supplied from the emergency system for essential electrical systems in nursing homes must have a distinctive color or marking so as to be readily identifiable.

    (a) True   (b) False

    Answer: _____   Section: _____._____

2. In a health care facility, receptacles and attachment plugs in a hazardous (classified) location within an anesthetizing area must be listed for use in Class I, Group _____ locations.

    (a) A   (b) B   (c) C   (d) D

    Answer: _____   Section: _____._____

3. Equivalent insulation and isolation to that required for the electrical distribution systems in patient care areas must be provided for communications, signaling systems, data system circuits, fire alarm systems, and systems less than _____, nominal in health care facilities.

    (a) 600V   (b) 120V   (c) 50V   (d) 24V

    Answer: _____   Section: _____._____

Article 518 Assembly Occupancies

This article covers all buildings or portions of buildings or structures specifically designed or intended for the assembly of 100 or more persons.

4. An assembly occupancy is a building, portion of a building, or structure designed or intended for the assembly of _____ or more persons.

    (a) 50   (b) 100   (c) 150   (d) 200

    Answer: _____   Section: _____._____

5. For temporary wiring in assembly occupancies, such as exhibition halls used for display booths, the wiring must be installed in accordance with Article 590, except _____.

    (a) the GFCI requirements of 590.6 do not apply
    (b) hard or extra-hard usage cords and cables are permitted to be laid on floors where protected from the general public
    (c) no cords are allowed
    (d) a and b

    Answer: _____   Section: _____._____

6. In assembly occupancies, nonmetallic raceways encased in not less than _____ of concrete are permitted.

    (a) 1 in.   (b) 2 in.   (c) 3 in.   (d) none of these

    Answer: _____   Section: _____._____

Article 520 Theaters, Audience Areas of Motion Picture and Television Studios, Performance Areas, and Similar Locations

This article covers all buildings or that part of a building or structure, indoor or outdoor, designed or used for presentation, dramatic, musical, motion picture projection, or similar purposes and to specific audience seating areas within motion picture or television studios.

7. •Article 520 locations include the performance area, which encompasses the stage and audience seating area associated with a _____ stage structure, whether indoors or outdoors, which is used for the presentation of theatrical or musical productions or public presentations.

    (a) temporary   (b) permanent   (c) a or b   (d) a and b

    Answer: _____   Section: _____._____

8. The wiring methods in theaters, audience areas of motion picture and television studios, performance areas, and similar locations for control, signal, and communications circuits can be _____.

    (a) communications circuits as provided in Article 800
    (b) Class 2 remote-control and signaling circuits as provided in Article 725
    (c) type NM cable
    (d) a or b, but not c

    Answer: _____   Section: _____._____

9. On fixed stage equipment, portable strip lights and connector strips must be wired with conductors having insulation rated suitable for the temperature but not less than _____.

    (a) 75°C   (b) 90°C   (c) 125°C   (d) 200°C

    Answer: _____   Section: _____._____

10. Flexible conductors, including cable extensions, used to supply portable stage equipment must be _____ cords or cables.

    (a) listed   (b) extra-hard usage   (c) hard usage   (d) a and b

    Answer: _____   Section: _____._____

Article 525 Carnivals, Circuses, Fairs, and Similar Events

This article covers the installation of portable wiring and equipment for carnivals, circuses, exhibitions, fairs, traveling attractions, and similar functions, including wiring in or on all structures.

11. Electrical wiring in and around water attractions such as bumper boats for carnivals, circuses, and fairs must comply with the requirements of Article 680—Swimming Pools, Fountains, and Similar Installations.

    (a) True   (b) False

    Answer: _____   Section: _____._____

12. At carnivals, circuses, and similar events, electrical equipment and wiring methods in or on rides, concessions, or other units must be provided with mechanical protection where such equipment or wiring methods are subject to _____.

    (a) public access   (b) physical damage   (c) exposure to the weather   (d) operator access

    Answer: _____   Section: _____._____

13. At carnivals, circuses, and similar events, service equipment must be mounted on a solid backing and be installed so as to be protected from the weather, unless _____.

    (a) the location is a mild climate   (b) installed for less than 90 days
    (c) of weatherproof construction   (d) a or b

    Answer: _____   Section: _____._____

14. When installed indoors for carnivals, circuses, and fairs, flexible cords and flexible cables must be listed for wet locations and must be sunlight resistant.

    (a) True   (b) False

    Answer: _____   Section: _____._____

15. Wiring for an amusement ride, attraction, tent, or similar structure must not be supported by any other ride or structure unless specifically designed for the purpose.

    (a) True   (b) False

    Answer: _____   Section: _____._____

16. Wiring for temporary lighting located inside tents and concession areas at carnivals, circuses, and fairs must be securely installed, and where subject to physical damage, must be provided with mechanical protection.

    (a) True   (b) False

    Answer: _____   Section: _____._____

17. GFCI protection for personnel is required at carnivals, circuses, and fairs for all 15 and 20A, 125V, single-phase receptacle outlets that are readily accessible to the general public.

    (a) True   (b) False

    Answer: _____   Section: _____._____

18.   GFCI protection is not permitted at carnivals, circuses, and fairs for _____.

(a) sign lighting   (b) equipment that is not readily accessible to the general public
(c) egress lighting   (d) circuits servicing spot lights

Answer: _____   Section: _____._____

Article 530 Motion Picture and Television Studios and Similar Locations

The requirements of this article apply to television studios and motion picture studios using either film or electronic cameras, and exchanges, factories, laboratories, stages, or a portion of the building in which film or tape more than 7/8 in. in width is exposed, developed, printed, cut, edited, rewound, repaired, or stored.

19.   Each receptacle of dc plugging boxes must be rated at not _____ when used on a stage or set of a motion picture studio.

(a) more than 30A   (b) less than 20A   (c) less than 30A   (d) more than 20A

Answer: _____   Section: _____._____

Article 540 Motion Picture Projection Rooms

The provisions of this article apply to motion picture projection rooms, motion picture projectors, and associated equipment of the professional and nonprofessional types using incandescent, carbon arc, xenon, or other light source equipment that develops hazardous gases, dust, or radiation.

20.   A switch for the control of parking lights in a theater may be installed inside the projection booth.

(a) True   (b) False

Answer: _____   Section: _____._____

Article 545 Manufactured Buildings

This article covers requirements for a manufactured building and building components as herein defined.

21.   The *NEC* specifies wiring methods for prefabricated buildings (manufactured buildings).

(a) True   (b) False

Answer: _____   Section: _____._____

22.   Service-entrance conductors for a manufactured building must be installed _____.

(a) after erection at the building site
(b) before erection only where the point of attachment is known prior to manufacture
(c) before erection at the building site
(d) a or b

Answer: _____   Section: _____._____

Article 547 Agricultural Buildings

The provisions of this article apply to agricultural buildings or those parts of buildings or adjacent areas where excessive dust or dust with water may accumulate, or where a corrosive atmosphere exists.

23. Agricultural buildings where a corrosive atmosphere exists include areas with conditions such as _____.

(a) poultry and animal excrement which may cause corrosive vapors
(b) corrosive particles which may combine with water
(c) an area that is damp and wet by reason of periodic washing
(d) all of these

Answer: _____   Section: _____._____

24. The distribution point is also known as the _____.

(a) center yard pole   (b) meter pole
(c) common distribution point   (d) all of these

Answer: _____   Section: _____._____

25. The purpose of the equipotential plane is to prevent a difference in voltage within the plane area.

(a) True   (b) False

Answer: _____   Section: _____._____

26. All cables installed in agricultural buildings must be secured within _____ of each cabinet, box, or fitting.

(a) 8 in.   (b) 12 in.   (c) 10 in.   (d) 18 in.

Answer: _____   Section: _____._____

27. In damp or wet locations of agricultural buildings, equipment enclosures and fittings must be located or equipped to prevent moisture from _____ within the enclosure, box, conduit body, or fitting.

(a) entering   (b) accumulating   (c) a or b   (d) none of these

Answer: _____   Section: _____._____

28. Where _____ may be present in an agricultural building, enclosures and fittings must have corrosion-resistance properties suitable for the conditions.

(a) wet dust   (b) corrosive gases or vapors   (c) other corrosive conditions   (d) any of these

Answer: _____   Section: _____._____

29. An equipotential plane is not required in dirt confinement areas containing metallic equipment that is accessible to animals and may become energized. GFCI protection must be provided for all 15 and 20A general-purpose receptacles located in the dirt confinement areas.

(a) True   (b) False

Answer: _____   Section: _____._____

30. Where livestock is housed, that portion of the equipment grounding conductor run underground to the building or structure from a distribution point must be insulated or covered _____.

    (a) aluminum   (b) copper   (c) copper-clad aluminum   (d) none of these

    Answer: _____   Section: _____._____

31. Outdoor livestock confinement areas, such as feedlots, must have equipotential planes installed around metallic equipment that is accessible to animals and may become energized. The equipotential plane must encompass the area around the equipment where the animal stands while accessing the equipment.

    (a) True   (b) False

    Answer: _____   Section: _____._____

Article 550 Mobile Homes, Manufactured Homes, and Mobile Home Parks

The provisions of this article cover the electrical conductors and equipment installed within or on mobile or manufactured homes, the conductors that connect mobile or manufactured homes to a supply of electricity, and the installation of electrical wiring, fixtures, and equipment.

32. In reference to mobile/manufactured homes, examples of portable appliances could be _____, but only if these appliances are cord connected and not hard wired.

    (a) refrigerators   (b) range equipment   (c) clothes washers   (d) all of these

    Answer: _____   Section: _____._____

33. For the purpose of the *Code*, unless otherwise indicated the term mobile home includes manufactured homes.

    (a) True   (b) False

    Answer: _____   Section: _____._____

34. The power supply to the mobile home must be _____.

    (a) one listed 50A mobile home power-supply cord with attachment plug
    (b) a permanently-installed feederv(c) a or b
    (d) none of these

    Answer: _____   Section: _____._____

35. Ground-fault circuit-interrupter (GFCI) protection in a mobile home is required for _____.

    (a) receptacle outlets installed outdoors and in compartments accessible from outside
    (b) receptacles within 6 ft of a wet bar sink and serving kitchen countertops
    (c) all receptacles in bathrooms including receptacles in luminaires (light fixtures)
    (d) all of these

    Answer: _____   Section: _____._____

36. The receptacle outlet for mobile and manufactured home heat tape that is used to protect cold water inlet piping must be _____ protected and it must be connected to an interior branch circuit other than a small appliance branch circuit where all of the outlets of the circuit are on the load side of the _____.

    (a) AFCI   (b) GFCI   (c) a or b   (d) none of these

    Answer: _____   Section: _____._____

37. All branch circuits that supply 15 and 20A, 125V outlets in bedrooms of mobile homes and manufactured homes must be protected by _____.

(a) GFCIs   (b) weatherproof-in-use covers
(c) AFCIs   (d) none of these

Answer: _____   Section: _____._____

38. •What is the total park electrical wiring system load, after applying the demand factors permitted in Article 550, for a small mobile home park having six mobile homes?

(a) 4,640 VA   (b) 27,840 VA   (c) 96,000 VA   (d) none of these

Answer: _____   Section: _____._____

39. Service equipment for a manufactured home can be installed in or on a manufactured home provided that all of seven conditions are met. Which of the following are included in the seven conditions?

(a) The manufacturer must include in its written installation instructions information indicating that the home must be secured in place by an anchoring system or installed on and secured to a permanent foundation.
(b) The manufacturer must include in its written installation instructions one method of grounding the service equipment at the installation site. The instructions must clearly state that other methods of grounding are found in Article 250.
(c) A red warning label must be mounted on or adjacent to the service equipment "WARNING DO NOT PROVIDE ELECTRICAL POWER UNTIL THE GROUNDING ELECTRODE SYSTEM IS INSTALLED AND CONNECTED".
(d) all of these

Answer: _____   Section: _____._____

40. An outdoor disconnecting means for a mobile home must be installed so the bottom of the enclosure is not less than _____ above the finished grade or working platform.

(a) 1 ft   (b) 2 ft   (c) 3 ft   (d) 6 ft

Answer: _____   Section: _____._____

41. Mobile home and manufactured home lot feeder circuit conductors must have adequate capacity for the loads supplied and must be rated at not less than _____ at 120/240V.

(a) 50A   (b) 60A   (c) 100A   (d) 200A

Answer: _____   Section: _____._____

Article 551 Recreational Vehicles and Recreational Vehicle Parks

The provisions of this article cover the electrical conductors and equipment other than low-voltage and automotive vehicle circuits or extensions thereof, installed within or on recreational vehicles, the conductors that connect recreational vehicles to a supply of electricity, and the installation of equipment and devices related to electrical installations within a recreational vehicle park.

42. A minimum of 20 percent of all recreational vehicle sites with electrical supply must each be equipped with a _____,125/250V receptacle.

(a) 15A   (b) 20A   (c) 30A   (d) 50A

Answer: _____   Section: _____._____

43. •Electrical service and feeders of a recreational vehicle park must be calculated at a minimum of _____ per site equipped with only 20A supply facilities (not including tent sites).

(a) 1,200 VA   (b) 2,400 VA   (c) 3,600 VA   (d) 9,600 VA

Answer: _____   Section: _____._____

Article 555 Marinas and Boatyards

This article covers the installation of wiring and equipment in the areas that comprise fixed or floating piers, wharves, docks, and other areas in marinas, boatyards, boat basins, boathouses, and similar occupancies that are used, or intended to be used, for the purpose of repair, berthing, launching, storing or fueling of small craft and the mooring of floating buildings. This article doesn't apply to docks or boathouses for single-family dwelling units.

44. Private, noncommercial docking facilities _____ for the use of the owner or residents of the associated single-family dwelling are not covered by Article 555.

(a) constructed   (b) occupied   (c) a or b   (d) a and d

Answer: _____   Section: _____._____

45. A _____ is an enclosed assembly that can include receptacles, circuit breakers, fused switches, fuses, watt-hour meter(s), and monitoring means approved for marine use. All such enclosures must have a weep hole to discharge condensation.

(a) marine power receptacle   (b) marine outlet   (c) marine power outlet   (d) any of these

Answer: _____   Section: _____._____

46. Service equipment for floating docks or marinas must be located _____ the floating structure.

(a) adjacent to   (b) on   (c) 100 ft from   (d) 20 ft from

Answer: _____   Section: _____._____

47. The feeder for six 30A receptacles supplying shore power for boats must be calculated at _____ percent of the sum of the rating of the receptacles.

(a) 70   (b) 80   (c) 90   (d) 100

Answer: _____   Section: _____._____

48. Where shore power accommodations provide two receptacles specifically for an individual boat slip, and these receptacles have different voltages, only the receptacle with the _____ is required to be calculated.

(a) smaller kW demand   (b) larger kW demand   (c) higher voltage   (d) none of these

Answer: _____   Section: _____._____

49. The disconnecting means for a boat must be readily accessible, not more than _____ from the receptacle it controls and must be in the supply circuit ahead of the receptacle.

(a) 12 in.   (b) 24 in.   (c) 30 in.   (d) none of these

Answer: _____   Section: _____._____

50. Fifteen and 20A, single-phase, 125V receptacles used for "other than shore power" in marinas used for storage, maintenance, or repair must be provided with _____.

    (a) lockouts   (b) GFCI protection for personnel
    (c) warning labels   (d) shore power adapters

    Answer: _____   Section: _____._____

51. Electrical wiring and equipment at marine craft repair facilities containing flammable or combustible liquids or gases must comply with the requirements contained in _____

    (a) Article 511   (b) Article 555   (c) Article 513   (d) a and b

    Answer: _____   Section: _____._____

Article 590 Temporary Installations

This article applies to temporary power and lighting for construction, remodeling, maintenance, repair, demolitions, and decorative lighting. This article also applies when temporary installations are necessary.

52. There is no time limit for temporary electrical power and lighting except that it must be removed upon completion of _____, or similar activities.

    (a) construction or remodeling   (b) maintenance or repair
    (c) demolition of buildings   (d) all of these

    Answer: _____   Section: _____._____

53. Temporary electrical power and lighting is permitted during emergencies and for _____.

    (a) tests   (b) experiments   (c) developmental work   (d) all of these

    Answer: _____   Section: _____._____

54. Services for temporary installations are not required to comply with the requirements of Article 230.

    (a) True   (b) False

    Answer: _____   Section: _____._____

55. NM and NMC cables can be used for temporary wiring as branch circuits in structures of a height of _____.

    (a) 18 ft   (b) 3 stories   (c) 4 stories   (d) no limit

    Answer: _____   Section: _____._____

56. Single insulated open conductors can be used for a period not to exceed 90 days for holiday decorative lighting and similar purposes when the circuit voltage-to-ground does not exceed _____.

    (a) 50V   (b) 125V   (c) 150V   (d) 277V

    Answer: _____   Section: _____._____

57. Receptacles for construction sites must not be installed on the _____ as temporary lighting or connected to _____ that supply temporary lighting.

    (a) same branch circuit, the same feeders
    (b) same feeders, the same ungrounded conductor of multiwire branch circuits
    (c) same branch circuit, the same ungrounded conductor of multiwire circuits
    (d) all of these

    Answer: _____   Section: _____._____

58. At construction sites, boxes are not required for temporary wiring splices of _____.

    (a) multiconductor cords   (b) multiconductor cables   (c) a or b   (d) none of these

    Answer: _____   Section: _____._____

59. For temporary installations, cable assemblies, as well as flexible cords and flexible cables, must be supported at intervals that ensure protection from physical damage. Support must be in the form of _____ or similar type fittings installed so as not to cause damage.

    (a) staples   (b) cable ties   (c) straps   (d) any of these

    Answer: _____   Section: _____._____

60. All _____, 125V, single-phase receptacle outlets that are not a part of the permanent wiring of the building or structure and are in use by personnel for temporary power must have ground-fault circuit-interrupter protection for personnel.

    (a) 15A   (b) 20A   (c) 30A   (d) all of these

    Answer: _____   Section: _____._____

61. Receptacles rated other than 125V single-phase 15, 20, and 30A for temporary installations must be protected by _____.

    (a) a GFCI device   (b) the Assured Equipment Grounding Conductor Program
    (c) an AFCI device   (d) a or b

    Answer: _____   Section: _____._____

Chapter 6 Special Equipment

Article 600 Electric Signs and Outline Lighting

This article covers the installation of conductors and equipment for electric signs and outline lighting as defined in Article 100. Electric signs and outline lighting include all products and installations that utilize neon tubing, such as signs, decorative elements, skeleton tubing, or art forms.

62. Electric signs and outline lighting—fixed, mobile, or portable-are not required to be listed.

    (a) True   (b) False

    Answer: _____   Section: _____._____

63. Branch circuits that supply signs and outline lighting systems containing incandescent and fluorescent forms of illumination must be rated not to exceed _____.

    (a) 20A   (b) 30A   (c) 40A   (d) 50A

    Answer: _____   Section: _____._____

64. Metal poles used to support signs can contain the sign circuit conductors, provided the _____ are installed in accordance with the requirements contained in 410.15(B).

    (a) poles   (b) conductors   (c) safety chains   (d) a and b

    Answer: _____   Section: _____._____

65. The disconnecting means for each circuit leading to a sign located within a fountain must be located in accordance with _____.

    (a) 430.102   (b) 440.14   (c) 680.12   (d) any of these

    Answer: _____   Section: _____._____

66. Sign and outline lighting enclosures for live parts other than lamps and neon tubing must _____.

    (a) have ample structural strength and rigidity   (b) be constructed of metal or must be listed
    (c) be at least 0.016 in. thick if of sheet steel   (d) all of these

    Answer: _____   Section: _____._____

67. Neon tubing, other than _____ accessible to pedestrians, must be protected from physical damage.

    (a) Class I, Division 1 locations   (b) dry location portable signs
    (c) fixed equipment   (d) wet location portable signs

    Answer: _____   Section: _____._____

68. The spacing in signs and outline lighting between wood or other combustible materials and an incandescent or HID lamp or lampholder must not be less than _____.

    (a) 18 in.   (b) 2 ft   (c) 2 in.   (d) 6 in.

    Answer: _____   Section: _____._____

69. A portable or mobile electric sign in a wet or damp location must have a ground-fault circuit interrupter _____.

    (a) located on the sign
    (b) located in the power supply cord within 12 in. of the attachment plug
    (c) as an integral part of the attachment plug of the supply cord
    (d) b or c

    Answer: _____   Section: _____._____

70. Ballasts, transformers, and electronic power supplies for signs installed in suspended ceilings can be connected to the branch circuit by a _____.

    (a) fixed wiring method   (b) flexible wiring method   (c) flexible cord   (d) a or b

    Answer: _____   Section: _____._____

Article 604 Manufactured Wiring Systems

The provisions of Article 604 apply to field-installed manufactured wiring systems used for branch circuits, remote-control circuits, signaling circuits, and communications circuits in accessible areas. The components of a listed manufactured wiring system can be assembled together at the jobsite.

71. A manufactured wiring system is a system assembled by a manufacturer, which cannot be inspected at the building site without _____.

(a) a permit   (b) a manufacturer's representative present
(c) damage or destruction to the assembly   (d) an engineer's supervision

Answer: _____   Section: _____._____

72. Manufactured wiring systems are permitted in _____ locations and in plenums and spaces used for environmental air, where installed in accordance with 300.22.

(a) accessible   (b) dry   (c) wet   (d) both a and b

Answer: _____   Section: _____._____

73. Each section of a manufactured wiring system must be marked to identify _____.

(a) its location   (b) the type of cable, flexible cord, or conduit
(c) the size of the wires installed   (d) its suitability for wet or damp locations

Answer: _____   Section: _____._____

Article 605 Office Furnishings (Wired Partitions)

This article covers electrical equipment, lighting accessories, and wiring systems used to connect, or contained in or on, relocatable partitions. Partitions can be fixed or freestanding and can have communications, signaling, and optical fiber cable wiring in addition to wiring for receptacles and lighting.

74. Wiring systems for the wiring of office furnishings must be identified as suitable for providing power for lighting accessories and appliances in wired partitions. These partitions are allowed to extend from the floor to above the ceiling.

(a) True   (b) False

Answer: _____   Section: _____._____

75. Wired partitions for office furnishings that are fixed (secured to building surfaces) must be permanently connected to the building electrical system by a Chapter 3 wiring method.

(a) True   (b) False

Answer: _____   Section: _____._____

Article 610 Cranes and Hoists

This article covers the installation of electrical equipment and wiring used in connection with cranes, monorail hoists, hoists, and all runways.

76. All exposed noncurrent-carrying metal parts of cranes, hoists, and accessories must _____ a continuous electrical conductor.

(a) be bonded with 6 AWG or larger conductors to   (b) be metallically joined together to
(c) have supplementary ground rods every 20 ft connected to   (d) not be grounded or made into

Answer: _____   Section: _____._____

Article 620 Elevators, Escalators, and Moving Walks

This article covers the installation of electrical equipment and wiring used in connection with elevators, dumbwaiters, escalators, moving walks, wheelchair lifts, and stairway chair lifts.

77. •The minimum size parallel conductors permitted for elevator lighting are _____, provided the combined ampacity is equivalent to at least that of a 14 AWG wire.

    (a) 14 AWG   (b) 20 AWG   (c) 16 AWG   (d) 1/0 AWG

    Answer: _____   Section: _____._____

78. A separate _____ is required for the elevator car lights, receptacle(s), auxiliary lighting power source, and ventilation on each elevator car.

    (a) branch circuit   (b) disconnecting means   (c) connection   (d) none of these

    Answer: _____   Section: _____._____

79. An elevator machine room _____ must be located at the point of entry to such machine rooms/machinery spaces.

    (a) directory   (b) lighting switch
    (c) control circuit disconnecting means   (d) emergency exit map

    Answer: _____   Section: _____._____

80. A separate _____ must supply the elevator hoistway pit lighting and receptacle(s). The required lighting must not be connected to the load side of a ground-fault circuit interrupter.

    (a) feeder   (b) sub-panel   (c) emergency system   (d) branch circuit

    Answer: _____   Section: _____._____

81. At least _____ 15 or 20A, 125V, single-phase, duplex receptacle(s) must be provided in the hoistway pit.

    (a) one   (b) two   (c) three   (d) four

    Answer: _____   Section: _____._____

82. Where multiple driving machines are connected to a single elevator, escalator, moving walk, or pumping unit, there must be one disconnecting means to disconnect the _____.

    (a) motor(s)   (b) control valve operating magnets
    (c) a and b   (d) none of these

    Answer: _____   Section: _____._____

83. No provision must be made to open or close the disconnecting means for an elevator from any other part of the premises. If sprinklers are installed in hoistways, machine rooms, control rooms, machinery spaces, or control spaces, the disconnecting means is permitted to automatically _____ the power supply to the affected elevator(s) prior to the application of water.

    (a) open   (b) close   (c) a or b   (d) none of these

    Answer: _____   Section: _____._____

84. Where there is more than one driving machine in an elevator machine room, the disconnecting means must be numbered to correspond to the identifying number of the _____.

(a) driving machine they control
(b) circuit feeding it
(c) panel it is fed from
(d) all of these

Answer: _____   Section: _____._____

85. All 15 and 20A, 125V single-phase receptacles installed in machine rooms and machinery spaces for elevators, escalators, moving walks, and lifts must have ground-fault circuit-interrupter protection by a _____.

(a) GFCI receptacle   (b) GFCI circuit breaker   (c) a or b   (d) none of these

Answer: _____   Section: _____._____

86. Each elevator must have a single means for disconnecting all ungrounded main power supply conductors for each unit _____.

(a) excluding the emergency power system
(b) including the emergency or standby power system
(c) excluding the emergency power system if it is automatic
(d) and the power supply may not be an emergency power system

Answer: _____   Section: _____._____

Article 625 Electric Vehicle Charging Systems

Article 625 covers conductors and equipment external to electric vehicles that are used for electric vehicle charging. This only applies to automotive-type vehicles for highway use.

87. According to Article 625, automotive-type vehicles for highway use include _____.

(a) passenger automobiles
(b) trucks
(c) neighborhood electric vehicles
(d) all of these

Answer: _____   Section: _____._____

88. For plug-connected electric vehicle supply equipment, the listed system of personnel protection can be _____.

(a) an integral part of the attachment plug
(b) in the power supply cable not more than 12 in. from the attachment plug
(c) a or b
(d) none of these

Answer: _____   Section: _____._____

89. Electric vehicle supply equipment that is identified for and intended to be interconnected to a vehicle, and also serve _____, must be listed as suitable for that purpose.

(a) as an optional standby system
(b) as an electric power production source
(c) to provide bidirectional power feed
(d) all of these

Answer: _____   Section: _____._____

Article 630 Electric Welders

Article 630 covers the wiring of arc welders, resistance welders, and other welding equipment connected to an electric supply system.

90. Feeder conductors that supply a group of welders must have an ampacity not less than the sum of the currents, as determined in accordance with 630.11(A) based on _____ percent of the two largest welders, 85 percent for the third largest welder, 70 percent for the fourth largest welder, and 60 percent for all remaining welders.

    (a) 90   (b) 100   (c) 125   (d) 250

    Answer: _____   Section: _____._____

91. A disconnecting means must be provided in the supply circuit for each arc welder that is not equipped with _____.

    (a) a governor   (b) a shunt trip breaker
    (c) an integral disconnect (d) ground-fault circuit-interrupter protection

    Answer: _____   Section: _____._____

92. Each resistance welder must have an overcurrent device rated or set at not more than _____ percent of the rated primary current of the welder.

    (a) 80   (b) 100   (c) 125   (d) 300

    Answer: _____   Section: _____._____

93. A _____ must be provided to disconnect each resistance welder and its control equipment from the supply circuit.

    (a) switch   (b) circuit breaker   (c) magnetic starter   (d) a or b

    Answer: _____   Section: _____._____

Article 640 Audio Signal Processing, Amplification, and Reproduction Equipment

This article covers equipment and wiring for audio signal generation, recording, processing, amplification and reproduction, distribution of sound, public address, speech input systems, temporary audio system installations, and electronic musical instruments such as electric organs, electric guitars, and electronic drums/percussion instruments.

94. Installed audio distribution cable that is not terminated at equipment and not identified for future use with a tag is considered abandoned.

    (a) True   (b) False

    Answer: _____   Section: _____._____

95. Amplifiers, loudspeakers, and other equipment covered by Article 640 must be so located or protected so as to guard against environmental or physical damage that might cause _____.

    (a) a fire   (b) shock   (c) personal hazard   (d) all of these

    Answer: _____   Section: _____._____

96. Audio system equipment supplied by branch circuit power must not be located within _____ of the inside wall of a pool, spa, hot tub, fountain, or tidal high-water mark.

    (a) 2 ft   (b) 10 ft   (c) 5 ft   (d) 18 in.

    Answer: _____   Section: _____._____

97. Flexible cords and flexible cables are not allowed for the electrical connection of permanently installed equipment racks of audio systems to the premises wiring to facilitate access to equipment.

    (a) True   (b) False

    Answer: _____   Section: _____._____

98. The number of conductors permitted in a single conduit or tubing in a permanent audio system installation is not required to follow the percentage fill specified in Table 1, Chapter 9.

    (a) True   (b) False

    Answer: _____   Section: _____._____

Article 645 Information Technology Equipment

Article 645 covers equipment, power-supply wiring, equipment interconnecting wiring, grounding, and bonding of information technology equipment and systems, including terminal units in an information technology equipment room.

99. An information technology equipment room must have _____.

    (a) a disconnecting means complying with 645.10.   (b) a separate heating/ventilating/air conditioning system
    (c) separation by fire-resistance rated walls, floors, and ceiling   (d) all of these

    Answer: _____   Section: _____._____

100. Branch-circuit conductors for data-processing equipment must have an ampacity not less than _____ of the total connected load.

    (a) 80 percent   (b) 100 percent   (c) 125 percent   (d) the sum

    Answer: _____   Section: _____._____

1. In a location where flammable anesthetics are employed, the entire area that extends _____ is classified as Class I, Division 1.

    (a) upward to the structural ceiling
    (c) upward to a level 5 ft above the floor

    (b) upward to a level 8 ft above the floor
    (d) 10 ft in all directions

    Answer: _____   Section: _____._____

2. A mobile home not intended as a dwelling unit such as a unit used for offices, construction job dormitories, or other similar uses, is still required to meet all of the provisions of Article 550 including the capacity of the circuits and the service size.

    (a) True   (b) False

    Answer: _____   Section: _____._____

3. A professional-type projector uses _____ film and has on each edge 212 perforations per meter, or a type using carbon arc, xenon, or other light source equipment that develops hazardous gases, dust, or radiation.

    (a) 35 mm   (b) 70 mm   (c) a or b   (d) none of these

    Answer: _____   Section: _____._____

4. A separate branch circuit must supply elevator machine room/machinery space lighting and receptacle(s). The required lighting must not be connected to the load side of _____.

    (a) a local subpanel
    (c) an HID type circuit breaker

    (b) an SWD type circuit breaker
    (d) a ground-fault circuit interrupter

    Answer: _____   Section: _____._____

5. All abandoned audio distribution cables must be removed.

    (a) True   (b) False

    Answer: _____   Section: _____._____

6. An electric vehicle that falls within the scope of Article 625 could be _____.

    (a) an automotive-type vehicle for highway use
    (c) an electric golf cart

    (b) an automotive-type vehicle for off-road use
    (d) any of these

    Answer: _____   Section: _____._____

7. At carnivals, circuses, and fairs GFCI protection is not required for receptacles that only facilitate the quick disconnecting and reconnecting of electrical equipment and are of the locking type.

    (a) True   (b) False

    Answer: _____   Section: _____._____

8. Audio system equipment (speakers) powered by a listed Class 2 power supply, or by the output of an amplifier listed for use with Class 2 wiring, must only be restricted in its placement by _____.

(a) the manufacturer's recommendations   (b) 640.10(A), within 6 ft of water

(c) the local authority having jurisdiction   (d) the desires of the owner

Answer: _____   Section: _____._____

9. Conductors that supply one or more resistance welders must be protected by an overcurrent device rated or set at not more than _____ percent of the conductor rating.

(a) 80   (b) 100   (c) 125   (d) 300

Answer: _____   Section: _____._____

10. Duty on escalator and moving walk driving machine motors must be rated as _____.

(a) full time   (b) continuous   (c) various   (d) long term

Answer: _____   Section: _____._____

11. Each arc welder must have overcurrent protection rated or set at not more than _____ percent of the rated primary current of the welder.

(a) 100   (b) 125   (c) 150   (d) 200

Answer: _____   Section: _____._____

12. Each commercial building, and each commercial occupancy with ground floor access for pedestrians, must have at least one outside sign outlet in an accessible location at each entrance. The outlet(s) must be supplied by a branch circuit rated at least _____ that supplies no other load.

(a) 15A   (b) 20A   (c) a or b   (d) none of these

Answer: _____   Section: _____._____

13. Each ride and concession at a carnival, circus, or similar event must be provided with a fused disconnect switch or circuit breaker within sight and within _____ of the operator's station. The disconnecting means must be readily accessible to the operator, including when the ride is in operation.

(a) 25 ft   (b) 6 ft   (c) 18 in.   (d) 10 ft

Answer: _____   Section: _____._____

14. Each sign and outline lighting system, or feeder/branch circuit supplying a sign or outline lighting system, must be controlled by an externally operable switch or circuit breaker that opens all _____ conductors.

(a) ungrounded   (b) grounded   (c) grounding   (d) all of these

Answer: _____   Section: _____._____

15. Electric vehicle supply equipment must have a listed system of protection against electric shock of personnel.

(a) True   (b) False

Answer: _____   Section: _____._____

16. Except as specifically modified by Article 590, all other requirements of the *Code* for permanent wiring apply to temporary wiring installations.

    (a) True   (b) False

    Answer: _____   Section: _____._____

17. Feeders to floating buildings are permitted to be installed in _____ where flexibility is required.

    (a) extra-hard usage portable power cable listed for both wet locations and sunlight resistance
    (b) liquidtight flexible metal conduit with approved fittings
    (c) liquidtight flexible nonmetallic conduit with approved fittings
    (d) all of these

    Answer: _____   Section: _____._____

18. For temporary wiring over 600V, nominal, suitable _____ must be provided to prevent access of other than authorized and qualified personnel.

    (a) fencing   (b) barriers   (c) signs   (d) a or b

    Answer: _____   Section: _____._____

19. General-purpose receptacles rated 125V, single-phase, _____ must be GFCI protected if they are located in an agricultural livestock building in an area that has an equipotential plane.

    (a) 15A   (b) 20A   (c) 30A   (d) a and b

    Answer: _____   Section: _____._____

20. In agricultural building locations where surfaces are periodically washed or sprayed with water, enclosures and fittings must be listed for use in wet locations and the enclosures must be weatherproof.

    (a) True   (b) False

    Answer: _____   Section: _____._____

21. In marinas and boatyards, transformers and enclosures must be specifically approved for the intended location. The bottom of enclosures for transformers must not be located below _____.

    (a) 2 ft above the dock   (b) 18 in. above the electrical datum plane
    (c) the electrical datum plane   (d) a dock

    Answer: _____   Section: _____._____

22. Loudspeakers of a permanent audio system which are installed in a fire-resistance rated partition, wall, or ceiling must be listed for the purpose or installed in an enclosure or recess that _____.

    (a) maintains the fire-resistance rating   (b) is no more than 4 in. deep
    (c) is no more than 6 ft 6 in. high   (d) all of these

    Answer: _____   Section: _____._____

23. Manufactured wiring systems must be constructed with _____.

    (a) listed Type AC or Type MC cable   (b) 10 or 12 AWG copper-insulated conductors
    (c) conductors that are suitable for nominal 600V   (d) all of these

    Answer: _____   Section: _____._____

24. Mobile home service equipment must be rated at not less than _____ at 120/240V, and provisions must be made for connecting a mobile home feeder assembly by a permanent wiring method.

    (a) 50A   (b) 60A   (c) 100A   (d) 200A

    Answer: _____   Section: _____._____

25. Multiwire branch circuits for temporary wiring must be provided with a means to disconnect simultaneously all _____ conductors at the power outlet or panelboard where the branch circuit originated.

    (a) underground   (b) overhead   (c) ungrounded   (d) grounded

    Answer: _____   Section: _____._____

26. Overhead wiring outside of tents and concession areas of carnivals and circuses which are accessible to pedestrians only, and where the voltage-to-ground does not exceed 150 must maintain a vertical clearance of _____ above finished grade, sidewalks, or from platforms, projections, or surfaces from which the wiring might be reached.

    (a) 3 ft   (b) 6 ft   (c) 8 ft   (d) 10 ft

    Answer: _____   Section: _____._____

27. Receptacles that provide shore power for boats must be rated not less than _____ and must be of the single outlet type.

    (a) 15A   (b) 20A   (c) 30A   (d) none of these

    Answer: _____   Section: _____._____

28. Signs and outline lighting system equipment installed in wet locations must be weatherproof and have drain holes unless they are listed watertight type.

    (a) True   (b) False

    Answer: _____   Section: _____._____

29. Temporary wiring must be _____ immediately upon the completion of construction or purpose for which the wiring was installed.

    (a) disconnected   (b) removed   (c) de-energized   (d) any of these

    Answer: _____   Section: _____._____

30. The bottom of sign and outline lighting enclosures must be at least _____ above areas accessible to vehicles unless protected from physical damage.

    (a) 12 ft   (b) 14 ft   (c) 16 ft   (d) 18 ft

    Answer: _____   Section: _____._____

31. The conductors to the hoistway door interlocks from the hoistway riser of an elevator must be flame retardant and suitable for a temperature of not less than _____, and the conductors must be SF or the equivalent.

    (a) 200°C   (b) 60°C   (c) 90°C   (d) 110°C

    Answer: _____   Section: _____._____

32. The demand used to calculate 45 receptacles in a boatyard feeder is _____ percent.

    (a) 90   (b) 80   (c) 70   (d) 50

    Answer: _____   Section: _____._____

33. The disconnecting means for an elevator or escalator must be an enclosed externally operable fused motor-circuit switch or circuit breaker capable of _____.

(a) interrupting 6 times the locked-rotor current   (b) being locked in the open position
(c) including overload protection   (d) serving as a transfer switch

Answer: _____   Section: _____._____

34. The distribution point is an electrical supply point from which _____ to agricultural buildings, associated farm dwelling(s), and associated buildings under single management are supplied.

(a) service drops or service laterals   (b) feeders or branch circuits
(c) a or b   (d) none of these

Answer: _____   Section: _____._____

35. The electrical connection between mechanically contiguous wired partitions (for office furnishings) is permitted to be a flexible cord if the cord _____.

(a) is extra-hard usage with 12 AWG or larger conductors
(b) has an insulated equipment grounding conductor
(c) is no longer than 2 ft and terminates at an attachment plug and connector with strain relief
(d) all of these

Answer: _____   Section: _____._____

36. The equipotential planes in an agricultural building must be bonded to the electrical grounding system. The bonding conductor must be copper, insulated, covered, or bare and not smaller than _____.

(a) 6 AWG   (b) 8 AWG   (c) 4 AWG   (d) 10 AWG

Answer: _____   Section: _____._____

37. The lighting switch for hoistway pits must be readily accessible from the _____.

(a) pit access door   (b) elevator car   (c) floor of the pit   (d) machinery room

Answer: _____   Section: _____._____

38. The maximum internal current that can flow through the line isolation monitor when any point of the isolated system is grounded must be _____ when used in a health care facility.

(a) 15A or less   (b) no more than 1A   (c) 1 mA   (d) 10 mA

Answer: _____   Section: _____._____

39. The maximum spacing of receptacle outlets over countertops in the kitchen in a mobile home is _____.

(a) 6 ft   (b) 12 ft   (c) 3 ft   (d) none of these

Answer: _____   Section: _____._____

40. The mobile home park secondary electrical distribution system to mobile home lots must be _____.

(a) 120/240V, 1-phase, 3-wire   (b) 208/208V, 3-phase, 4-wire
(c) either a or b   (d) none of these

Answer: _____   Section: _____._____

41. The pilot light provided within a portable stage switchboard enclosure must have overcurrent protection rated or set at not more than _____.

    (a) 10A   (b) 15A   (c) 20A   (d) 30A

    Answer: _____   Section: _____._____

42. The plans, specifications, and other building details for construction of manufactured buildings are included in the _____ details.

    (a) manufactured building   (b) building component   (c) building structure   (d) building system

    Answer: _____   Section: _____._____

43. The provisions of Article 604 apply to field-installed manufactured wiring systems using off-site manufactured subassemblies for branch circuits, remote-control circuits, signaling circuits, and communications circuits in _____ areas.

    (a) accessible   (b) only patient care   (c) hazardous (classified)   (d) concealed

    Answer: _____   Section: _____._____

44. The wiring methods permitted in theaters, audience areas of motion picture and television studios, performance areas, and similar locations are _____.

    (a) any metal raceway
    (b) nonmetallic raceways encased in 2 in. of concrete
    (c) Types MC or AC cable with an insulated equipment grounding conductor
    (d) any of these

    Answer: _____   Section: _____._____

45. The working space clearance for a distribution panelboard located in a recreational vehicle must be no less than _____.

    (a) 24 in. wide   (b) 30 in. deep   (c) 30 in. wide   (d) a and b

    Answer: _____   Section: _____._____

46. Type NM cable is an acceptable wiring method in agricultural buildings.

    (a) True   (b) False

    Answer: _____   Section: _____._____

47. Types NM and NMC cable are permitted to be used for temporary installations in any dwelling, building, or structure without height limitation or limitation by building construction type and without concealment when installed as _____.

    (a) branch circuits   (b) feeders   (c) a or b   (d) none of these

    Answer: _____   Section: _____._____

48. Vegetation cannot be used for support of overhead spans of _____.

    (a) branch circuits   (b) feeders
    (c) holiday lighting branch circuits with proper strain relief   (d) a or b

    Answer: _____   Section: _____._____

49. Where multiple services or separately derived systems or both supply rides, attractions, and other structures of carnival, circuses, fairs, and similar events, all sources of supply that serve rides, attractions, or other structures separated by less than _____ must be bonded to the same grounding electrode system.

(a) 12 ft   (b) 8 ft   (c) 16 ft   (d) 6 ft

Answer: _____   Section: _____._____

50. Which of the following wiring methods are permitted to be installed in an assembly occupancy?

(a) Metal raceways.
(b) Type MC cable.
(c) Type AC cable containing an insulated equipment grounding conductor.
(d) all of these

Answer: _____   Section: _____._____

(• Indicates that 75% or fewer exam takers get the question correct)

1. Where a nonmetallic wireway is used as a pull box for insulated conductors 4 AWG or larger, the distance between raceway and cable entries enclosing the same conductor must not be less than that required in 314.28(A)(1) for straight pulls and 314.28(A)(2) for angle pulls.

    (a) True   (b) False

    Answer: _____   Section: _____._____

2. Where a portion of the dwelling unit basement is finished into one or more habitable rooms, each separate unfinished portion must have a receptacle outlet installed.

    (a) True   (b) False

    Answer: _____   Section: _____._____

3. Where a service raceway enters a building or structure from a(n) _____ it must be sealed in accordance with 300.5(G).

    (a) transformer vault   (b) underground distribution system
    (c) cable tray   (d) overhead rack

    Answer: _____   Section: _____._____

4. Where a transformer supplies an electric fire pump motor, it must be sized no less than _____ percent of the sum of the fire pump motor(s) and pressure maintenance pump motors, and 100 percent of any associated fire pump accessory equipment supplied by the transformer.

    (a) 100   (b) 125   (c) 250   (d) 300

    Answer: _____   Section: _____._____

5. Where a wireway is used as a pull box for insulated conductors 4 AWG or larger, the distance between raceway and cable entries enclosing the same conductor must not be less than that required in 314.28(A)(1) for straight pulls and 314.28(A)(2) for angle pulls.

    (a) True   (b) False

    Answer: _____   Section: _____._____

6. Where an ac system operating at less than 1,000V is grounded at any point, the _____ conductors must be run to each service disconnecting means and must be bonded to each disconnect enclosure.

    (a) ungrounded   (b) grounded   (c) grounding   (d) none of these

    Answer: _____   Section: _____._____

7. Where batteries are used for _____ in auxiliary engines of emergency systems, the authority having jurisdiction must require periodic maintenance.

    (a) starting   (b) control or ignition   (c) a and b   (d) none of these

    Answer: _____   Section: _____._____

8. Where batteries are used for _____ in auxiliary engines of legally required standby systems, the authority having jurisdiction must require periodic maintenance.

    (a) control   (b) starting or ignition   (c) a and b   (d) none of these

    Answer: _____   Section: _____._____

9. Where CNG (compressed natural gas) vehicles are repaired or stored, the area within _____ in. of the ceiling is classified as Class I, Division 2, except where ventilation of at least 1 cu ft per minute per sq ft (cfm/sq. ft) of ceiling area is taken from a point within 18 in. of the highest point in the ceiling of major repair garages.

    (a) 6   (b) 12   (c) 18   (d) 24

    Answer: _____   Section: _____._____

10. Where communications wires and cables are installed in a raceway, the raceway must be of a type permitted in Chapter 3 and must be installed in accordance with Chapter 3 requirements, or a listed nonmetallic raceway may be used that complies with 800.182.

    (a) True   (b) False

    Answer: _____   Section: _____._____

11. Where conductors are run in parallel in multiple raceways or cables, the equipment grounding conductor, where used, must be run in parallel in each raceway or cable.

    (a) True   (b) False

    Answer: _____   Section: _____._____

12. Where fixed multioutlet assemblies used in other than dwelling units or the guest rooms of hotels or motels are employed, each _____ or fraction thereof of each separate and continuous length of multioutlet assembly must be considered as one outlet of not less than 180 VA capacity where appliances are unlikely to be used simultaneously.

    (a) 5 ft   (b) 5 1/2 ft   (c) 6 ft   (d) 6 1/2 ft

    Answer: _____   Section: _____._____

13. Where flexibility is necessary, securing LFMC is not required for lengths not exceeding _____ at terminals.

    (a) 2 ft   (b) 3 ft   (c) 4 ft   (d) 6 ft

    Answer: _____   Section: _____._____

14. Where flexible cords are used in ambient temperatures exceeding _____ the temperature correction factors from Table 310.16 that correspond to the temperature rating of the cord must be applied to the ampacity from Table 400.5(A) or 400.5(B).

    (a) 60°C   (b) 30°C   (c) 75°C   (d) 90°C

    Answer: _____   Section: _____._____

15. Where nails or screws are likely to penetrate nonmetallic-sheathed cable or electrical nonmetallic tubing installed through metal framing members, a steel sleeve, steel plate, or steel clip not less than _____ in thickness must be used to protect the cable or tubing. A thinner plate that provides equal or better protection may be used if listed and marked.

    (a) 1/16 in.   (b) 1/8 in.   (c) 1/2 in.   (d) none of these

    Answer: _____   Section: _____._____

16. Where nonmetal underground conduit with conductors (NUCC) enters a box, fitting, or other enclosure, a bushing or adapter must be provided to protect the conductor or cable from abrasion unless the design of the box, fitting, or enclosure is such as to afford equivalent protection.

    (a) True   (b) False

    Answer: _____   Section: _____._____

17. Where service entrance conductors are paralleled in two or more raceways or cables, the bonding jumper for each raceway or cable must be based on the size of the _____ in each raceway or cable.

    (a) overcurrent protection for conductors   (b) grounded conductors
    (c) service entrance conductors   (d) sum of all conductors in the raceway

    Answer: _____   Section: _____._____

18. Where the load is computed on volt-amperes per square meter or square foot basis, the wiring system up to and including the branch-circuit _____ must be provided to serve not less than the calculated load.

    (a) wiring   (b) protection   (c) panelboard(s)   (d) all of these

    Answer: _____   Section: _____._____

19. Where the premises wiring system contains feeders supplied from more than one voltage system, each ungrounded (hot) conductor, where accessible, must be identified by the system. Identification can be by _____ or other approved means. Such identification must be permanently posted at each feeder panelboard or similar feeder distribution equipment.

    (a) color-coding   (b) marking tape   (c) tagging   (d) a, b, or c

    Answer: _____   Section: _____._____

20. Which of the following areas of an aircraft hangar are not classified as a Class I, Division 1 or 2 location?

    (a) Any pit or depression below the level of the hangar floor.
    (b) Areas adjacent to and not suitably cut off from the hangar.
    (c) Areas within the vicinity of aircraft.
    (d) Adjacent areas where adequately ventilated and where effectively cut off from the classified area of the hangar.

    Answer: _____   Section: _____._____

21. Which of the following conductor types are required to be used when FMC is installed in a wet location?

    (a) THWN   (b) XHHW   (c) THW   (d) any of these

    Answer: _____   Section: _____._____

22. Which of the following is not a standard size for fuses or inverse-time circuit breakers?

    (a) 45A   (b) 70A   (c) 75A   (d) 80A

    Answer: _____   Section: _____._____

23. A receptacle installed in a wet location, where the product intended to be plugged into it is not attended while in use, shall have an enclosure that is weatherproof with the attachment plug cap inserted or removed.

(a) True   (b) False

Answer: _____   Section: _____._____

24. Which of the following switches must indicate whether they are in the open (off) or closed (on) position?

(a) General-use switches.   (b) Motor-circuit switches.   (c) Circuit breakers.   (d) all of these

Answer: _____   Section: _____._____

25. Which of the following wiring methods are permitted in a Class I, Division 1 location?

(a) Threaded rigid metal conduit (b) Threaded IMC   (c) MI cable   (d) all of these

Answer: _____   Section: _____._____

26. Wiring methods and equipment installed behind panels designed to permit access (such as suspended-ceiling panels) must be so arranged and secured so as to allow the removal of panels and access to the electrical equipment.

(a) True   (b) False

Answer: _____   Section: _____._____

27. Working space cannot be used for _____.

(a) storage   (b) raceways   (c) lighting   (d) accessibility

Answer: _____   Section: _____._____

28. _____ is permitted to be installed in messenger-supported wiring.

(a) Multiconductor service-entrance cable   (b) Mineral Insulated (Type MI) cable
(c) Multiconductor underground feeder cable   (d) all of these

Answer: _____   Section: _____._____

29. •_____ identified for use on lighting track must be designed specifically for the track on which they are to be installed.

(a) Fittings   (b) Receptacles   (c) Devices   (d) all of these

Answer: _____   Section: _____._____

30. •Aluminum and copper-clad aluminum of the same circular mil size and insulation have _____.

(a) the same physical characteristics   (b) the same termination
(c) the same ampacity   (d) different ampacities

Answer: _____   Section: _____._____

31. •Warning signs for over 600V must read: Warning - High Voltage - Keep Out.

(a) True   (b) False

Answer: _____   Section: _____._____

32. •When devices or plug-in connections for tapping off feeders or branch circuits from busways include an externally operable fusible switch that is out of reach, _____ must be provided for operation of the disconnecting means from the floor.

    (a) ropes   (b) chains   (c) hook sticks   (d) any of these

    Answer: _____   Section: _____._____

33. •When the dc system consists of a _____, the grounding electrode conductor must not be smaller than the neutral conductor and not smaller than 8 AWG copper.

    (a) 2-wire balancer set   (b) 3-wire balancer set
    (c) balancer winding with overcurrent protection   (d) b or c

    Answer: _____   Section: _____._____

34. A _____ circuit is a circuit, other than field wiring, in which any arc or thermal effect produced under intended operating conditions of the equipment is not capable of igniting the flammable gas-air, vapor-air, or dust-air mixture under specified test conditions.

    (a) nonconductive   (b) branch   (c) nonincendive   (d) closed

    Answer: _____   Section: _____._____

35. A 10 AWG single strand (solid) copper wire has a cross-sectional area of _____

    (a) 0.008 sq in.   (b) 0.101 sq in.   (c) 0.012 sq in.   (d) 0.106 sq in.

    Answer: _____   Section: _____._____

36. A box must not be required where cables or conductors from cable trays are installed in bushed conduit and tubing used as support or protection against _____.

    (a) abuse   (b) unauthorized access   (c) physical damage   (d) tampering

    Answer: _____   Section: _____._____

37. A capacitor operating at over 600V must be provided with means to reduce the residual voltage to 50V or less within _____ after it is disconnected from the source of supply.

    (a) 15 seconds   (b) 45 seconds   (c) 1 minute   (d) 5 minutes

    Answer: _____   Section: _____._____

38. A circuit breaker with a _____ voltage rating, such as 240V or 480V, is permitted to be used where the nominal voltage between any two conductors does not exceed the circuit breaker's voltage rating.

    (a) straight   (b) slash   (c) high   (d) low

    Answer: _____   Section: _____._____

39. A field-installed wiring system for branch circuits designed for installation under carpet squares is defined as _____.

    (a) underfloor wiring   (b) undercarpet wiring
    (c) flat conductor cable   (d) underfloor conductor cable

    Answer: _____   Section: _____._____

40. A fuse or an overcurrent trip unit of a circuit breaker must be connected in series with each ungrounded _____.

    (a) device   (b) conductor   (c) branch circuit   (d) all of these

    Answer: _____   Section: _____._____

41. A generator set for a required standby system must _____.

    (a) have means for automatically starting the prime movers
    (b) have two hours of fuel supply for full demand operation available onsite if the prime mover is an internal combustion engine
    (c) not be solely dependent on public utility gas system
    (d) all of these

    Answer: _____   Section: _____._____

42. A large single panel, frame, or assembly of panels on which switches, overcurrent and other protective devices, buses, and instruments are mounted is a _____. They are generally accessible from the rear as well as from the front and are not intended to be installed in cabinets.

    (a) switchboard   (b) panel box   (c) switch box   (d) panelboard

    Answer: _____   Section: _____._____

43. A mobile home that is factory-equipped with gas or oil-fired central heating equipment and cooking appliances is permitted to be supplied with a listed mobile home power-supply cord rated _____.

    (a) 30A   (b) 35A   (c) 40A   (d) 50A

    Answer: _____   Section: _____._____

44. A motor for general use must be marked with a time rating of _____.

    (a) continuous   (b) 30 or 60 minutes   (c) 5 or 15 minutes   (d) any of these

    Answer: _____   Section: _____._____

45. A motor terminal housing with rigidly-mounted motor terminals must have a minimum of _____ between line terminals for a 230V motor.

    (a) 1/4 in.   (b) 3/8 in.   (c) 1/2 in.   (d) 5/8 in.

    Answer: _____   Section: _____._____

46. A vented alkaline-type battery operating at less than 250V must be installed with not more than _____ cells in the series circuit of any one tray.

    (a) 10   (b) 12   (c) 18   (d) 20

    Answer: _____   Section: _____._____

47. A(n) _____ system must supply major electrical equipment necessary for patient care and basic hospital operation.

    (a) emergency   (b) equipment   (c) life safety   (d) none of these

    Answer: _____   Section: _____._____

48. All accessible portions of abandoned network-powered broadband cable must be removed.

(a) True   (b) False

Answer: _____   Section: _____._____

49. All extensions from flat cable assemblies must be made by approved wiring methods within the _____ that is/are installed at either end of the flat cable assembly runs.

(a) end-caps   (b) junction boxes   (c) surface metal raceway   (d) underfloor metal raceway

Answer: _____   Section: _____._____

50. All fixed outdoor deicing and snow melting equipment must be provided with a means for disconnection from all _____ conductors.

(a) grounded neutral   (b) grounding   (c) ungrounded   (d) all of these

Answer: _____   Section: _____._____

(• Indicates that 75% or fewer exam takers get the question correct)

Article 645 Information Technology Equipment (continue)

1. Cables listed for the purpose can be used to interconnect separate data-processing units in information technology equipment rooms. Where run on the surface of the floor, the cables must be protected by _____.

   (a) a GFCI circuit breaker   (b) approved means   (c) duct tape   (d) metal raceways only

   Answer: _____   Section: _____._____

2. Under a raised floor, liquidtight flexible metal conduit is permitted to enclose branch-circuit conductors for information technology communications equipment.

   (a) True   (b) False

   Answer: _____   Section: _____._____

3. Ventilation in the underfloor area of an information equipment room can be used in that room only, and the ventilation system must be arranged so that upon the detection of fire or products of combustion in the underfloor area, the circulation of air will cease.

   (a) True   (b) False

   Answer: _____   Section: _____._____

4. _____ cables such as CL2, CM, or CATV are permitted within the raised floor area of an information technology equipment room.

   (a) Control   (b) Signal   (c) Communications   (d) all of these

   Answer: _____   Section: _____._____

5. Abandoned cables under an information technology room raised floor must be removed, unless the cables are contained within a metal raceway.

   (a) True   (b) False

   Answer: _____   Section: _____._____

6. Signal and communications cables that extend beyond the information technology equipment room are required to comply only with Article 645.

   (a) True   (b) False

   Answer: _____   Section: _____._____

7. Where a pushbutton is used as a means to disconnect power in the information technology equipment room, pushing the button "in" must disconnect the power.

    (a) True   (b) False

    Answer: _____   Section: _____._____

8. Each unit of an information technology system supplied by a branch circuit must have a manufacturer's nameplate that includes the _____.

    (a) rating in volts   (b) operating frequency   (c) maximum load in amperes   (d) all of these

    Answer: _____   Section: _____._____

Article 647 Sensitive Electronic Equipment

A technical power system (called "balanced power" by some) is a separately derived, 120V line-to-line, single-phase, 3-wire system with 60V-to-ground used for sensitive electronic equipment.

9. The purpose of a 60/120V power system is to reduce objectionable noise in sensitive electronic equipment locations. Its use is restricted to _____ occupancies that are under close supervision by qualified personnel.

    (a) commercial   (b) industrial   (c) a and b   (d) none of these

    Answer: _____   Section: _____._____

10. Junction boxes used in sensitive electronic equipment systems must be clearly marked to indicate _____.

    (a) the installer's name   (b) the system voltage   (c) the distribution panel   (d) b and c

    Answer: _____   Section: _____._____

11. Voltage drop on sensitive electronic equipment systems must not exceed _____ percent for branch circuits.

    (a) 1.5   (b) 3   (c) 2.5   (d) 5

    Answer: _____   Section: _____._____

12. Permanently-wired utilization equipment and receptacles in sensitive electronic equipment systems must be grounded with a separate equipment grounding conductor run with the circuit conductors to an equipment grounding bus prominently marked _____.

    (a) "Technical Equipment Ground"   (b) "Equipment Ground Bar"
    (c) "Green"   (d) "Isolation Bonding"

    Answer: _____   Section: _____._____

Article 660 X-Ray Equipment

This article covers all X-ray equipment operating at any frequency or voltage for industrial or other nonmedical or nondental use.

13. X-ray equipment mounted on a permanent base equipped with wheels and/or casters for moving while completely assembled is defined as _____.

    (a) portable   (b) mobile   (c) movable   (d) room

    Answer: _____   Section: _____._____

14. The ampacity requirements for a disconnecting means for X-ray equipment must be based on the greater of _____ percent of the input required for the momentary rating or 100 percent of the input required for the long-time rating.

    (a) 125   (b) 100   (c) 50   (d) none of these

    Answer: _____   Section: _____._____

15. Size 18 or 16 AWG fixture wires are permitted for the control and operating circuits of X-ray and auxiliary equipment when protected by an overcurrent protection device not larger than _____.

    (a) 15A   (b) 20A   (c) 25A   (d) 30A

    Answer: _____   Section: _____._____

Article 670 Industrial Machinery

This article covers the definition of, the nameplate data for, and the size and overcurrent protection of supply conductors to industrial machinery.

16. Where overcurrent protection is provided as part of an industrial machine, the machine must be marked to read, _____.

    (a) "Overcurrent Protection Provided At Machine Supply Terminals"
    (b) "This Unit Contains Overcurrent Protection"
    (c) "Fuses Or Circuit Breaker Enclosed"
    (d) "Overcurrent Protected"

    Answer: _____   Section: _____._____

Article 675 Electrically Driven or Controlled Irrigation Machines

The provisions of this article apply to electrically driven or controlled irrigation machines, and to the branch circuits and controllers for such equipment.

17. An electrically-driven or -controlled machine with one or more motors that are not hand-portable, and used primarily to transport and distribute water for agricultural purposes, is called a(n) _____.

    (a) irrigation machine   (b) electric water distribution system
    (c) center pivot irrigation machine   (d) automatic water distribution system

    Answer: _____   Section: _____._____

Article 680 Swimming Pools, Spas, Hot Tubs, Fountains, and Similar Installations

The scope of Article 680 is limited to the installation of electric wiring and equipment that supplies swimming, wading, therapeutic and decorative pools, fountains, hot tubs, spas, and hydromassage bathtubs, whether permanently installed or storable.

18. •A spa or hot tub is a hydromassage pool or tub for recreational or therapeutic use designed for the immersion of users. They are not generally designed or intended to have the contents drained or discharged after each use.

    (a) True   (b) False

    Answer: _____   Section: _____._____

19. A wet-niche luminaire (lighting fixture) is intended to be installed in a _____.

    (a) transformer   (b) forming shell   (c) hydromassage bathtub   (d) all of these

    Answer: _____   Section: _____._____

20. Fixed or stationary pool, outdoor spa, and hot tub equipment is permitted to be cord-and-plug connected to facilitate the removal or disconnection for maintenance or repair. The flexible cord must _____.

    (a) not exceed 3 ft except for storable pools
    (b) have a copper equipment grounding conductor not smaller than 12 AWG
    (c) terminate in a grounding-type attachment plug
    (d) all of these

    Answer: _____   Section: _____._____

21. Overhead utility service conductors that operate at not over 750 volts-to-ground must maintain a _____ clearance in any direction to the water level, edge of water surface, base of diving platform, or permanently anchored raft.

    (a) 14 ft   (b) 16 ft   (c) 20 ft   (d) 22 1/2 ft

    Answer: _____   Section: _____._____

22. Overhead network-powered broadband communications systems conductors must be located no less than _____ from the water's edge of swimming and wading pools, or the base of diving structures.

    (a) 10 ft   (b) 12 ft   (c) 18 ft   (d) none of these

    Answer: _____   Section: _____._____

23. Underground rigid nonmetallic wiring located less than 5 ft from the inside wall of a pool or spa must be buried not less than _____

    (a) 6 in.   (b) 10 in.   (c) 12 in.   (d) 18 in.

    Answer: _____   Section: _____._____

24. Underground outdoor pool or spa equipment rooms or pits must have adequate drainage to prevent water accumulation during normal operation or filter maintenance.

    (a) True   (b) False

    Answer: _____   Section: _____._____

25. The "maintenance" disconnect for pool equipment applies to all utilization equipment, including lighting.

    (a) True   (b) False

    Answer: _____   Section: _____._____

26. Pool-associated motors must be grounded using a minimum size 12 AWG insulated copper conductor and this grounding conductor must be installed in any wiring method employed, which could include _____.

    (a) rigid nonmetallic conduit   (b) electrical metallic tubing where installed on or within buildings
    (c) flexible metal conduit   (d) a or b

    Answer: _____   Section: _____._____

27. Receptacles that provide power for water-pump motors or for other loads directly related to the circulation and sanitation system must be located at least _____ from the inside walls of the pool.

(a) 3 ft   (b) 5 ft   (c) 10 ft   (d) 12 ft

Answer: _____   Section: _____._____

28. One 15 or 20A, single-phase, 125V receptacle can be installed not less than _____, measured horizontally, from the inside wall of the pool at a dwelling unit if the dimensions of the lot do not allow the required receptacle outlet to be 10 ft from the water.

(a) 3 ft   (b) 5 ft   (c) 6 ft   (d) none of these

Answer: _____   Section: _____._____

29. All outdoor 15 and 20A, single-phase, 125V through 250V receptacles for pool, spa, and hot tub pump motors must be _____.

(a) AFCI protected   (b) GFCI protected   (c) approved   (d) listed

Answer: _____   Section: _____._____

30. Luminaires or ceiling fans mounted less than 12 ft above the water level cannot be installed above or within _____ of an outdoor pool, fountain, or spa.

(a) 3 ft   (b) 5 ft   (c) 10 ft   (d) 8 ft

Answer: _____   Section: _____._____

31. A pool transformer used for the supply of underwater luminaires, together with the transformer enclosure, is required to _____.

(a) be of the isolated-winding type with an ungrounded secondary
(b) have a grounded metal barrier between the primary and secondary windings
(c) be listed for the purpose
(d) all of these

Answer: _____   Section: _____._____

32. Forming shells for wet-niche luminaires must be installed with the top level of the fixture lens not less than _____ below the normal water level of the pool or spa.

(a) 6 in.   (b) 12 in.   (c) 18 in.   (d) 24 in.

Answer: _____   Section: _____._____

33. All wet-niche luminaires installed in swimming pools must be removable from the water for relamping or normal maintenance and must be installed in such a manner that personnel can reach the luminaire for relamping, maintenance, or inspection _____.

(a) while the pool is drained   (b) while the person is on the deck or a dry location
(c) during construction   (d) all of these

Answer: _____   Section: _____._____

34. Electrical metallic tubing is permitted for branch-circuit wiring for underwater luminaires where installed on buildings. Where installed within buildings, electrical nonmetallic tubing, Type MC cable, or electrical metallic tubing is permitted.

(a) True   (b) False

Answer: _____   Section: _____._____

35. A pool light junction box that is connected to a conduit that extends directly to a forming shell or mounting bracket of a no-niche luminaire (fixture) must be _____ for this use.

    (a) listed   (b) labeled   (c) marked   (d) a and b

    Answer: _____   Section: _____._____

36. Junction boxes for pool lighting must not be located less than _____ from the inside wall of a pool unless separated by a fence or wall.

    (a) 3 ft   (b) 4 ft   (c) 6 ft   (d) 8 ft

    Answer: _____   Section: _____._____

37. The enclosure for a transformer or ground-fault circuit interrupter connected to a conduit that extends directly to a pool light forming shell must be _____ for this purpose.

    (a) labeled   (b) listed   (c) identified   (d) a and b

    Answer: _____   Section: _____._____

38. The feeder to a swimming pool panelboard at a separate building or structure is permitted to be supplied with any Chapter 3 wiring method provided the feeder has a separate insulated copper equipment grounding conductor.

    (a) True   (b) False

    Answer: _____   Section: _____._____

39. •When installing equipotential bonding of pool and spa equipment, a solid 8 AWG copper conductor must be run back to the service equipment. This conductor must be unbroken.

    (a) True   (b) False

    Answer: _____   Section: _____._____

40. •When bonding together pool reinforcing steel and welded wire fabric (wire-mesh) with tie-wire, the tie-wires must be _____.

    (a) stainless steel   (b) accessible   (c) made tight   (d) none of these

    Answer: _____   Section: _____._____

41. •Which of the following must be bonded?

    (a) Metal parts of electrical equipment associated with the pool water circulating system.   (b) Pool structural steel.
    (c) Metal fittings within or attached to the pool.   (d) all of these

    Answer: _____   Section: _____._____

42. The components that are required to be connected to the equipotential bonding grid of a swimming pool must be connected using a minimum size of 8 AWG solid _____ conductor.

    (a) insulated   (b) bare   (c) covered   (d) any of these

    Answer: _____   Section: _____._____

43. The electric motors, controllers, and wiring for an electrically operated pool cover must be _____.

    (a) located at least 5 ft from the inside wall of the pool   (b) separated from the pool by a permanent barrier
    (c) both a and b   (d) either a or b

    Answer: _____   Section: _____._____

44. Radiant heating cables embedded in or below the pool deck _____.

   (a) must not be installed within 5 ft horizontally from the inside walls of the pool
   (b) must be mounted at least 12 ft vertically above the pool deck
   (c) are not permitted
   (d) none of these

   Answer: _____   Section: _____._____

45. 15 and 20 amp, single-phase, 125V receptacles located within _____ of the inside walls of a storable pool must be protected by a ground-fault circuit interrupter.

   (a) 8 ft   (b) 10 ft   (c) 15 ft   (d) 20 ft

   Answer: _____   Section: _____._____

46. In spas or hot tubs, a clearly labeled emergency shutoff or control switch for the purpose of stopping the motors(s) that provide power to the recirculation system and jet system must be installed. The emergency shutoff control switch must be _____ to the users and located not less than 5 ft away, and within sight of, the spa or hot tub. This requirement does not apply to single-family dwelling units.

   (a) accessible   (b) readily accessible   (c) available   (d) none of these

   Answer: _____   Section: _____._____

47. Listed packaged spa or hot tub equipment assemblies or self-contained spas or hot tubs installed outdoors are permitted to use flexible connections utilizing _____.

   (a) liquidtight flexible metal conduit or liquidtight flexible nonmetallic conduit in lengths of not more than 6 ft.
   (b) cord-and-plug connections with cords not longer than 15 ft, where GFCI protected
   (c) a or b
   (d) none of these

   Answer: _____   Section: _____._____

48. The interior wiring for the motor, heater, and control loads that are part of an outdoor installation of a self-contained spa or hot tub, at a one-family dwelling or structure associated with a one-family dwelling, can use any Chapter 3 wiring method that contains an insulated 12 AWG or larger copper equipment grounding conductor.

   (a) True   (b) False

   Answer: _____   Section: _____._____

49. At least one 15 or 20A, 125V receptacle must be located a minimum of _____ (and a maximum of 10 ft) from the inside wall of a spa or hot tub installed indoors.

   (a) 2 ft   (b) 5 ft   (c) 18 in.   (d) no minimum

   Answer: _____   Section: _____._____

50. Receptacles that provide power for an indoor spa or hot tub must be _____.

   (a) 240V minimum   (b) GFCI protected   (c) a or b   (d) a and b

   Answer: _____   Section: _____._____

51. Luminaires and ceiling fans located over or within 5 ft, measured horizontally, from the inside walls of an indoor spa or hot tub must have a mounting height of not less than _____ above the maximum water level when GFCI protection is provided.

    (a) 4.7 ft   (b) 5 ft   (c) 7 ft 6 in.   (d) 12 ft

    Answer: _____   Section: _____._____

52. Surface-mounted luminaires _____ located over or within 5 ft, measured horizontally, from the inside walls of an indoor spa or hot tub are permitted to be installed at less than 7 ft 6 in. above the maximum water level when GFCI protection is provided.

    (a) with a glass or plastic globe
    (b) with a nonmetallic body or a metallic body isolated from contact
    (c) suitable for use in a damp location
    (d) all of these

    Answer: _____   Section: _____._____

53. Metal fittings within or attached to an indoor spa or hot tub structure must be _____.

    (a) bonded   (b) insulated   (c) removed   (d) concealed

    Answer: _____   Section: _____._____

54. Metal conduit and metal piping within _____ of the inside walls of an indoor spa or hot tub, and not separated from the indoor spa or hot tub by a permanent barrier, must be bonded.

    (a) 4 ft   (b) 5 ft   (c) 7 ft   (d) 12 ft

    Answer: _____   Section: _____._____

55. Small conductive surfaces of an indoor spa or hot tub, such as air and water jets not likely to become energized, are not required to be bonded. Other nonelectric equipment, such as towel bars or mirror frames, which are not connected to metallic piping, are not required to be bonded.

    (a) True   (b) False

    Answer: _____   Section: _____._____

56. All metal parts associated with an indoor spa or hot tub must be bonded by _____.

    (a) the interconnection of threaded metal piping and fittings
    (b) metal-to-metal mounting on a common frame or base
    (c) a copper bonding jumper (insulated, covered, or bare) not smaller than 8 AWG solid
    (d) any of these

    Answer: _____   Section: _____._____

57. The branch circuit supplying submersible fountain equipment must be _____, unless the equipment is listed for operation at not more than 15V and is supplied by a pool transformer complying with 680.23(A)(2).

    (a) 240V   (b) protected by a ground-fault circuit interrupter
    (c) both a and b   (d) none of these

    Answer: _____   Section: _____._____

58. The maximum length of exposed cord in a fountain must be _____.

    (a) 3 ft   (b) 4 ft   (c) 6 ft   (d) 10 ft

    Answer: _____   Section: _____._____

59.   All metal piping systems associated with a fountain must be bonded to the equipment grounding conductor of the _____.

(a) branch circuit supplying the fountain
(b) bonding grid
(c) equipotential plane
(d) locally-driven ground rod

Answer: _____   Section: _____._____

60.   All cord-and-plug connected equipment in fountains _____ must have ground-fault circuit-interrupter protection.

(a) except pumps
(b) including power supply cords
(c) less than 6 ft high
(d) except power supply cords

Answer: _____   Section: _____._____

61.   Each circuit supplying a sign within or adjacent to a fountain must _____.

(a) have ground-fault circuit-interrupter protection
(b) be equipped with a lock out
(c) operate at less than 50V
(d) be an intrinsically safe circuit

Answer: _____   Section: _____._____

62.   All 15 and 20A, single-phase, 125V through 250V receptacles located within _____ of a fountain edge must have GFCI protection.

(a) 8 ft
(b) 10 ft
(c) 15 ft
(d) 20 ft

Answer: _____   Section: _____._____

63.   GFCI protection is required for all 125V, single-phase receptacles not exceeding 30A and located within 5 ft measured _____ from the inside walls of a hydromassage bathtub.

(a) vertically
(b) horizontally
(c) across
(d) none of these

Answer: _____   Section: _____._____

64.   All metal piping systems, metal parts of electrical equipment, and pump motors associated with a hydromassage tub must be bonded together with a(n) _____ solid copper bonding jumper not smaller than 8 AWG.

(a) insulated
(b) covered
(c) bare
(d) any of these

Answer: _____   Section: _____._____

Article 690 Solar Photovoltaic Systems

The provisions of this article apply to solar photovoltaic electrical energy systems that may be interactive with other electrical power production sources or stand-alone, with or without electrical energy storage such as batteries. These systems may have ac or dc output for utilization.

65.   Any structure with a photovoltaic power system that is not connected to a utility service source and is a stand-alone system must have a permanent plaque or directory on the exterior of the structure that identifies the location of system disconnecting means and states that the structure contains a stand-alone electrical power system.

(a) True
(b) False

Answer: _____   Section: _____._____

Article 692 Fuel Cell Systems

This article identifies the requirements for the installation of fuel cell power systems, which may be stand-alone or interactive with other electrical power production sources and may be with or without electrical energy storage such as batteries. These systems may have ac or dc output for utilization.

66. A fuel cell is an electrochemical system that consumes fuel to produce an electric current. The main chemical reaction used in a fuel cell to produce electrical power is not combustion.

(a) True   (b) False

Answer: _____   Section: _____._____

67. The fuel cell system must be evaluated and _____ for its intended application prior to installation.

(a) approved   (b) identified   (c) listed   (d) marked

Answer: _____   Section: _____._____

Article 695 Fire Pumps

Article 695 covers the electric power sources and interconnecting circuits for electric motor-driven fire pumps. It also covers switching and control equipment dedicated to fire pump drivers. Article 695 doesn't apply to sprinkler system pumps in one- and two-family dwellings or to pressure-maintenance (jockey) pumps.

68. For fire pump motors, the _____ must be selected to carry indefinitely the sum of the locked-rotor current of the fire pump motor(s), pressure maintenance pump motor(s), and the full-load current of any associated fire pump accessory equipment connected to this power supply.

(a) overcurrent protective device(s)   (b) pump motor conductors
(c) a and b   (d) none of these

Answer: _____   Section: _____._____

69. The primary overcurrent protective device for a transformer supplying a fire pump must carry the sum of the locked-rotor current of the fire pump motor(s) and pressure maintenance pump motor(s), and the full-load current of any associated fire pump accessory equipment when connected to this power supply _____.

(a) for 15 minutes   (b) for 45 minutes   (c) for 3 hours   (d) indefinitely

Answer: _____   Section: _____._____

70. The _____ for a transformer that supplies fire pumps must carry indefinitely the sum of the locked-rotor current of the fire pump motor(s) and the pressure maintenance pump motor(s), and the full-load current of the associated fire pump accessory equipment when connected to this power supply.

(a) primary overcurrent protective device(s)   (b) pump motor conductors
(c) both a and b   (d) none of these

Answer: _____   Section: _____._____

71. Feeder conductors supplying fire-pump motors and accessory equipment must be sized no less than _____ percent of the sum of the motor full-load currents as listed in Article 430, plus 100 percent of the ampere rating of the fire-pump accessory equipment.

(a) 100   (b) 125   (c) 250   (d) 600

Answer: _____   Section: _____._____

72. Ground-fault protection of equipment _____ for fire pumps.

(a) is not permitted   (b) is permitted
(c) is allowed   (d) must be approved by the AHJ

Answer: _____   Section: _____._____

73. When a fire-pump motor is operating at 115 percent of its full-load current rating, the supply voltage at the motor terminals must not drop more than _____ percent below the voltage rating of the motor.

(a) 5   (b) 10   (c) 15   (d) any of these

Answer: _____   Section: _____._____

Chapter 7 Special Conditions

Article 700 Emergency Power Systems

The requirements of Article 700 apply only to the wiring methods for "emergency systems" that are essential for safety to human life and required by federal, state, municipal, or other regulatory codes. When normal power is lost, emergency systems must be capable of supplying emergency power in 10 seconds or less.

74. Emergency systems are generally installed where artificial illumination is required for safe exiting and for panic control in buildings occupied by large numbers of persons, such as _____ and similar institutions.

(a) hotels   (b) theaters and sports arenas
(c) health care facilities   (d) all of these

Answer: _____   Section: _____._____

75. Except as modified by Article 700, all requirements contained in the *NEC* Chapters 1 through 4 apply to installations of emergency systems.

(a) True   (b) False

Answer: _____   Section: _____._____

76. Emergency systems that are tested upon installation and found to be acceptable to the authority having jurisdiction (AHJ) are not required to undergo any future tests unless the equipment is modified.

(a) True   (b) False

Answer: _____   Section: _____._____

77. A written record must be kept of required tests and maintenance on emergency systems.

(a) True   (b) False

Answer: _____   Section: _____._____

78. An emergency system must have adequate capacity to safely carry _____ that are expected to operate simultaneously on the emergency system.

(a) all of the loads   (b) 80 percent of the total loads
(c) up to 200A of the loads   (d) 300 percent of the total loads

Answer: _____   Section: _____._____

79. A portable or temporary alternate source _____ whenever the emergency generator is out of service for major maintenance or repair.

    (a) is not required   (b) is recommended   (c) must be available   (d) must be avoided

    Answer: _____   Section: _____._____

80. An emergency transfer switch can supply _____.

    (a) emergency loads   (b) computer equipment   (c) UPS equipment   (d) all of these

    Answer: _____   Section: _____._____

81. A sign _____ be placed at the service-entrance equipment indicating the type and location of on-site emergency power sources.

    (a) must   (b) should   (c) is not required to   (d) is not allowed to

    Answer: _____   Section: _____._____

82. Emergency circuit wiring must be designed and located to minimize the hazards that might cause failure because of _____.

    (a) flooding   (b) fire   (c) icing   (d) all of these

    Answer: _____   Section: _____._____

83. A storage battery supplying emergency lighting and power must maintain not less than 87 1/2 percent of full voltage at total load for a period of at least _____ hour(s).

    (a) 1   (b) 1 1/2   (c) 2   (d) 2 1/2

    Answer: _____   Section: _____._____

84. Where a generator for emergency circuits is installed outdoors and equipped with a readily accessible disconnecting means located within sight of the building or structure supplied, an additional disconnecting means is not required where ungrounded conductors pass through the building or structure.

    (a) True   (b) False

    Answer: _____   Section: _____._____

85. In emergency systems, no appliances and no lamps other than those required for emergency use, may be supplied by _____.

    (a) emergency lighting circuits   (b) multiwire branch circuits
    (c) HID rated circuit breakers   (d) a and b

    Answer: _____   Section: _____._____

86. The switches installed in emergency lighting circuits must be arranged so that only _____ will have control of emergency lighting.

    (a) the authority having jurisdiction   (b) authorized persons
    (c) automated means   (d) qualified persons

    Answer: _____   Section: _____._____

87. All manual switches for controlling emergency circuits must be in locations convenient to authorized persons responsible for their _____.

    (a) maintenance   (b) actuation   (c) inspection   (d) evaluation

    Answer: _____   Section: _____._____

88. The alternate source for emergency systems must be required to have ground-fault protection of equipment.

(a) True   (b) False

Answer: _____   Section: _____._____

Article 701 Legally Required Standby Power Systems

Legally required standby systems provide electric power to aid in firefighting, rescue operations, control of health hazards, and similar operations, and are required by federal, state or municipal governments, or other regulatory codes. When normal power is lost, legally required systems must be capable of automatically supplying standby power in 60 seconds or less, instead of the 10 seconds or less required of emergency systems.

89. A legally required standby system is intended to automatically supply power to _____.

(a) those systems classed as emergency systems   (b) selected loads
(c) a and b   (d) none of these

Answer: _____   Section: _____._____

90. Legally required standby systems that are tested upon installation and found to be acceptable to the authority having jurisdiction (AHJ) are not required to undergo any future tests unless the equipment is modified.

(a) True   (b) False

Answer: _____   Section: _____._____

91. A written record must be kept of required tests and maintenance on legally required standby systems.

(a) True   (b) False

Answer: _____   Section: _____._____

92. A legally required standby system must have adequate capacity to safely carry _____ that are expected to operate simultaneously on the standby system.

(a) all of the loads   (b) 80 percent of the total loads
(c) up to 200A of the loads   (d) 300 percent of the total loads

Answer: _____   Section: _____._____

93. The alternate power source (generator, UPS, etc.) is permitted to supply legally required standby and optional standby system loads where automatic selective load pickup and load shedding is provided as needed to ensure adequate power to the legally required standby systems.

(a) True   (b) False

Answer: _____   Section: _____._____

94. Means to bypass and isolate the transfer switch equipment are not permitted on legally required standby systems.

(a) True   (b) False

Answer: _____   Section: _____._____

95. Audible and visual signal devices must be provided on legally required standby systems, where practicable, to indicate _____.

(a) derangement of the standby source   (b) that the standby source is carrying load
(c) that the battery charger is not functioning   (d) all of these

Answer: _____   Section: _____._____

96. Legally required standby system wiring is permitted to occupy the same raceways, cables, boxes, and cabinets with other general-purpose wiring.

(a) True   (b) False

Answer: _____   Section: _____._____

97. Where a generator for legally required circuits is installed outdoors and equipped with a readily accessible disconnecting means located within sight of the building or structure supplied, an additional disconnecting means is not required where ungrounded conductors pass through the building or structure.

(a) True   (b) False

Answer: _____   Section: _____._____

98. Individual unit equipment (battery packs) for legally required standby illumination must consist of _____.

(a) a rechargeable battery with a battery charging means
(b) provisions for one or more lamps on the equipment, remote, or both
(c) a relaying device arranged to energize the lamps automatically upon failure
(d) all of these

Answer: _____   Section: _____._____

99. The branch circuit feeding the unit equipment for legally required standby illumination must be the same branch circuit that serves the normal lighting in the area, but the unit must be connected ahead of any local switches.

(a) True   (b) False

Answer: _____   Section: _____._____

100. The alternate source for legally required standby systems is not required to have ground-fault protection of equipment.

(a) True   (b) False

Answer: _____   Section: _____._____

1. Power cables, communications cables, connecting cables, interconnecting cables, and receptacles associated with the information technology equipment are permitted under a raised floor, provided the area under the floor is not accessible after installation.

   (a) True   (b) False

   Answer: _____   Section: _____._____

2. A disconnecting means for X-ray equipment must have adequate capacity for at least _____ percent of the input required for the momentary rating of the equipment or _____ percent of the input required for the long-time rating of the equipment, whichever is greater

   (a) 50, 100   (b) 100, 100   (c) 50, 125   (d) 125, 125

   Answer: _____   Section: _____._____

3. A ground-fault circuit interrupter (GFCI) must be installed in the branch circuit supplying swimming pool luminaires that operate at more than _____ to eliminate shock hazard during relamping.

   (a) 6V   (b) 14V   (c) 15V   (d) 18V

   Answer: _____   Section: _____._____

4. A portable electric sign cannot be placed in or within _____ from the inside walls of a fountain.

   (a) 3 ft   (b) 5 ft   (c) 10 ft   (d) none of these

   Answer: _____   Section: _____._____

5. A sign must be placed at the service equipment indicating the _____ of on-site legally required standby power sources.

   (a) type   (b) location   (c) manufacturer   (d) a and b

   Answer: _____   Section: _____._____

6. A spa or hot tub installed outdoors is permitted to be bonded by metal-to-metal mounting on a common frame. The metal bands or hoops used to secure wooden staves _____.

   (a) are not be required to be bonded   (b) must be bonded
   (c) must be covered with insulating material   (d) are not allowed

   Answer: _____   Section: _____._____

7. All exposed noncurrent-carrying metal parts of an information technology system must be _____.

   (a) grounded in accordance with Article 250   (b) double insulated
   (c) fed from GFCI-protected circuits   (d) a or b

   Answer: _____   Section: _____._____

8.   An assembly of electrically interconnected electrolytic cells supplied by a source of dc power is called a(n) _____.

     (a) battery pack   (b) cell line   (c) electrolytic cell bank   (d) battery storage bank

     Answer: _____   Section: _____._____

9.   An underground rigid nonmetallic raceway must be not less than _____ from the inside wall of the pool or spa, unless space limitations prevent otherwise.

     (a) 8 ft   (b) 10 ft   (c) 5 ft   (d) 25 ft

     Answer: _____   Section: _____._____

10. Article 700 applies to the installation, operation, and maintenance of emergency systems consisting of circuits and equipment intended to supply, distribute, and control electricity for _____ in required facilities when the normal electrical supply or system is interrupted.

     (a) illumination   (b) power   (c) HVAC systems only   (d) a and b

     Answer: _____   Section: _____._____

11. Branch-circuit wiring for underwater luminaires must be installed in _____.

     (a) rigid metal conduit or intermediate metal conduit
     (b) liquidtight flexible nonmetallic conduit or rigid nonmetallic conduit
     (c) any raceway wiring method
     (d) a or b

     Answer: _____   Section: _____._____

12. Cables for communications systems such as _____ must be located no less than 10 ft from the water's edge of swimming and wading pools, diving structures, observation stands, towers, or platforms.

     (a) telephone   (b) radio   (c) CATV   (d) all of these

     Answer: _____   Section: _____._____

13. Conductors supplying a single fire pump motor must be sized in accordance with the requirements of 430.22 and 695.7.

     (a) True   (b) False

     Answer: _____   Section: _____._____

14. Electrical devices and controls not associated with an spa or hot tub must be located a minimum of _____ from the inside walls of the indoor spa or hot tub, or be bonded to the indoor spa or hot tub system.

     (a) 4.7 ft   (b) 5 ft   (c) 7 ft 6 in.   (d) 12 ft

     Answer: _____   Section: _____._____

15. Emergency lighting systems must be designed and installed so that the failure of any individual lighting element, such as the burning out of a light bulb, will not leave in total darkness any space that requires emergency illumination.

     (a) True   (b) False

     Answer: _____   Section: _____._____

16. Emergency transfer equipment, including automatic transfer switches, must be _____.

    (a) automatic   (b) identified for emergency use
    (c) approved by the authority having jurisdiction (d) any of these

    Answer: _____   Section: _____._____

17. Equipment for a fountain that is supplied by a flexible cord must have all exposed noncurrent-carrying metal parts grounded by an insulated copper equipment grounding conductor that is an integral part of the cord.

    (a) True   (b) False

    Answer: _____   Section: _____._____

18. Ground-fault circuit interrupters (GFCI) protecting a 120V wet-niche light on a pool or spa must only be of the circuit-breaker type.

    (a) True   (b) False

    Answer: _____   Section: _____._____

19. Hydromassage bathtub equipment must be _____ without damaging the building structure or building finish.

    (a) readily accessible   (b) accessible   (c) within sight   (d) none of these

    Answer: _____   Section: _____._____

20. In dwelling units, a 125V receptacle is required to be installed a minimum of 10 ft and a maximum of 20 ft from the inside wall of the pool.

    (a) True   (b) False

    Answer: _____   Section: _____._____

21. In outdoor pool areas, ceiling-suspended (paddle) fans installed above the pool or the area extending _____ horizontally from the inside walls of the pool must be installed at a height not less than 12 ft above the maximum water level of the pool.

    (a) 3 ft   (b) 5 ft   (c) 10 ft   (d) 12 ft

    Answer: _____   Section: _____._____

22. In swimming pools, the junction box connected to a conduit that extends to the forming shell of the luminaire (fixture) must be listed as a pool light junction box. In addition, when the luminaire operates at over 15V, the junction box must be located not less than _____ above the ground level or pool deck, or not less than _____ above the maximum water level.

    (a) 8 in., 4 in.   (b) 4 in., 8 in.   (c) 6 in., 12 in.   (d) 12 in., 6 in.

    Answer: _____   Section: _____._____

23. Interconnecting cables under raised floors that support information technology equipment must be listed as Type _____ cable having adequate fire-resistant characteristics suitable for use under raised floors of an information technology equipment room.

    (a) RF   (b) UF   (c) LS   (d) DP

    Answer: _____   Section: _____._____

24. Junction boxes connected to a conduit that extends directly to a forming shell must be provided with a number of grounding terminals that must be no fewer than _____ the number of conduit entries.

(a) one more than   (b) two more than   (c) the same as   (d) none of these

Answer: _____   Section: _____._____

25. Luminaires installed in fountains must be _____.

(a) installed with the top of the luminaire lens below the normal water level
(b) listed for above-water use
(c) a and b
(d) a or b

Answer: _____   Section: _____._____

26. Metal parts of electric equipment associated with an indoor spa or hot tub water circulating system must be bonded.

(a) True   (b) False

Answer: _____   Section: _____._____

27. Panelboards for sensitive electronic equipment systems are allowed to be standard single-phase panelboards with the requirements that _____.

(a) 2 pole common-trip circuit breakers are used
(b) circuit breakers are identified for operation at the system voltage
(c) the system is clearly marked on the face of the panel or inside cover
(d) all of these

Answer: _____   Section: _____._____

28. Power to fire pump motors must be supplied by a reliable source. This source must have the capacity to carry the locked-rotor current of the fire pump motor(s), the pressure maintenance pump motors, and the full-load current of any associated fire pump equipment. This source can be _____.

(a) a separate service or a tap located ahead of but not within the utility service disconnecting means
(b) an on-site power supply, such as a generator
(c) a or b
(d) a and b

Answer: _____   Section: _____._____

29. Receptacles must not be less than _____ from the inside walls of a storable pool.

(a) 8 ft   (b) 10 ft   (c) 15 ft   (d) 20 ft

Answer: _____   Section: _____._____

30. Receptacles rated 125V, and 30A or less, within 10 ft of the inside walls of an indoor spa or hot tub, must be _____.

(a) removed   (b) on individual circuits only
(c) GFCI protected   (d) at least 12 in. above the maximum water level

Answer: _____   Section: _____._____

31. Recessed luminaires _____ located over or within 5 ft, measured horizontally, from the inside walls of an indoor spa or hot tub are permitted to be installed at less than 7 ft 6 in. above the maximum water level when GFCI protection is provided.

    (a) with a glass or plastic lens   (b) with nonmetallic or electrically isolated metal trim
    (c) suitable for use in a damp location   (d) all of these

    Answer: _____   Section: _____._____

32. Secondary overcurrent protection is permitted for transformers supplying fire pumps.

    (a) True   (b) False

    Answer: _____   Section: _____._____

33. Stainless steel, brass, copper, or copper alloy clamps labeled as being suitable for the purpose are acceptable for connection of the bonding conductor to the equipotential bonding grid of a swimming pool.

    (a) True   (b) False

    Answer: _____   Section: _____._____

34. Structures with a utility service and a photovoltaic system must have a permanent plaque or directory that identifies the location of the service disconnecting means and the photovoltaic system disconnecting means, if they are not at the same location.

    (a) True   (b) False

    Answer: _____   Section: _____._____

35. Testing all emergency lighting and power systems during maximum anticipated load conditions must be avoided so as not to tax the emergency system unnecessarily.

    (a) True   (b) False

    Answer: _____   Section: _____._____

36. Testing all legally required standby system lighting and power systems during maximum anticipated load conditions must be avoided so as not to tax the standby system unnecessarily.

    (a) True   (b) False

    Answer: _____   Section: _____._____

37. The branch-circuit overcurrent protection devices for legally required standby systems must be accessible only to _____.

    (a) the authority having jurisdiction   (b) authorized persons
    (c) the general public   (d) qualified persons

    Answer: _____   Section: _____._____

38. The branch-circuit overcurrent protection devices in emergency circuits must be accessible to _____ only.

    (a) the authority having jurisdiction   (b) authorized person
    (c) the general public   (d) qualified persons

    Answer: _____   Section: _____._____

39. The electric motor and controller for an electrically operated pool cover must be _____.

    (a) GFCI protected   (b) located at least 10 ft from the inside wall of the poo
    (c) both a and b   (d) either a or b

    Answer: _____   Section: _____._____

40. The maintenance disconnecting means required for swimming pool equipment must be _____.

    (a) readily accessible   (b) within sight of its equipment
    (c) accessible   (d) a and b

    Answer: _____   Section: _____._____

41. The pool structure, including the reinforcing metal of the pool shell and deck, must be bonded together.

    (a) True   (b) False

    Answer: _____   Section: _____._____

42. The scope of Article 680 includes _____.

    (a) wading and decorative pools   (b) fountains
    (c) hydromassage bathtubs   (d) all of these

    Answer: _____   Section: _____._____

43. To ensure that the emergency system meets or exceeds the original installation specification, the _____ must conduct or witness an acceptance test of the complete emergency system upon installation and periodically afterward.

    (a) electrical engineer   (b) authority having jurisdiction
    (c) qualified person   (d) manufacturer's representative

    Answer: _____   Section: _____._____

44. To ensure that the legally required standby system meets or exceeds the original installation specification, the _____ must conduct or witness an acceptance test of the complete emergency system upon installation.

    (a) electrical engineer   (b) authority having jurisdiction
    (c) qualified person   (d) manufacturer's representative

    Answer: _____   Section: _____._____

45. Transfer equipment for legally required systems, including automatic transfer switches, must be _____. Transfer equipment must be designed and installed to prevent the inadvertent interconnection of normal and alternate sources of supply in any operation of the transfer equipment.

    (a) automatic   (b) identified for standby use
    (c) approved by the authority having jurisdiction (d) all of these

    Answer: _____   Section: _____._____

46. Under raised floors of information technology equipment rooms, power cables, communications cables, connecting and interconnecting cables, and associated boxes, connectors, plugs, and receptacles listed as part of or for information technology equipment _____.

    (a) are not allowed

    (b) must be secured in place

    (c) are not required to be secured in place

    (d) must be installed only in rigid metal conduit

    Answer: _____ Section: _____._____

47. Voltage drop on sensitive electronic equipment systems must not exceed _____ percent for feeder and branch-circuit conductors combined.

    (a) 1.5   (b) 3   (c) 2.5   (d) 5

    Answer: _____ Section: _____._____

48. Where acceptable to the authority having jurisdiction (AHJ), connections ahead of and not within the same cabinet, enclosure, or vertical switchboard section as the service disconnecting means are permitted for _____ standby service.

    (a) emergency   (b) legally required   (c) optional   (d) all of these

    Answer: _____ Section: _____._____

49. Where an internal combustion engine is used as the prime mover for an emergency system, an on-site fuel supply must be provided for not less than _____ hours of full-demand operation of the system.

    (a) 2   (b) 3   (c) 4   (d) 5

    Answer: _____ Section: _____._____

50. Wiring from emergency source or emergency source distribution overcurrent protection to emergency loads must be kept entirely independent of all other wiring and equipment except in _____.

    (a) transfer equipment enclosures

    (b) exit or emergency luminaires supplied from two sources

    (c) a common junction box attached to exit or emergency luminaires supplied from two sources

    (d) all of these

    Answer: _____ Section: _____._____

1. All lights and receptacles installed in theater dressing rooms adjacent to the mirrors and above the dressing table counter(s), must be controlled by wall switches in the dressing rooms.

    (a) True   (b) False

    Answer: _____   Section: _____._____

2. All theater fixed stage switchboards that are not completely enclosed, dead-front and dead-rear or recessed into a wall, must be provided with a metal hood extending the full length of the board to protect all equipment on the board from falling objects.

    (a) True   (b) False

    Answer: _____   Section: _____._____

3. An apparatus enclosed in a case that is capable of withstanding an explosion of a specified gas or vapor that may occur within it, and of preventing the ignition of a specified gas or vapor surrounding the enclosure by sparks, flashes, or explosion of the gas or vapor within, and that operates at such an external temperature that a surrounding flammable atmosphere will not be ignited is defined as a(n) _____.

    (a) overcurrent protection device   (b) thermal apparatus
    (c) explosionproof apparatus   (d) bomb casing

    Answer: _____   Section: _____._____

4. An atmosphere classified as Group E contains combustible metal dusts.

    (a) True   (b) False

    Answer: _____   Section: _____._____

5. An autotransformer, used as part of a ballast for supplying lighting units and which raises the voltage to more than 300V, must be supplied by a(n) _____ system.

    (a) high leg   (b) grounded   (c) listed   (d) identified

    Answer: _____   Section: _____._____

6. An electrically operated pipe organ must have both the generator and motor frame grounded or _____.

    (a) the generator and motor must be effectively insulated from ground
    (b) the generator and motor must be effectively insulated from ground and from each other
    (c) the generator must be effectively insulated from ground and from the motor driving it
    (d) both must have double insulation

    Answer: _____   Section: _____._____

7.   An irrigation machine may have hand-portable motors.

     (a) True   (b) False

     Answer: _____   Section: _____._____

8.   An open span length of 200 ft for antenna conductors of hard-drawn copper located at an amateur transmitting and receiving station requires a minimum conductor size of _____.

     (a) 14 AWG   (b) 12 AWG   (c) 10 AWG   (d) 8 AWG

     Answer: _____   Section: _____._____

9.   Audible and visual signal devices for an emergency system must be provided, when practicable, for the purpose(s) of indicating _____.

     (a) that the battery is carrying load   (b) derangement of the emergency source
     (c) that the battery charger is not functioning   (d) all of these

     Answer: _____   Section: _____._____

10. Bare conductors must be securely and rigidly supported so that the minimum clearance between bare current-carrying metal parts of different potential mounted on the same surface will not be less than 2 in., nor less than _____, for parts that are in free air.

     (a) 1/4 in.   (b) 1/2 in.   (c) 1 in.   (d) 2 in.

     Answer: _____   Section: _____._____

11. Cablebus is ordinarily assembled at the _____.

     (a) point of installation   (b) manufacturer's location   (c) distributor's location   (d) none of these

     Answer: _____   Section: _____._____

12. Class 2 and 3 control conductors must be installed in raceways including _____ when used in hoistways.

     (a) rigid metal conduit   (b) electrical metallic tubing   (c) intermediate metal conduit   (d) all of these

     Answer: _____   Section: _____._____

13. Conductors located above a heated ceiling are considered as operating in an ambient temperature of _____.

     (a) 86°C   (b) 30°C   (c) 50°C   (d) 20°C

     Answer: _____   Section: _____._____

14. Conductors supplying outlets for arc and xenon projectors of the professional type must not be smaller than _____ and must be of sufficient size for the projector employed.

     (a) 12 AWG   (b) 10 AWG   (c) 8 AWG   (d) 6 AWG

     Answer: _____   Section: _____._____

15. Conductors with thermoplastic and fibrous outer braid, such as TBS insulation, are used for wiring _____.

     (a) switchboards only   (b) in a dry location   (c) in a wet location   (d) luminaires

     Answer: _____   Section: _____._____

16. Conduit bodies containing conductors larger than 6 AWG must have a cross-sectional area at least twice that of the largest conduit to which they are connected.

    (a) True   (b) False

    Answer: _____   Section: _____._____

17. Dry-type transformers installed indoors rated over _____ must be installed in a vault.

    (a) 1,000V   (b) 112 1/2 kVA   (c) 50,000V   (d) 35,000V

    Answer: _____   Section: _____._____

18. Each continuous-duty motor of _____ or less that is not permanently installed, not automatically started, and is within sight of the controller, is permitted to be protected against overload by the branch-circuit short-circuit and ground-fault protective device.

    (a) 1 hp   (b) 2 hp   (c) 3 hp   (d) 4 hp

    Answer: _____   Section: _____._____

19. Each electric appliance must be provided with a(n) _____ giving the identifying name and the rating in volts and amperes, or in volts and watts.

    (a) pamphlet   (b) nameplate   (c) auxiliary statement (d) owner's manual

    Answer: _____   Section: _____._____

20. Electric equipment must not be installed in rooms or pits that do not have drainage that adequately prevents water accumulation only during abnormal operation.

    (a) True   (b) False

    Answer: _____   Section: _____._____

21. Electric heaters of the cord-and-plug connected immersion type must be constructed and installed so that current-carrying parts are effectively _____ from electrical contact with the substance in which they are immersed.

    (a) isolated   (b) protected   (c) insulated   (d) all of these

    Answer: _____   Section: _____._____

22. Electric pipe organ circuits must be arranged so that all 26 AWG and 28 AWG conductors are protected from overcurrent by an overcurrent protection device rated at not more than _____.

    (a) 20A   (b) 15A   (c) 6A   (d) none of these

    Answer: _____   Section: _____._____

23. Except by special permission, no conductor larger than _____ AWG can be installed in a cellular metal floor raceway.

    (a) 1/0   (b) 4/0   (c) 1   (d) no restriction

    Answer: _____   Section: _____._____

24. Feeders supplying 15 and 20A receptacle branch circuits are permitted to be protected by a ground-fault circuit interrupter in lieu of the provisions for such interrupters as specified in 210.8 and Article 590.

    (a) True   (b) False

    Answer: _____   Section: _____._____

25. Fixed electric space-heating equipment must be installed to provide the _____ spacing between the equipment and adjacent combustible material, unless it has been found to be acceptable where installed in direct contact with combustible material.

    (a) required   (b) minimum   (c) maximum   (d) safest

    Answer: _____   Section: _____._____

26. Flat conductor cable cannot be installed in _____.

    (a) dwelling units   (b) schools   (c) hospitals   (d) any of these

    Answer: _____   Section: _____._____

27. FMT must be used _____.

    (a) in dry and damp locations   (b) for direct burial   (c) in lengths over 6 ft   (d) for a maximum of 1,000V

    Answer: _____   Section: _____._____

28. For applications where underground circuits must be buried deeper than shown in a specific underground ampacity table or figure, the following ampacity derating factor is permitted to be used: _____ percent per increased foot of depth for all values of Rho.

    (a) 3   (b) 6   (c) 9   (d) 12

    Answer: _____   Section: _____._____

29. For cellular concrete floor raceways, junction boxes must be _____ the floor grade and sealed against the free entrance of water or concrete.

    (a) leveled to   (b) above   (c) below   (d) perpendicular to

    Answer: _____   Section: _____._____

30. For each farm building or load supplied by _____ or more branch circuits, the load for feeders, service-entrance conductors, and service equipment must be computed in accordance with demand factors not less than indicated in Table 220.102.

    (a) one   (b) two   (c) three   (d) four

    Answer: _____   Section: _____._____

31. For services exceeding 600V, nominal, the isolating switch must be accessible to _____.

    (a) all occupants   (b) qualified personnel only   (c) a height of 8 ft   (d) any of these

    Answer: _____   Section: _____._____

32. For straight pulls, the length of a pull box must not be less than _____ times the outside diameter, over sheath, of the largest shielded or lead covered conductor or cable entering the box on systems over 600V.

    (a) 18   (b) 16   (c) 36   (d) 48

    Answer: _____   Section: _____._____

33. General-use _____ switches must be used only to control permanently-installed incandescent luminaires unless otherwise listed for control of other loads.

    (a) dimmer   (b) fan speed control (c) timer   (d) all of these

    Answer: _____   Section: _____._____

34. General-use branch circuits using flat conductor cable must not exceed _____.

    (a) 15A   (b) 20A   (c) 30A   (d) 40A

    Answer: _____   Section: _____._____

35. Ground-fault protection of equipment must be provided for electric heat tracing and heating panels installed on pipelines or vessels except in certain industrial installations where there is alarm indication of ground faults.

    (a) True   (b) False

    Answer: _____   Section: _____._____

36. If a set of 120/240V service conductors terminates at a through-the-roof raceway or approved support, with less than 6 ft of these conductors passing over the roof overhang, the minimum clearance above the roof for these service conductors is _____.

    (a) 12 in.   (b) 18 in.   (c) 2 ft   (d) 5 ft

    Answer: _____   Section: _____._____

37. In a cablebus, the size and number of conductors must be that for which the cablebus is designed, and in no case smaller than _____ AWG.

    (a) 1/0   (b) 2/0   (c) 3/0   (d) 4/0

    Answer: _____   Section: _____._____

38. In anesthetizing locations, low-voltage equipment that is frequently in contact with the bodies of persons or has exposed current-carrying elements must _____.

    (a) operate on an electrical potential of 10V or less   (b) be moisture resistant
    (c) be intrinsically safe or double-insulated   (d) all of these

    Answer: _____   Section: _____._____

39. In Article 200, connected so as to be capable of carrying current (as distinguished from connection through electromagnetic induction) defines the term _____.

    (a) effectively grounded   (b) electrically connected   (c) grounded system   (d) none of these

    Answer: _____   Section: _____._____

40. In cellular concrete floor raceways, a cell is defined as a single, enclosed _____ space in a floor made of precast cellular concrete slabs, the direction of the cell being parallel to the direction of the floor member.

    (a) circular   (b) oval   (c) tubular   (d) hexagonal

    Answer: _____   Section: _____._____

41. In health care facilities, patient bed receptacles located in general care areas must be supplied by at least two branch circuits, generally one from the normal system and one from the emergency system. The branch circuits for these receptacles are allowed to originate from two separate transfer switches on the emergency system.

    (a) True   (b) False

    Answer: _____   Section: _____._____

42. In locations where electrical equipment is likely to be exposed to _____, enclosures or guards must be so arranged and of such strength as to prevent such damage.

(a) air circulation   (b) physical damage   (c) magnetic fields   (d) weather

Answer: _____   Section: _____._____

43. In network-powered broadband communications systems, all separate electrodes can be bonded together using a minimum size jumper of _____ copper.

(a) 10 AWG   (b) 8 AWG   (c) 6 AWG   (d) 4 AWG

Answer: _____   Section: _____._____

44. Incandescent luminaires must be marked with the maximum lamp wattage. Luminaires requiring ballasts or transformers must be plainly marked with their electrical _____ and the manufacturer's name, trademark, or other suitable means of identification.

(a) characteristics   (b) rating   (c) frequency   (d) none of these

Answer: _____   Section: _____._____

45. Individual open conductors and cables other than service-entrance cables must not be installed within _____ of grade level or where exposed to physical damage.

(a) 8 ft   (b) 10 ft   (c) 12 ft   (d) 15 ft

Answer: _____   Section: _____._____

46. Knife switches rated for more than 1,200A at 250V or less _____.

(a) are used only as isolating switches   (b) may be opened under load   (c) should be placed so that gravity tends to close them   (d) should be connected in parallel

Answer: _____   Section: _____._____

47. Lampholders installed in wet or damp locations must be of the _____ type.

(a) waterproof   (b) weatherproof   (c) moistureproof   (d) moisture-resistant

Answer: _____   Section: _____._____

48. Lampholders installed over highly combustible material must be of the _____ type.

(a) industrial   (b) switched   (c) unswitched   (d) residential

Answer: _____   Section: _____._____

49. Loop wiring in an underfloor raceway _____ to be a splice or tap.

(a) is considered   (b) must not be considered   (c) is not permitted   (d) none of these

Answer: _____   Section: _____._____

50. Luminaires with more than one lampholder must be wired so that the _____ of each lampholder is connected to the same circuit conductor or terminal.

(a) stem   (b) arm   (c) supplemental protection   (d) screw-shell

Answer: _____   Section: _____._____

(• Indicates that 75% or fewer exam takers get the question correct)

Article 702 Optional Standby Power Systems

Optional standby systems are intended to protect public or private facilities or property where life safety doesn't depend on the performance of the system. These systems are typically installed to provide an alternate source of electric power for such facilities as industrial and commercial buildings, farms, and residences, and to serve loads that, when stopped during any power outage, could cause discomfort, serious interruption of a process, or damage to a product or process. Optional standby systems are intended to supply on-site generated power to loads selected by the customer either automatically or manually.

1. Article 702 applies to _____ generators used for backup power to telecommunications facilities, water and wastewater pump stations, as well as homes and offices.

    (a) permanently installed   (b) portable   (c) a and b   (d) none of these

    Answer: _____   Section: _____._____

2. Optional standby systems must have adequate capacity and rating for the supply of _____.

    (a) all emergency lighting and power loads
    (b) all equipment intended to be operated at one time
    (c) 100 percent of the appliance loads and 50 percent of the lighting loads
    (d) 100 percent of the lighting loads and 75 percent of the appliance loads

    Answer: _____   Section: _____._____

3. For optional standby systems, the temporary connection of a portable generator without transfer equipment is permitted, where written safety procedures are in place and conditions of maintenance and supervision ensure that only qualified persons will service the installation, and where the normal supply is physically isolated by _____.

    (a) a lockable disconnecting means   (b) the disconnection of the normal supply conductors
    (c) an extended power outage   (d) a or b

    Answer: _____   Section: _____._____

4. A sign must be placed at the service-entrance equipment indicating the _____ of on-site optional standby power sources.

    (a) type   (b) location   (c) manufacturer   (d) a and b

    Answer: _____   Section: _____._____

5. If the transfer switch for a portable generator switches the _____ conductor, then it is being used as a separately derived system and the portable generator must be grounded in accordance with 250.30.

    (a) phase   (b) equipment grounding   (c) grounded neutral   (d) all of these

    Answer: _____ Section: _____._____

6. Where a generator for an optional standby system is installed outdoors and equipped with a readily accessible disconnecting means located _____, an additional disconnecting means is not required where ungrounded conductors serve or pass through the building or structure.

    (a) inside the building or structure   (b) within sight of the building or structure
    (c) inside the generator enclosure   (d) a or c

    Answer: _____ Section: _____._____

Article 720 Circuits and Equipment Operating at Less Than 50V

Article 720 applies to electrical installations that operate below 50V, either direct current or alternating current. Other installations that operate below 50V and are covered in Articles 411, 551, 650, 669, 725, and 760 aren't required to comply with Article 720.

7. Circuits and equipment operating at less than 50V must use receptacles that are rated at not less than _____.

    (a) 10A   (b) 15A   (c) 20A   (d) 30A

    Answer: _____ Section: _____._____

Article 725 Class 1, Class 2, and Class 3 Remote-Control, Signaling, and Power-Limited Circuits

Article 725 contains the requirements for remote-control, signaling, and power-limited circuits that aren't an integral part of a device or appliance.

- Remote-Control Circuit—A circuit that controls other circuits through a relay or solid-state device. For example, a circuit that controls the coil of a motor starter or lighting contactor.
- Signaling Circuit—A circuit that supplies energy to an appliance or device that gives a visual and/or audible signal. For example, a circuit for doorbells, buzzers, code-calling systems, signal lights, annunciators, burglar alarms, and other indication or alarm devices.

8. Due to its power limitations, a Class 2 circuit is safe from a fire initiation standpoint and provides acceptable protection from electric shock

    (a) True   (b) False

    Answer: _____ Section: _____._____

9. All accessible portions of abandoned Class 2, Class 3, and PLTC cables must be removed.

    (a) True   (b) False

    Answer: _____ Section: _____._____

10. Class 1, 2, and 3 cables installed _____ on the surface of ceilings and sidewalls must be supported by the building structure in such a manner that the cable will not be damaged by normal building use.

    (a) exposed   (b) concealed   (c) hidden   (d) a and b

    Answer: _____ Section: _____._____

11. Remote-control circuits to safety-control equipment must be classified as _____ if the failure of the equipment to operate introduces a direct fire or life hazard.

(a) Class 1   (b) Class 2   (c) Class 3   (d) Class I, Division 1

Answer: _____   Section: _____._____

12. Where damage to remote-control circuits of safety control equipment would introduce a hazard, all conductors of such remote-control circuits shall be installed in rigid metal conduit, intermediate metal conduit, rigid nonmetallic conduit, electrical metallic tubing, Type MI cable, Type MC cable, or be otherwise suitably protected from physical damage.

(a) True   (b) False

Answer: _____   Section: _____._____

13. A Class 1 signaling circuit must not exceed _____.

(a) 130V   (b) 150V   (c) 220V   (d) 600V

Answer: _____   Section: _____._____

14. Class 1 circuit conductors supplied by the secondary of a single-phase transformer having only a 2-wire (single-voltage) secondary are permitted to be protected by overcurrent protection provided on the primary side of the transformer, provided _____.

(a) primary protection is in accordance with 450.3
(b) primary protection does not exceed the value determined by multiplying the secondary conductor ampacity by the secondary to primary transformer voltage ratio
(c) branch circuit conductors are 90-degree rated
(d) a and b.

Answer: _____   Section: _____._____

15. Power-supply and Class 1 circuit conductors are permitted to occupy the same cable, enclosure, or raceway _____.

(a) only where the equipment powered is functionally associated
(b) only where the circuits involved are not a mixture of ac and dc
(c) under no circumstances
(d) none of these

Answer: _____   Section: _____._____

16. When required, the maximum overcurrent protection in amperes for a noninherently-limited Class 2 remote-control circuit is _____.

(a) 1.0A   (b) 2.0A   (c) 5.0A   (d) 7.5A

Answer: _____   Section: _____._____

17. Equipment supplying Class 2 or Class 3 circuits must be durably marked where plainly visible to indicate _____.

(a) each circuit that is a Class 2 or Class 3 circuit   (b) the circuit VA rating
(c) the size of the conductors serving each circuit   (d) all of these

Answer: _____   Section: _____._____

18. Conductors of Class 2 and Class 3 circuits must not be placed in any enclosure, raceway, cable, or similar fittings with conductors of Class 1 or electric light or power conductors, except when they are _____.

    (a) insulated for the maximum voltage   (b) totally comprised of aluminum conductors
    (c) separated by a barrier   (d) all of these

    Answer: _____   Section: _____._____

19. Class 2 and Class 3 circuits are permitted within the same cable, raceway, or enclosure provided that the insulation of the Class 2 circuit conductors meet the requirements for Class 3 circuits.

    (a) True   (b) False

    Answer: _____   Section: _____._____

20. Raceways must not be used as a means of support for Class 2 or Class 3 circuit conductors.

    (a) True   (b) False

    Answer: _____   Section: _____._____

21. The accessible portion of abandoned Class 2 and Class 3 cables installed in duct, plenums, or other spaces used for environmental air must be _____.

    (a) removed   (b) identified as abandoned   (c) a or b   (d) none of these

    Answer: _____   Section: _____._____

22. Class 2 or Class 3 cables installed in hazardous (classified) locations must be Type _____, as permitted by 501.4(B), 502.4(B), and 504.20.

    (a) CL2R   (b) PLTC   (c) CL2P   (d) CL3P

    Answer: _____   Section: _____._____

23. Class 2 and Class 3 riser cables listed as suitable for use in a vertical run in a shaft, or from floor to floor are _____.

    (a) CL2P and CL3P   (b) CL2R and CL3R   (c) CL2 and CL3   (d) PLCT

    Answer: _____   Section: _____._____

Article 727 Instrumentation Tray Cable (Type ITC)

Instrumentation tray cable (ITC) is used in industrial establishments where the conditions of maintenance and supervision assure that only qualified persons will service the installation.

24. Instrumentation tray cable is used for instrumentation and control circuits operating at _____.

    (a) 300V or less and 0.5A or less   (b) 150V or less and 5A or less
    (c) 480V or less and 10A or less   (d) over 600V

    Answer: _____   Section: _____._____

25. Type ITC cable can be installed with power, lighting, and Class 1 circuits.

    (a) True   (b) False

    Answer: _____   Section: _____._____

26. Overcurrent protection for Type ITC cable must not exceed _____ for 20 AWG and larger conductors.

(a) 3A   (b) 5A   (c) 10A   (d) 15A

Answer: _____   Section: _____._____

Article 760 Fire Alarm Systems

Article 760 covers the installation of wiring and equipment for fire alarm systems. Fire alarm systems include fire detection and alarm notification, voice communications, guard's tour, sprinkler waterflow, and sprinkler supervisory systems.

27. Article 760 covers the requirements for the installation of wiring and equipment of _____.

(a) communications systems   (b) antennas   (c) fire alarm systems   (d) fiber optics

Answer: _____   Section: _____._____

28. Class 2, Class 3, and PLTC cables that are not terminated at equipment and not identified for future use with a tag will be considered as abandoned.

(a) True   (b) False

Answer: _____   Section: _____._____

29. Fire alarm circuits installed in ducts, plenums, and other air-handling spaces must be installed in accordance with the requirements contained in 300.22.

(a) True   (b) False

Answer: _____   Section: _____._____

30. Fire alarm circuits installed in _____ locations must comply with 110.11, 300.6, and 310.9.

(a) corrosive   (b) damp   (c) wet   (d) any of these

Answer: _____   Section: _____._____

31. Exposed fire alarm circuit cables must be supported by the building structure using straps, staples, hangers, or similar fittings designed and installed so as not to damage the cable.

(a) True   (b) False

Answer: _____   Section: _____._____

32. Fire alarm circuits must be identified at all terminal and junction locations. The identification must be in a manner that will prevent unintentional interference with the fire alarm signaling circuit during _____.

(a) installation   (b) testing and servicing   (c) renovations   (d) all of these

Answer: _____   Section: _____._____

33. The power source for a nonpower-limited fire alarm (NPLFA) circuit cannot be supplied through a(n) _____.

(a) ground-fault circuit interrupter   (b) arc-fault circuit interrupter
(c) inverse-time circuit breaker   (d) a or b

Answer: _____   Section: _____._____

34. Overcurrent protection devices for nonpower-limited fire alarm (NPLFA) circuits must be located at the point where the conductor to be protected _____.

(a) terminates at the load   (b) is spliced to any other conductor
(c) receives its supply   (d) none of these

Answer: _____   Section: _____._____

35. Nonpower-limited fire alarm (NPLFA) circuit conductors are permitted to be in the same cable, enclosure, or raceway with power-supply circuits only where connected to the same equipment.

(a) True   (b) False

Answer: _____   Section: _____._____

36. Conductors for nonpower-limited fire alarm circuits must be _____.

(a) solid copper   (b) stranded copper   (c) copper or aluminum   (d) a or b

Answer: _____   Section: _____._____

37. Where installed exposed, fire alarm cables must be _____.

(a) adequately supported   (b) installed in such a way as to be protected against physical damage
(c) none of these   (d) a and b

Answer: _____   Section: _____._____

38. Exposed power-limited fire alarm circuit cables may be installed in _____ when passing through a floor or wall to a height of 7 ft above the floor, unless adequate protection is afforded by the building construction or an equivalent solid guard is provided.

(a) rigid metal conduit   (b) rigid nonmetallic conduit   (c) electrical metallic tubing   (d) any of these

Answer: _____   Section: _____._____

39. The listing requirements for power-limited fire alarm (PLFA) circuit sources are found in Tables 12(A) and 12(B) of _____.

(a) Article 760   (b) Chapter 9   (c) Article 300   (d) Annex C

Answer: _____   Section: _____._____

40. Power-limited fire alarm circuits are permitted to be reclassified and installed as _____ if the power-limited fire alarm circuit markings required by 760.42 are eliminated, and the entire circuit is installed in a Chapter 3 wiring method in accordance with Part II of Article 760.

(a) intrinsically safe circuits   (b) ground-fault protected circuits
(c) nonpower-limited circuits   (d) Class I, Division 2

Answer: _____   Section: _____._____

41. Conductors of lighting or power may occupy the same enclosure or raceway with conductors of power-limited fire alarm circuits.

(a) True   (b) False

Answer: _____   Section: _____._____

42. Audio system circuits described in 640.9(C) and using Class 2 or Class 3 wiring methods are not permitted to be installed in the same cable or raceway with _____.

(a) other audio system circuits   (b) power-limited fire alarm conductors or cables

(c) a or b   (d) none of these

Answer: _____   Section: _____._____

43. Power-limited fire alarm circuit cables installed within buildings in an air-handling space used for environmental air must use _____ conductors when not installed in a raceway.

(a) FPL   (b) CL3P   (c) OFNP   (d) FPLP

Answer: _____   Section: _____._____

44. Coaxial cables used in power-limited fire alarm systems must have an overall insulation rating of not less than _____.

(a) 100V   (b) 300V   (c) 600V   (d) 1,000V

Answer: _____   Section: _____._____

Article 770 Optical Fiber Cables and Raceways

Article 770 covers the installation of optical fiber cables, which contain optical fibers used to transmit light for control, signaling, and communication. This article also contains the installation requirements for raceways that contain and support the optical fiber cables. Requirements are also contained in this article for composite cables (often called "hybrid" in the field) that combine optical fibers with current-carrying metallic conductors.

45. All accessible portions of abandoned optical fiber cable must be removed.

(a) True   (b) False

Answer: _____   Section: _____._____

46. Conductive optical fiber cables contain noncurrent-carrying conductive members such as metallic _____.

(a) strength members   (b) vapor barriers   (c) armor or sheath   (d) any of these

Answer: _____   Section: _____._____

47. When optical fiber cable is installed in a raceway, the raceway must be of a type permitted in Chapter 3 and the raceway must be installed in accordance with Chapter 3 requirements.

(a) True   (b) False

Answer: _____   Section: _____._____

48. Access to equipment must not be prohibited by an accumulation of optical fiber cables that prevent the removal of access panels. This includes suspended-ceiling panels.

(a) True   (b) False

Answer: _____   Section: _____._____

49. Exposed optical fiber cables must be supported by the building structure using straps, staples, hangers, or similar fittings designed and installed so as not to damage the cable.

    (a) True   (b) False

    Answer: _____   Section: _____._____

50. _____ is a conductive, general-purpose type of optical fiber cable that may be installed as wiring within buildings.

    (a) FPLP   (b) CL2P   (c) OFPN   (d) OFC

    Answer: _____   Section: _____._____

51. Optical fibers are permitted within the same composite cable as electric light, power, and Class 1 circuits operating at 600V, or less where the functions of the optical fibers and the electrical conductors are associated.

    (a) True   (b) False

    Answer: _____   Section: _____._____

52. Optical fibers are permitted in the same cable, and conductive and nonconductive optical fiber cables are permitted in the same cable tray, enclosure, or raceway with conductors of Class 2 and Class 3 circuits in compliance with Article 725.

    (a) True   (b) False

    Answer: _____   Section: _____._____

53. Types OFNG, OFN, OFCG, and OFC optical fiber cables may be used as risers when _____.

    (a) encased in a metal raceway
    (b) located in a fireproof shaft having a fire-stop at each floor
    (c) none of these
    (d) a or b

    Answer: _____   Section: _____._____

54. Optical fiber riser cables listed as suitable for use in a vertical run in a shaft or from floor to floor are Types _____.

    (a) OFNP and OFCP   (b) OFNR and OFCR   (c) OFNG and OFCG   (d) OFN and OFC

    Answer: _____   Section: _____._____

55. Optical fiber cables listed as suitable for general-purpose use, with the exception of risers, plenums, and other space used for environmental air are Types _____.

    (a) OFNP and OFCP   (b) OFNR and OFCR   (c) OFNG and OFCG   (d) OFN and OFC

    Answer: _____   Section: _____._____

Chapter 8 Communications Systems

Article 800 Communications Circuits

This article covers the installation requirements for telephone wiring and for other related telecommunications purposes such as computer Local Area Networks (LANs), and outside wiring for fire and burglar alarm systems connected to central stations.

56. Communications circuits and equipment installed in a location that is _____ in accordance with Article 500 must comply with the applicable requirements contained in Chapter 5.

(a) designed   (b) classified   (c) located   (d) approved

Answer: _____   Section: _____._____

57. Equipment intended to be electrically connected to a telecommunications network must be listed for the purpose.

(a) True   (b) False

Answer: _____   Section: _____._____

58. Communications cables installed _____ on the surface of ceilings and sidewalls must be supported by the building structure in such a manner that the cable will not be damaged by normal building use.

(a) exposed   (b) concealed   (c) hidden   (d) a and b

Answer: _____   Section: _____._____

59. Where overhead communications wires and cables enter buildings, they must _____.

(a) where practicable, be located below the electric light or power conductors
(b) not be attached to a cross-arm that carries electric light or power conductors
(c) have a vertical clearance of not less than 8 ft from all points of roofs above which they pass
(d) all of these

Answer: _____   Section: _____._____

60. The metallic sheath of communications cable entering buildings must be _____.

(a) grounded at the point of emergence through an exterior wall
(b) grounded at the point of emergence through a concrete floor slab
(c) interrupted as close to the point of entrance as practicable by an insulating joint
(d) any of these

Answer: _____   Section: _____._____

61. Limiting the length of the primary protector grounding conductors for communications circuits on one- and two-family dwellings reduces differences in potential between the building's _____ and communications systems during lightning events.

(a) power   (b) fire alarm   (c) lighting   (d) lightning protection

Answer: _____   Section: _____._____

62. In communications circuits, all separate electrodes are permitted to be bonded together using a minimum jumper size of _____ copper.

(a) 10 AWG   (b) 8 AWG   (c) 6 AWG   (d) 4 AWG

Answer: _____   Section: _____._____

63. Communications wires and cables are not required to be listed and marked where the length of the cable within the building, measured from its point of entrance, does not exceed_____ and the cable enters the building from the outside and is terminated in an enclosure or on a listed primary protector.

(a) 25 ft   (b) 30 ft   (c) 50 ft   (d) 100 ft

Answer: _____   Section: _____._____

64. Communications cable risers penetrating more than one floor, or cables installed in vertical runs in a shaft, must be Type CMR. Listed communications cables are also allowed when _____.

(a) encased in metal raceways   (b) located in a fireproof shaft with firestops at each floor
(c) a or b   (d) none of these

Answer: _____   Section: _____._____

65. Communications plenum cable must be _____ as being suitable for use in ducts, plenums, and other spaces used for environmental air.

(a) marked   (b) identified   (c) approved   (d) listed

Answer: _____   Section: _____._____

Article 810 Radio and Television Equipment

This article covers antenna systems for radio and television receiving equipment, amateur radio transmitting and receiving equipment, and certain features of transmitter safety. It also includes antennas such as multi-element, vertical rod and dish, and the wiring and cabling that connect them to the equipment.

66. Coaxial cables that connect antennas to equipment must be installed in accordance with Article 820.

(a) True   (b) False

Answer: _____   Section: _____._____

67. Soft-drawn or medium-drawn copper lead-in conductors for receiving antenna systems are permitted where the maximum span between points of support is less than _____.

(a) 35 ft   (b) 30 ft   (c) 20 ft   (d) 10 ft

Answer: _____   Section: _____._____

68. Outdoor antennas and lead-in conductors for radio and television equipment must not cross over open conductors of electric light or power circuits, and must be kept well away from all such circuits to avoid the possibility of accidental contact. Where proximity to open electric light or power service conductors of less than 250V between conductors cannot be avoided, the installation must provide a clearance of at least _____.

(a) 2 ft   (b) 6 ft   (c) 8 ft   (d) 5 ft

Answer: _____   Section: _____._____

69. The receiving station outdoor wire-strung antenna conductor with a span of 75 ft must be at least _____ if a copper-clad steel conductor is used.

(a) 10 AWG   (b) 12 AWG   (c) 14 AWG   (d) 17 AWG

Answer: _____   Section: _____._____

70. Underground antenna conductors for radio and television receiving equipment must be separated at least _____ from any light, power, or Class 1 circuit conductors.

    (a) 6 ft   (b) 5 ft   (c) 12 in.   (d) 18 in.

    Answer: _____   Section: _____._____

71. Indoor antenna lead-in conductors for radio and television receiving equipment are permitted to be in the same enclosure with conductors of other wiring systems where separated by an effective, permanently installed barrier.

    (a) True   (b) False

    Answer: _____   Section: _____._____

72. Antenna discharge units must be located outside the building. They may never be located indoors.

    (a) True   (b) False

    Answer: _____   Section: _____._____

73. The grounding conductor for an antenna mast or antenna discharge unit must be run to the grounding electrode in as straight a line as practicable.

    (a) True   (b) False

    Answer: _____   Section: _____._____

74. If a separate grounding electrode is installed for the radio and television equipment, it must be bonded to the building's electrical power grounding electrode system with a conductor not smaller than _____ AWG.

    (a) 10   (b) 8   (c) 6   (d) 1/0

    Answer: _____   Section: _____._____

75. Unshielded lead-in antenna conductors for amateur transmitting stations attached to buildings must be firmly mounted at least _____ clear of the surface of the building on nonabsorbent insulating supports.

    (a) 1 in.   (b) 2 in.   (c) 3 in.   (d) 4 in.

    Answer: _____   Section: _____._____

Article 820 Community Antenna Television (CATV) and Radio Distribution Systems

This article covers the installation of coaxial cables to distribute limited-energy high-frequency signals for television, cable TV, and closed-circuit television (CCTV), which is often used for security purposes. This article also covers premises wiring of satellite TV systems where the dish antenna is outside and covered by Article 810.

76. CATV cable not terminated at equipment and not identified for future use with a tag is considered abandoned.

    (a) True   (b) False

    Answer: _____   Section: _____._____

77. The coaxial cable for community antenna television (CATV) and radio systems is permitted to deliver low-energy power to equipment that is directly associated with the radio frequency distribution system if voltage is not over _____ volts and if the current supply is from a transformer or other energy-limiting device.

    (a) 600   (b) 120   (c) 60   (d) 1,000

    Answer: _____   Section: _____._____

78. CATV cables installed _____ on the surface of ceilings and sidewalls must be supported by the building structure in such a manner that the cable will not be damaged by normal building use.

    (a) exposed   (b) concealed   (c) hidden   (d) a and b

    Answer: _____   Section: _____._____

79. Where practicable, coaxial cables for a CATV system must be separated by at least _____ from lightning conductors.

    (a) 3 in.   (b) 6 in.   (c) 6 ft   (d) 2 ft

    Answer: _____   Section: _____._____

80. The conductor used to ground the outer cover of a coaxial cable must be _____.

    (a) insulated   (b) 14 AWG minimum   (c) bare   (d) a and b

    Answer: _____   Section: _____._____

81. Limiting the length of the primary protector grounding conductors for community antenna television and radio systems on one- and two-family dwellings reduces differences in potential between the building's _____ and communications systems during lightning events.

    (a) power   (b) fire alarm   (c) lighting   (d) lightning protection

    Answer: _____   Section: _____._____

82. The grounding conductor for a CATV system must be connected to the nearest accessible location included on the list in 820.100(B)(1) when the building _____.

    (a) has a grounding means   (b) is without a grounding means
    (c) has an emergency transfer switch   (d) is wired using a metallic cable or raceway system

    Answer: _____   Section: _____._____

83. A bonding jumper not smaller than _____ copper or equivalent must be connected between the antenna system's grounding electrode and the power grounding electrode system at the building or structure served where separate electrodes are used for the CATV system.

    (a) 12 AWG   (b) 8 AWG   (c) 6 AWG   (d) 4 AWG

    Answer: _____   Section: _____._____

84. Coaxial cable is permitted to be placed in a raceway, compartment, outlet box, or junction box with the conductors of light or power circuits, or Class 1 circuits when _____.

    (a) installed in rigid metal conduit   (b) separated by a permanent barrier
    (c) insulated   (d) none of these

    Answer: _____   Section: _____._____

85. CATV cables installed in ducts, plenums, and other spaces used for environmental air, and not inside of a raceway, must be Type CATVP.

(a) True   (b) False

Answer: _____   Section: _____._____

Article 830 Network-Powered Broadband Communications Systems

This article contains the installation requirements for network-powered broadband communications systems where powered from the communications utility network for voice, audio, video, data, and interactive services through a network interface unit (NIU). An example of a network-powered broadband communications system is hybrid fiber-coaxial (HFC) cable used for video/audio conferencing or interactive multimedia entertainment systems.

86. Network-powered broadband cable not terminated at equipment and not identified for future use with a tag is considered abandoned.

(a) True   (b) False

Answer: _____   Section: _____._____

87. Network-powered broadband cables installed _____ on the surface of ceilings and sidewalls must be supported by the structural components of the building in such a manner that the cable will not be damaged by normal building use.

(a) exposed   (b) concealed   (c) hidden   (d) a and b

Answer: _____   Section: _____._____

88. Where network-powered broadband communications system aerial cables are installed outside and entering buildings, they must _____.

(a) be located below the electric light or power conductors, where practicable
(b) not be attached to a cross-arm that carries electric light or power conductors
(c) have a vertical clearance of not less than 8 ft from all points of roofs above which they pass
(d) all of these

Answer: _____   Section: _____._____

89. In one- and two-family and multifamily dwellings, the grounding conductor for network-powered broadband communications systems must be as short as permissible, not to exceed _____ in length.

(a) 5 ft   (b) 6 ft   (c) 10 ft   (d) 20 ft

Answer: _____   Section: _____._____

90. In one- and two-family dwellings where it is not practicable to achieve an overall maximum primary protector grounding conductor length of 20 ft or less for network-powered broadband communications systems, a separate _____ communications ground rod must be driven and be bonded to the power grounding electrode system with a 6 AWG conductor.

(a) 5 ft   (b) 8 ft   (c) 10 ft   (d) 20 ft

Answer: _____   Section: _____._____

91. Network-powered broadband communications system cables must be separated at least 2 in. from conductors of _____ circuits.

(a) power   (b) electric light   (c) Class 1   (d) any of these

Answer: _____   Section: _____._____

Chapter 9 Tables

Conductor and Raceway Specifications

92. The percentage of conduit fill for two conductors is _____ percent.

    (a) 40   (b) 31   (c) 53   (d) 30

    Answer: _____   Section: _____._____

93. When calculating raceway conductor fill, equipment grounding conductors must _____.

    (a) not be counted   (b) have the actual dimensions used
    (c) not be counted if in a nipple   (d) not be counted if for a wye three-phase balanced load

    Answer: _____   Section: _____._____

94. When conduit nipples 24 in. or shorter are installed, the ampacity adjustment factor for more than three current-carrying conductors _____ to this condition.

    (a) does not apply   (b) must be applied

    Answer: _____   Section: _____._____

95. The inside diameter of 1 in. IMC is _____

    (a) 1.000 in.   (b) 1.105 in.   (c) 0.826 in.   (d) 0.314 in.

    Answer: _____   Section: _____._____

96. The circular mil area of a 12 AWG conductor is _____.

    (a) 10,380   (b) 26,240   (c) 6,530   (d) 6,350

    Answer: _____   Section: _____._____

97. A 10 AWG 7-strand copper wire has a cross-sectional area of _____

    (a) 0.007 sq in.   (b) 0.011 sq in.   (c) 0.012 sq in.   (d) 0.106 sq in.

    Answer: _____   Section: _____._____

98. A 250 kcmil bare cable has a conductor diameter of _____

    (a) 0.557 in.   (b) 0.755 in.   (c) 0.575 in.   (d) 0.690 in.

    Answer: _____   Section: _____._____

99. The ac ohms-to-neutral impedance per 1,000 ft of 2/0 AWG copper conductor in a steel raceway is _____.

    (a) 0.06 ohms   (b) 0.10 ohms   (c) 0.22 ohms   (d) 0.11 ohms

    Answer: _____   Section: _____._____

100. Annex C contains tables that list the number of conductors or fixture wires permitted in a raceway when the conductors are all of the same size and type.

    (a) True   (b) False

    Answer: _____   Section: _____._____

Unit 12
NEC Practice Quiz
Articles 702 through Chapter 9

(• Indicates that 75% or fewer exam takers get the question correct)

1. Optional standby systems are typically installed to provide an alternate source of power for _____.

    (a) data-processing and communication systems
    (b) emergency systems for health care facilities
    (c) emergency systems for hospitals
    (d) none of these

    Answer: _____ Section: _____._____

2. •Cables and conductors of Class 2 and Class 3 circuits _____ be placed in any cable, cable tray, compartment, enclosure, man-hole, outlet box, device box, raceway, or similar fitting with conductors of electric light, power, Class 1, nonpower-limited fire alarm circuits, and medium power network-powered broadband communications circuits.

    (a) may   (b) must not   (c) a and b   (d) none of these

    Answer: _____ Section: _____._____

3. A rigid metal conduit nipple (1 1/2 in.) with three conductors can be filled to an area of _____

    (a) 0.882 sq in.   (b) 1.072 sq in.   (c) 1.243 sq in.   (d) 1.343 sq in.

    Answer: _____ Section: _____._____

4. Access doors to the transmitter enclosure of a radio or TV station must have interlocks to disconnect the power to the transmitter when any access door is opened, if the voltage between conductors is over _____.

    (a) 150V   (b) 250V   (c) 350V   (d) 480V

    Answer: _____ Section: _____._____

5. Access to electrical equipment must not be denied by an accumulation of cables that prevents removal of panels, including suspended-ceiling panels.

    (a) True   (b) False

    Answer: _____ Section: _____._____

6. Access to equipment must not be denied by an accumulation of (CATV) wires and cables that prevent the removal of panels. This does not apply to suspended-ceiling panels.

    (a) True   (b) False

    Answer: _____ Section: _____._____

7. Access to equipment must not be prohibited by an accumulation of _____ that prevents the removal of access panels. This includes suspended-ceiling panels.

    (a) wires   (b) cables   (c) ductwork   (d) a and b

    Answer: _____ Section: _____._____

8. An outdoor wire-strung antenna conductor of a receiving station with a 75 ft span using a hard-drawn copper conductor must not be less than _____.

   (a) 10 AWG   (b) 12 AWG   (c) 14 AWG   (d) 17 AWG

   Answer: _____   Section: _____._____

9. Audible and visual signal devices must be provided on optional standby systems, where practicable, to indicate _____.

   (a) derangement of the optional standby source   (b) that the optional standby source is carrying load
   (c) that the battery charger is not functioning   (d) a and b

   Answer: _____   Section: _____._____

10. Audio system circuits described in 640.9(C), and using Class 2 or Class 3 wiring methods, are not permitted to be installed in the same cable or raceway with _____.

    (a) other audio system circuits   (b) Class 2 conductors or cables
    (c) Class 3 conductors or cables .   (d) b or c

    Answer: _____   Section: _____._____

11. Cables and conductors of two or more power-limited fire alarm circuits can be installed in the same cable, enclosure, or raceway.

    (a) True   (b) False

    Answer: _____   Section: _____._____

12. Class 1 control circuits using 18 AWG conductors must use insulation types including _____.

    (a) RFH-2, RFHH-2, or RFHH-3   (b) TF, TFF, TFN, or TFFN
    (c) RHH, RHW, THWN, or THHN   (d) a and b

    Answer: _____   Section: _____._____

13. Class 1, 2, and 3 cables installed _____ to framing members must be protected against physical damage from penetration by screws or nails by 1 1/4 in. separation from the framing member or by a suitable metal plate in accordance with 300.4(D).

    (a) exposed   (b) concealed   (c) parallel   (d) all of these

    Answer: _____   Section: _____._____

14. Class 2 and Class 3 cables listed as suitable for general-purpose use with the exception of risers, ducts, plenums, and other spaces used for environmental air, are _____.

    (a) CL2P and CL3P   (b) CL2R and CL3R   (c) CL2 and CL3   (d) PLCT

    Answer: _____   Section: _____._____

15. Class 2 or Class 3 cables, installed in vertical runs penetrating more than one floor or installed in a shaft, must be type _____.

    (a) CL2R   (b) CL3R   (c) CL2P   (d) a or b

    Answer: _____   Section: _____._____

16. Class 2, Class 3, and PLTC cable that is not terminated at equipment and not identified for future use with a tag is considered abandoned.

    (a) True   (b) False

    Answer: _____   Section: _____._____

17. Coaxial cables for community antenna television systems installed in vertical runs and penetrating more than one floor or cables installed in vertical runs in a shaft, must be Type _____.

    (a) CATV   (b) CATVX   (c) CATVR   (d) any of these

    Answer: _____   Section: _____._____

18. Communications _____ cable must be listed as being suitable for use in a vertical run in a shaft, or from floor to floor, and must also be listed as having fire-resistant characteristics capable of preventing the carrying of fire from floor to floor.

    (a) plenum   (b) riser   (c) general-purpose   (d) none of these

    Answer: _____   Section: _____._____

19. Communications cables not terminated at both ends with a connector or other equipment and not identified for future use with a tag are considered abandoned.

    (a) True   (b) False

    Answer: _____   Section: _____._____

20. Communications wires and cables must be separated by at least 2 in. from conductors of _____ circuits.

    (a) power   (b) lighting   (c) Class 1   (d) any of these

    Answer: _____   Section: _____._____

21. Community antenna television (CATV) and radio system coaxial cables are not required to be listed and marked where the length of the cable within the building, measured from its point of entrance, does not exceed _____, the cable enters the building from the outside, and the cable is terminated at a grounding block.

    (a) 25 ft   (b) 30 ft   (c) 50 ft   (d) 100 ft

    Answer: _____   Section: _____._____

22. Conductive optical fiber cables are permitted to occupy the same cable tray or raceway with conductors for electric light, power, and Class 1 circuits.

    (a) True   (b) False

    Answer: _____   Section: _____._____

23. Each conductor of a lead-in from an outdoor antenna must be provided with a listed antenna discharge unit.

    (a) True   (b) False

    Answer: _____   Section: _____._____

24. Exposed network-powered broadband cables must be secured to structural components by straps, staples, hangers, or similar fittings designed and installed so as not to damage the cable.

    (a) True   (b) False

    Answer: _____   Section: _____._____

25. Fire alarm cables installed _____ to framing members must be protected against physical damage from penetration by screws or nails by 1 1/4 in. separation from the framing member or by a suitable metal plate in accordance with 300.4(D).

    (a) exposed   (b) concealed   (c) parallel   (d) all of these

    Answer: _____   Section: _____._____

26. Fire alarm circuits installed in any _____ must be installed in accordance with Articles 500 through 516 and Article 517, Part IV.

   (a) outdoor location   (b) hazardous (classified) location
   (c) place of assembly   (d) patient care area

   Answer: _____   Section: _____._____

27. Fire alarm equipment supplying PLFA circuits must be durably marked where plainly visible to indicate each circuit that is _____.

   (a) supplied by a nonpower-limited fire alarm circuit   (b) a power-limited fire alarm circuit
   (c) a fire alarm circuit   (d) none of these

   Answer: _____   Section: _____._____

28. Fire alarm systems include _____.

   (a) fire detection and alarm notification   (b) guard's tour
   (c) sprinkler water flow   (d) all of these

   Answer: _____   Section: _____._____

29. For nonpower-limited fire alarm circuits, an 18 AWG conductor is considered protected if the overcurrent device protecting the system is not over _____.

   (a) 15A   (b) 10A   (c) 20A   (d) 7A

   Answer: _____   Section: _____._____

30. If the transfer switch for a portable generator does not switch the _____ conductor, then it is not a separately derived system and the equipment grounding conductor must be bonded to the system grounding electrode.

   (a) phase   (b) equipment grounding   (c) grounded neutral   (d) all of these

   Answer: _____   Section: _____._____

31. In one- and two-family dwellings where it is not practicable to achieve an overall maximum primary protector grounding conductor length of 20 ft for communications systems, a separate _____ or longer communications ground rod must be driven and it must be bonded to the power grounding electrode system with a 6 AWG conductor.

   (a) 5 ft   (b) 8 ft   (c) 10 ft   (d) 20 ft

   Answer: _____   Section: _____._____

32. In one- and two-family dwellings where it is not practicable to achieve an overall maximum grounding conductor length of _____ for CATV, a separate ground must be used as specified in 250.52(A)(5), (6), or (7). It must be bonded to the power grounding electrode system with a copper conductor no smaller than 6 AWG.

   (a) 5 ft   (b) 8 ft   (c) 10 ft   (d) 20 ft

   Answer: _____   Section: _____._____

33. Listed plenum optical fiber raceways, listed riser optical fiber raceways, or listed general-purpose optical fiber raceways installed in accordance with 770.154 can be installed as _____ in any type of listed raceway permitted in Chapter 3.

   (a) innerduct   (b) ductfill   (c) busway   (d) a or b

   Answer: _____   Section: _____._____

34. Nonconductive optical fiber cable contains no metallic members and no other _____ materials.

    (a) electrically conductive   (b) inductive   (c) synthetic   (d) insulating

    Answer: _____   Section: _____._____

35. Nonpower-limited fire alarm circuit conductors of sizes _____ must be of the types included in 760.27(B) or other types of insulation listed for nonpower-limited fire alarm circuit use. Conductors larger than 16 AWG must comply with Article 310.

    (a) 16 and 18 AWG   (b) 14 and 12 AWG   (c) 14 AWG and larger   (d) all of these

    Answer: _____   Section: _____._____

36. Optical fiber plenum cables listed as suitable for use in ducts, plenums, and other space used for environmental air are Types _____.

    (a) OFNP and OFCP   (b) OFNR and OFCR   (c) OFNG and OFCG   (d) OFN and OFC

    Answer: _____   Section: _____._____

37. Outdoor antennas and lead-in conductors must be securely supported and the lead-in conductors must be securely attached to the antenna, but they must not be attached to the electric service mast.

    (a) True   (b) False

    Answer: _____   Section: _____._____

38. Overcurrent protection devices for Class 1 circuit protection must be located at the point where the conductor to be protected _____.

    (a) terminates to the load   (b) is spliced to any other conductor
    (c) receives its supply   (d) none of these

    Answer: _____   Section: _____._____

39. Power-limited fire alarm cables installed as wiring within buildings must be _____ as being resistant to the spread of fire.

    (a) marked FR   (b) listed   (c) identified   (d) color coded

    Answer: _____   Section: _____._____

40. Splices and terminations of nonpower-limited fire alarm circuits must be made in _____ fittings, boxes, enclosures, fire alarm devices, or utilization equipment.

    (a) identified   (b) listed   (c) approved   (d) none of these

    Answer: _____   Section: _____._____

41. The ac ohms-to-neutral impedance per 1,000 ft of 4/0 AWG aluminum in a steel raceway is the same as the ohms-to-neutral impedance of 1,000 ft of _____ copper installed in a steel raceway.

    (a) 1 AWG   (b) 1/0 AWG   (c) 2/0 AWG   (d) 250 kcmil

    Answer: _____   Section: _____._____

42. The area in sq in. for a 1/0 AWG bare aluminum conductor is _____

    (a) 0.087 sq in.   (b) 0.109 sq in.   (c) 0.137 sq in.   (d) 0.173 sq in.

    Answer: _____   Section: _____._____

43. The conductors contained within Type ITC cable must be rated 300V, and not smaller than _____ AWG nor larger than _____ AWG.

    (a) 18,10   (b) 16, 8   (c) 22, 12   (d) 14, 1/0

    Answer: _____   Section: _____._____

44. The cross-section area (in.2) of a 12 THHN is _____.

    (a) 0.0133   (b) 0.0233   (c) 0.0321   (d) 0.0147

    Answer: _____   Section: _____._____

45. The grounding conductor for an antenna mast or antenna discharge unit must not be smaller than 10 AWG copper.

    (a) True   (b) False

    Answer: _____   Section: _____._____

46. The grounding conductor for an antenna must be _____.

    (a) True   (b) False

    Answer: _____   Section: _____._____

47. The outer conductive shield of a coaxial cable must be grounded at the building premises as close to the point of cable entrance or attachment as practicable.

    (a) True   (b) False

    Answer: _____   Section: _____._____

48. When conduit nipples 24 in. or shorter are installed, the ampacity adjustment factor for more than three current-carrying conductors _____ to this condition.

    (a) does not apply   (b) must be applied

    Answer: _____   Section: _____._____

49. When practical, a separation of at least _____ must be maintained between communications wires and cables on buildings and lightning conductors.

    (a) 6 ft   (b) 8 ft   (c) 10 ft   (d) 12 ft

    Answer: _____   Section: _____._____

50. Where exposed to contact with electric light or power conductors, the noncurrent-carrying metallic members of optical fiber cables entering buildings must be _____.

    (a) grounded as close as possible to emergence through an exterior wall
    (b) grounded as close as possible to emergence through a concrete floor slab
    (c) interrupted as close to the point of entrance as practicable by an insulating joint
    (d) any of these

    Answer: _____   Section: _____._____

1. Means must be provided to disconnect simultaneously all _____ supply conductors to the phase converter.

   (a) ungrounded   (b) grounded   (c) grounding   (d) all of these

   Answer: _____   Section: _____._____

2. No _____ splices or taps may be made within or on a luminaire (fixture).

   (a) unapproved   (b) untested   (c) uninspected   (d) unnecessary

   Answer: _____   Section: _____._____

3. Nonmetallic cable trays must be made of _____ material.

   (a) fire-resistant   (b) waterproof   (c) corrosive   (d) flame-retardant

   Answer: _____   Section: _____._____

4. On circuits over 600V, nominal, where energized live parts are exposed, the minimum clear workspace must not be less than _____ high.

   (a) 3 ft   (b) 5 ft   (c) 6 ft   (d) 6 1/2 ft

   Answer: _____   Section: _____._____

5. Open conductors entering or leaving locations subject to dampness, wetness, or corrosive vapors must have _____ formed on them and must then pass upward and inward from the outside of the buildings, or from the damp, wet, or corrosive location, through noncombustible, nonabsorbent, insulating tubes.

   (a) weather heads   (b) drip loops   (c) identification   (d) blisters

   Answer: _____   Section: _____._____

6. Open conductors must be separated by at least _____ from metal raceways, piping, or other conducting material, and from any exposed lighting, power, or signaling conductor, or must be separated by a continuous and firmly-fixed nonconductor in addition to the insulation of the conductor.

   (a) 2 in.   (b) 2 1/2 in.   (c) 3 in.   (d) 3 1/2 in.

   Answer: _____   Section: _____._____

7. Overload relays and other devices for motor overload protection that are not capable of _____ must be protected by fuses or circuit breakers, or a motor short circuit protector.

   (a) opening short circuits   (b) clearing overloads   (c) opening ground faults   (d) a or c

   Answer: _____   Section: _____._____

8. Receptacles, receptacle housings, and self-contained devices used with flat conductor cable systems must be _____.

    (a) rated a minimum of 20A   (b) rated a minimum of 15A   (c) identified for this use   (d) none of these

    Answer: _____   Section: _____._____

9. Resistance heating elements of embedded deicing and snow-melting _____ must not be installed where they bridge expansion joints unless provision is made for expansion and contraction.

    (a) cables   (b) units   (c) panels   (d) all of these

    Answer: _____   Section: _____._____

10. Resistance-type heating elements in electric space-heating equipment must be protected at not more than _____.

    (a) 95 percent of the nameplate value   (b) 60A
    (c) 48A   (d) 150 percent of the rated current

    Answer: _____   Section: _____._____

11. Service-entrance conductors entering, or on the exterior of, buildings or other structures must be insulated.

    (a) True   (b) False

    Answer: _____   Section: _____._____

12. Service-lateral conductors must have _____.

    (a) adequate mechanical strength   (b) sufficient ampacity for the loads computed
    (c) a and b   (d) none of these

    Answer: _____   Section: _____._____

13. Sheet steel boxes not over 100 cu in. in size must be made from steel at least _____ thick.

    (a) 0.0625 in.   (b) 0.0757 in.   (c) 0.075 in.   (d) 0.025 in.

    Answer: _____   Section: _____._____

14. Single, locking, and grounding-type receptacles for water-pump motors or other loads directly related to the circulation and sanitation system of a permanently installed pool or fountain can be located _____ from the inside walls of the pool or fountain, if the receptacle is GFCI protected.

    (a) 3 to 6 ft   (b) 5 to 10 ft   (c) 10 to 15 ft   (d) 10 to 20 ft

    Answer: _____   Section: _____._____

15. Switchboards that have any exposed live parts must be installed in permanently _____ locations, and then only where under competent supervision and accessible only to qualified persons.

    (a) dry   (b) mounted   (c) supported   (d) all of these

    Answer: _____   Section: _____._____

16. The _____ of conductors used in prewired ENT manufactured assemblies must be identified by means of a printed tag or label attached to each end of the manufactured assembly.

    (a) type   (b) size   (c) quantity   (d) all of these

    Answer: _____   Section: _____._____

17. The ac ohms-to-neutral impedance per 1,000 ft of 4/0 AWG aluminum conductor in a steel raceway is _____.

    (a) 0.06 ohms   (b) 0.10 ohms   (c) 0.22 ohms   (d) 0.11 ohms

    Answer: _____   Section: _____._____

18. The ampacity of supply branch-circuit conductors and the overcurrent protection devices for X-ray equipment must not be less than _____.

    (a) 50 percent of the momentary rating   (b) 100 percent of the long-time rating
    (c) the larger of a or b   (d) the smaller of a or b

    Answer: _____   Section: _____._____

19. The authority having jurisdiction may judge a location utilized for _____ as nonhazardous, providing there is positive ventilation and the conditions of the *Code* are met.

    (a) drying or curing   (b) dipping and coating   (c) spraying operations   (d) none of these

    Answer: _____   Section: _____._____

20. The building disconnecting means for a one circuit installation that supplies only limited loads of a single branch circuit must have a rating of not less than _____.

    (a) 15A   (b) 20A   (c) 25A   (d) 30A

    Answer: _____   Section: _____._____

21. The continuous current-carrying capacity of 1 1/2 sq in. copper busbar mounted in an unventilated enclosure is _____.

    (a) 500A   (b) 750A   (c) 650A   (d) 1,500A

    Answer: _____   Section: _____._____

22. The essential electrical systems in a health care facility must have sources of power from _____.

    (a) a normal source generally supplying the entire electrical system
    (b) one or more alternate sources for use when the normal source is interrupted
    (c) a or b
    (d) a and b

    Answer: _____   Section: _____._____

23. The flexible cord conductor identification of the grounded circuit conductor required in the *Code* must consist of one of six methods. One method is a tracer in a braid of any color contrasting with that of the braid and _____ in the braid of the other conductor or conductors.

    (a) a solid color   (b) no tracer   (c) two tracers   (d) none of these

    Answer: _____   Section: _____._____

24. The ground-fault protection system for service equipment must be _____ when first installed on site.

    (a) a Class A device   (b) identified   (c) turned on   (d) performance tested

    Answer: _____   Section: _____._____

25. The maximum load permitted on a heating element in a pool heater must not exceed _____.

    (a) 20A   (b) 35A   (c) 48A   (d) 60A

    Answer: _____   Section: _____._____

26. The minimum depth of clear working space in front of electrical equipment for 5,000V, nominal-to-ground is _____ when there are exposed live parts on both sides of the workspace.

    (a) 4 ft   (b) 5 ft   (c) 6 ft   (d) 9 ft

    Answer: _____   Section: _____._____

27. The minimum size conductor for operating control and signaling circuits in an elevator is _____.

    (a) 20 AWG   (b) 16 AWG   (c) 14 AWG   (d) 12 AWG

    Answer: _____   Section: _____._____

28. The minimum size conductor permitted for Type MC cable is _____ AWG.

    (a) 18 copper   (b) 14 copper   (c) 12 copper   (d) none of these

    Answer: _____   Section: _____._____

29. The minimum spacing of busbars of opposite polarity held in free air inside a panelboard is _____ when operating at not over 125V, nominal.

    (a) 1/2 in.   (b) 1 in.   (c) 2 in.   (d) 4 in.

    Answer: _____   Section: _____._____

30. The *NEC* requires series-rated installations to be field-marked to indicate the maximum level of fault-current for which the system has been installed.

    (a) True   (b) False

    Answer: _____   Section: _____._____

31. The percentage of conduit fill for five conductors is _____ percent.

    (a) 35   (b) 60   (c) 40   (d) 55

    Answer: _____   Section: _____._____

32. The photovoltaic disconnecting means must _____.

    (a) be installed at a readily accessible location either outside of a building or structure or inside nearest the point of entrance of the system conductors
    (b) be suitable for the prevailing conditions
    (c) consist of not more than six switches or six circuit breakers
    (d) all of these

    Answer: _____   Section: _____._____

33. The residual voltage of a capacitor, rated not over 600V, must be reduced to 50V or less within _____ after the capacitor is disconnected from the source of supply.

    (a) 15 seconds   (b) 45 seconds   (c) 1 minute   (d) 2 minutes

    Answer: _____   Section: _____._____

34. The size of the branch-circuit overcurrent protective devices and conductors for an electrode-type boiler, rated less than 50 kW and not greater than 600V, must be calculated on the basis of _____.

    (a) 125 percent of the total load excluding motors   (b) 125 percent of the total load including motors
    (c) 150 percent of the nameplate value   (d) 100 percent of the nameplate value

    Answer: _____   Section: _____._____

35. Type FC cable is an assembly of parallel conductors formed integrally with an insulating material web specifically designed for field installation in surface metal raceways.

    (a) True   (b) False

    Answer: _____   Section: _____._____

36. Type IGS cable is a factory assembly of one or more conductors, each individually insulated and enclosed in a loose-fit, non-metallic flexible conduit as an integrated gas spacer cable rated _____ volts.

    (a) 0 through 6,000   (b) 600 through 6,000   (c) 0 through 600   (d) 3,000 through 6,000

    Answer: _____   Section: _____._____

37. Type MI cable must be securely supported at intervals not exceeding _____.

    (a) 3 ft   (b) 3 1/2 ft   (c) 5 ft   (d) 6 ft

    Answer: _____   Section: _____._____

38. When determining the number of conductors that are considered as current-carrying, a grounding conductor is _____.

    (a) counted as one current-carrying conductor
    (b) considered to be a current-carrying conductor but not counted
    (c) considered to be a noncurrent-carrying conductor and is not counted
    (d) counted as one conductor for each ground wire in the raceway

    Answer: _____   Section: _____._____

39. When individual open conductors enter a building or other structure through tubes, _____ must be formed on the conductors before they enter the tubes.

    (a) drop loops   (b) knots   (c) drip loops   (d) none of these

    Answer: _____   Section: _____._____

40. When the calculated number of conductors, all of the same size, that may be installed in a conduit or in tubing includes a decimal, the next higher whole number must be used when this decimal is _____ or larger.

    (a) 0.40   (b) 0.60   (c) 0.70   (d) 0.80

    Answer: _____   Section: _____._____

41. When used as open wiring on insulators, conductors that are _____ AWG or larger, supported on solid knobs, must be securely tied to the knobs by tie wires having an insulation equivalent to that of the conductor.

    (a) 14   (b) 12   (c) 10   (d) 8

    Answer: _____   Section: _____._____

42. Where knob-and-tube conductors pass through wood cross members in plastered partitions, conductors must be protected by non-combustible, nonabsorbent, insulating tubes extending not less than _____ beyond the wood member.

(a) 2 in.   (b) 3 in.   (c) 4 in.   (d) 6 in.

Answer: _____   Section: _____._____

43. Where practicable, a separation of at least _____ must be maintained between any network-powered broadband communications cable on buildings and lightning conductors.

(a) 6 ft   (b) 8 ft   (c) 10 ft   (d) 12 ft

Answer: _____   Section: _____._____

44. Where the outer sheath of Type MI cable is made of copper, it must provide an adequate path for equipment grounding purposes.

(a) True   (b) False

Answer: _____   Section: _____._____

45. Which of the following statements about Type MI cable is correct?

(a) It may be used in any hazardous location.
(b) A single run of cable must not contain more than the equivalent of four quarter bends.
(c) It must be securely supported at intervals not exceeding 10 ft.
(d) none of these

Answer: _____   Section: _____._____

46. It is permissible to extend busways vertically through dry floors if totally enclosed (unventilated) where passing through, and for a minimum distance of _____ above the floor to provide adequate protection from physical damage.

(a) 6 ft   (b) 6 1/2 ft   (c) 8 ft   (d) 10 ft

Answer: _____   Section: _____._____

47. For installations consisting of not more than two 2-wire branch circuits, the building disconnecting means must have a rating of not less than _____.

(a) 15A   (b) 20A   (c) 25A   (d) 30A

Answer: _____   Section: _____._____

48. HDPE is permitted to be installed _____.

(a) where subject to chemicals for which the conduit is listed   (b) in cinder fill
(c) in direct burial installations in earth or concrete   (d) all of these

Answer: _____   Section: _____._____

49. Power distribution blocks installed in metal wireways must be listed.

(a) True   (b) False

Answer: _____   Section: _____._____

50. The requirements in "Annexes" must be complied with.

(a) True   (b) False

Answer: _____   Section: _____._____

Discount 25% off

Electrical Theory Library

Do you know where electricity comes from? To be able to say yes to that question, you must understand a bit about the physics of matter. What value does a brief study of the nature of matter have for the student of electrical theory? Only when you know the theory can you truly have confidence in the practical aspects of your electrical work.

Discount 25% off

Calculations Library

Electrical Calculations must be mastered to become successful in the electrical trade. You must understand how to perform the important electrical calculations specified in the National Electrical Code. The detailed videos/DVDs are taped from live classes and take you step-by-step through the calculations. If you just need Calculations, then these libraries are for you.

Discount 20% off

Any Online Training Course

Interactive Online Training is available. Many states are now accepting online testing for Continuing Education credits. Go online today and see if your state is on the list and view selected chapters for FREE. Don't get frustrated trying to find a local class or miss valuable time at work if your state accepts this convenient solution.